Work Out
Numeracy

Ted Penketh

MACMILLAN

First edition 1987
Reprinted four times
Second edition 1996

Published by
MACMILLAN PRESS LTD
Houndmills, Basingstoke, Hampshire RG21 6XS
and London
Companies and representatives
throughout the world

ISBN 0–333–66270–9

A catalogue record for this book is available
from the British Library.

10   9   8   7   6   5   4   3   2   1
05   04   03   02   01   00   99   98   97   96

Printed in Hong Kong

Contents

How to Use this Book

The aim of this book is to provide a working knowledge of basic mathematics and, at the same time, to concentrate on essential topics that occur in first-level examinations.

The book has sufficient material to cover the syllabus for NCVQ Core Skills Levels 1 and 2, Application of Number, and City and Guilds and GCSE Numeracy examinations; also, GCSE candidates who are looking for a medium grade will find plenty of help in this book.

The methods used for each chapter are similar: a brief revision or statement of facts for the heading given; a large number of worked examples to cover all levels of the examinations mentioned; and numerous exercises and multiple choice questions to meet the ever-increasing demand for those asking for more practice. Where any question proves difficult it can be answered by careful reference to the worked examples.

To keep pace with everyday life the sections on percentages and graphs have been increased considerably. Many worked examples reflect up-to-date changes and conditions, while all exercises and multiple choice questions are new.

Significant changes have been made in this second edition, with much additional material to satisfy the changing demands of first examinations. Opportunity has been taken also to bring the use of the calculator into operation after appropriate chapters, and guidance is given where this is applicable. I am very grateful to those who have written making suggestions along these lines.

Mathematics is an enjoyable subject, not something of which to be frightened, and it is hoped that this book will go some way to being a springboard for higher things.

Ted Penketh
September 1995

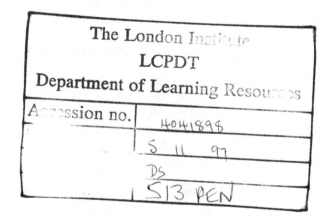

Acknowledgements

The author and publishers wish to thank the following, who have been of assistance in the compilation of this book or who have kindly given permission for the use of copyright material to illustrate particular points: British Airways, British Rail, Casio Electronics Co. Ltd, the Department of Transport, the Electoral Reform Society, *The Guardian*, HM Statistical Office, *The Independent*, ParcelForce, The Post Office, Ribble Bus Company.

Every effort has been made to trace all the copyright holders, but if any have been overlooked the publishers will be pleased to make the necessary arrangements at the first opportunity.

1 Number

1 How Big is a Number?

The size of a number depends on the position (place value) of the figures and the size of the figures.

Worked example 1

Write 68 in words.

68 is 6 tens and 8 units and is written sixty-eight.

Worked example 2

Write 437 in words.

437 is 4 hundreds, 3 tens and 7 units and is written four hundred and thirty-seven.

Worked example 3

Write 2006 in words.

2006 is 2 thousands, 0 hundreds, 0 tens and 6 units and is written two thousand and six.

Remember that the place value headings can be written in order of size:

Millions	Hundred thousands	Ten thousands	Thousands	Hundreds	Tens	Units
2	4	6	3	8	5	1

The number 2 463 851 is two million, four hundred and sixty-three thousand, eight hundred and fifty-one.

Worked example 4

Write eight hundred and twenty-five in figures.

Eight hundred and twenty-five is 825.

Worked example 5

Write two million six hundred thousand three hundred and ninety-six in figures.

Two million six hundred thousand three hundred and ninety-six is 2 600 396.

Exercise 1

Write the following in words. The first two are completed for you.

1   46 is *forty-six*

2   508 is *five hundred and eight*

3   36   4   52   5   69   6   94

7	483	**8**	937	**9**	608	**10**	370
11	2147	**12**	4836	**13**	3058	**14**	7040
15	38 476	**16**	83 721	**17**	50 478	**18**	46 284
19	40 065	**20**	570 745	**21**	5 930 657	**22**	4 060 874
23	10 001	**24**	3027				

Exercise 2

Write the following in figures. The first two are completed for you.

1 Seventy-three is *73*

2 One hundred and nine is *109*

3 One hundred and sixty-four

4 Three hundred and forty-nine

5 Two hundred and seven

6 Two thousand five hundred and eighty-three

7 Five thousand nine hundred and eighteen

8 Nine thousand and six

9 Seven thousand and seventy-seven

10 Fifteen thousand two hundred and ninety-four

11 Twenty-four thousand six hundred and thirty-three

12 Two hundred and fifteen thousand

13 Two hundred and sixty-two

14 Five hundred and twenty-two thousand nine hundred and six

15 Nine hundred and eighteen thousand and twenty-four

16 Eighteen million

17 Two million six hundred thousand five hundred and three

18 What does the figure 2 represent in 64 295?

19 What does the figure 5 represent in 157 384?

20 What does the figure 2 represent in 2645?

21 What does the figure 0 represent in 34 076?

22 What does the figure 8 represent in 859 395?

23 What does the figure 3 represent in 20 306?

24 What does the figure 4 represent in 594 216?

2 Addition

Begin by adding figures in the right-hand column.

Worked example 6

$$\begin{array}{r} 54 \\ + \underline{32} \\ \underline{86} \end{array}$$ *Answer 86*

2 and 4 make 6. Write 6 in the units column of the answer.
3 and 5 make 8. Write 8 in the tens column of the answer.

Worked example 7

$$\begin{array}{r} 51 \\ + \underline{47} \\ \underline{98} \end{array}$$ *Answer 98*

7 and 1 make 8
4 and 5 make 9

Where figures have to be carried from one column to the next then use the method with which you are familiar.

Worked example 8

```
  47        47
+ 26      + 26
   1
  ──        ──
  73        73
                1
```

Thus 1 and 2 make 3 and 4 makes 7.
Answer 73

> 6 and 7 make 13. Write figure 3 in the answer and carry 1 into the next column, putting it either alongside and slightly below the next figure or beneath the answer line as shown.

Worked example 9

Find the sum of 127, 32, 79 and 256.

Where numbers are not given in columns then put them into columns before beginning the addition:

```
    127
     32
     79
+   256
    1 2
    ───
    494        Answer 494
```

As a matter of habit I always begin at the bottom of the column and add upwards.

Where there are a lot of numbers always *check* the addition by starting at the top and adding downwards. If the two answers do not coincide then repeat the additions until they do.

Worked example 10

Find the sum of 4275, 384, 1009, 369 and 57.

Write the numbers in columns:

```
   4275
    384
   1009
    369
+    57
   1 2 3
   ─────
   6094        Answer 6094
```

> 7 and 9 make 16, and 9 makes 25, and 4 makes 29, and 5 makes 34.
> Write 4 in the answer and carry 3.
> *Check:* 5 and 4 make 9, and 9 makes 18, and 9 makes 27, and 7 makes 34.

Exercise 3

Complete the following additions. The first two are completed for you.

```
1     36       2     15       3     23       4     41
    + 12          +  9          + 45          + 58
     ──            ──            ──            ──
      48            24


5     46       6     87       7     79       8    254
    + 28          + 42          + 31          +  45
     ──            ──            ──            ───


9     83      10    376      11     48      12    737
     379             54            748            86
    + 63          + 277         + 302         + 492
     ──            ───           ───           ───


13    48      14    956      15   2765      16    381
     724             48            805            927
    + 74          + 189          1736             84
     ──            ───          +  820         + 846
                                 ────           ───
```

17	439	18	628	19	709	20	485
	3836		75		3093		54
	265		1363		507		3573
+	937	+	6307	+	9460	+	628

21	403	22	38	23	927	24	77
	87		1069		84		828
	1005		827		5106		60
	690	+	507		387		3208
+	59			+	49	+	99

Exercise 4

Find the sum of the following numbers. The first two are completed for you.

1 15 + 48 + 27

$$
\begin{array}{r}
15 \\
48 \\
+\ 27 \\
{\scriptstyle 2} \\
\hline
90
\end{array}
$$ *Answer 90*

2 9 + 84 + 16 + 305

$$
\begin{array}{r}
9 \\
84 \\
16 \\
+\ 305 \\
{\scriptstyle 1\ 2} \\
\hline
414
\end{array}
$$ *Answer 414*

3 63 + 47 + 321

4 74 + 32 + 58

5 476 + 839 + 51

6 38 + 174 + 291 + 80

7 69 + 46 + 73

8 60 + 409 + 107 + 58 + 33

9 427 + 483 + 76 + 807

10 46 + 28 + 943 + 173 + 607

11 38 + 127 + 55 + 83

12 189 + 36 + 507 + 284

13 836 + 47 + 92 + 152

14 53 + 839 + 194 + 56

15 2008 + 406 + 91 + 307

16 63 + 4087 + 61 + 754

17 254 + 407 + 63 + 54

18 427 + 538 + 941 + 28

19 407 + 637 + 48 + 953

20 176 + 508 + 3005 + 61

21 296 + 30 + 473 + 57

22 4035 + 894 + 728 + 17

23 68 + 2007 + 908 + 890

24 34 + 75 + 2587 + 503

3 Addition from Information Given

Many questions are written in sentences, and it becomes a matter of sorting out which things have to be added together.

Worked example 11

A darts player in a pub throws six darts. He scores 20, 5 and 1, and then 19, 17 and 3. How many does he score?

He scores on each of the six darts.
The scores are 20, 5, 1, 19, 17 and 3.
Add them together:

$$
\begin{array}{r}
20 \\
5 \\
1 \\
19 \\
17 \\
+\ 3 \\
{\scriptstyle 2} \\
\hline
+\ 65
\end{array}
$$ *Answer 65*

Worked example 12   A salesman in the course of a week had to travel from Oxford to London (57 miles), then to Cambridge (54 miles), then to Leeds (145 miles), then to Manchester (40 miles), then to Birmingham (80 miles), and then home to Oxford (another 64 miles). How far did he travel in the week and, using his route, how far is it from Manchester to Oxford?

There are two questions being asked:
(a)   How far did he travel in the week?
Total distance he travelled = 57 miles + 54 miles + 145 miles
$$+ \ 40 \text{ miles} + 80 \text{ miles} + 64 \text{ miles}$$
$$= 440 \text{ miles}$$
(b)   How far is it from Manchester to Oxford using his route?
Manchester to Birmingham =   80 miles
Birmingham to Oxford   =   64 miles
Manchester to Oxford   = 144 miles

Exercise 5

Figure 1.1 is part of a mileage chart from a road atlas. To find the distance between two towns follow the columns of figures from each town, horizontally or vertically, until they coincide. This is the distance to the nearest mile.

From the mileage chart find how far it is from

1   London to Aberdeen   2   London to Edinburgh

3   Leeds to Manchester   4   Norwich to Aberystwyth

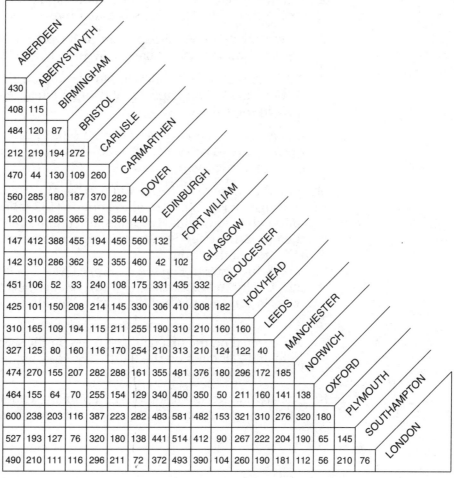

Figure 1.1 Mileage chart

5 Carlisle to Plymouth

6 Aberdeen to Holyhead

7 Birmingham to Norwich via Oxford

8 Plymouth to Aberdeen via Leeds

9 Southampton to Carlisle via Oxford and Manchester

10 London to Edinburgh via Norwich, Leeds and Carlisle

11 Dover to Carlisle via London, Oxford, Birmingham and Manchester

12 Dover to Aberystwyth via Oxford, Birmingham and Carmarthen

13 Plymouth to Aberdeen via Bristol, Leeds, Carlisle and Edinburgh

14 Edinburgh to Dover via Carlisle, Manchester, Norwich and London

15 Bristol to Fort William via Leeds, Carlisle, Edinburgh and Aberdeen

Exercise 6

1 John with his first three darts of a match threw 8, 19 and 57. What did he score?

2 Three different packets of sweets held 23, 27 and 26 sweets respectively. How many sweets were there altogether?

3 The attendances at Watford's ground for the first three home games of the season were 9424, 12 685 and 8378. What was the total attendance for the first three home games?

4 A golfer scored 5, 3, 4, 7, 4, 6, 3, 5 and 8 in his first nine holes of a competition. What was his score after nine holes?

5 A newsboy delivered 33 papers on each weekday, 41 on Saturday and 46 on Sunday. How many newspapers did he deliver in a whole week?

6 A salesman drove 126 miles on Monday, 83 on Tuesday, 247 on Wednesday, 156 on Thursday and 49 on Friday. How many miles did he drive in these five days?

7 A branch of Marks & Spencer had 10 890, 12 245 and 19 833 customers on the first three days of a quiet week. How many customers were there altogether over the three days?

8 A journey from Manchester and back went as follows: Manchester to Nottingham (71 miles), then to London (132 miles), then to Oxford (57 miles), then to Cardiff (109 miles), then to Birmingham (108 miles), and then to Manchester (88 miles). Using the same route, and going the same way, how far is it from
(a) Manchester to London   (b) Oxford to Birmingham
(c) Cardiff to Manchester   (d) Manchester to Oxford
(e) Nottingham to Cardiff   (f) London to Manchester?

9 A holiday journey by car to Florence from Preston took 4 days. 262 miles was covered on the first day, 297 miles on the second, 319 miles on the third and 268 miles on the fourth day. How far, using this route, is it from Preston to Florence?

10 The attendance at ten sessions of a primary school class was 33, 33, 31, 31, 34, 33, 34, 34, 29 and 27. What was the total attendance for the week?

4 Subtraction

Subtract using the method you have been taught.

Worked example 13

What is the difference between 88 and 43?

$$\begin{array}{r} 88 \\ -\ 43 \\ \hline 45 \end{array}$$ *Answer 45*

8 take away 3 leaves 5. Write 5 in the units column of the answer.
8 take away 4 leaves 4. Write 4 in the tens column of the answer.

Worked example 14

From 659 take 237.

$$\begin{array}{r} 659 \\ -\ 237 \\ \hline 422 \end{array}$$ *Answer 422*

9 take away 7 leaves 2. Write 2 in the answer.
5 take away 3 leaves 2. Write 2 in the answer.
6 take away 2 leaves 4. Write 4 in the answer.

Worked example 15

From 73 take away 28.

Two methods can be used in this example, and I would advise continuing the method you have been taught.

Method 1

$$\begin{array}{r} ^{6}\cancel{7}^{1}3 \\ -\ 28 \\ \hline 45 \end{array}$$ *Answer 45*

3 take away 8 cannot be done, so a 10 is used from the 7 in the next column and added to the 3 to make 13.
13 take away 8 is 5. Place 5 in the answer.
The 7 in the tens column has become 6.
6 take away 2 is 4. Place 4 in the answer.

Method 2

$$\begin{array}{r} ^{1}73 \\ -\ 28 \\ \hline ^{1}45 \end{array}$$ *Answer 45*

3 take away 8 cannot be done so 10 is added to the 3 to make 13.
13 take away 8 is 5. Place 5 in the answer.
Because we added 10 to the top line we must add one 10 to the bottom line and the 2 becomes 3.
7 take away 3 is 4. Write 4 in the answer.

Worked example 16

$$\begin{array}{r} ^{1}\cancel{2}^{3}\cancel{4}^{1}7 \\ -\ 169 \\ \hline 78 \end{array}$$ *Answer 78*

Worked example 17

$$\begin{array}{r} ^{0}\cancel{1}^{9}\cancel{0}^{9}\cancel{0}^{1}1 \\ -\ 257 \\ \hline 744 \end{array}$$ *Answer 744*

Exercise 7

Find the difference between the numbers given. The first two are completed for you.

1	$\overset{3\ 1}{45}$ $-\ 28$ $\overline{17}$	2	$\overset{1\ ^{1}0\ 1}{216}$ $-\ 38$ $\overline{178}$	3	58 $-\ 24$ $\overline{}$	4	79 $-\ 65$ $\overline{}$
5	63 $-\ 37$ $\overline{}$	6	42 $-\ 17$ $\overline{}$	7	52 $-\ 36$ $\overline{}$	8	253 $-\ 85$ $\overline{}$
9	317 $-\ 138$ $\overline{}$	10	493 $-\ 274$ $\overline{}$	11	284 $-\ 98$ $\overline{}$	12	2158 $-\ 349$ $\overline{}$
13	3748 $-\ 2457$ $\overline{}$	14	4920 $-\ 4646$ $\overline{}$	15	1060 $-\ 953$ $\overline{}$	16	604 $-\ 318$ $\overline{}$
17	3005 $-\ 999$ $\overline{}$	18	428 $-\ 137$ $\overline{}$	19	1003 $-\ 626$ $\overline{}$	20	450 $-\ 105$ $\overline{}$
21	305 $-\ 88$ $\overline{}$	22	921 $-\ 875$ $\overline{}$	23	5005 $-\ 789$ $\overline{}$	24	1608 $-\ 929$ $\overline{}$

Exercise 8

The first two are completed for you.

1 A newsagent starts the day with 260 newspapers, and when the shop closes he has 43 left. How many has he sold?

The number sold is the difference between the number of papers at the start of the day and the number left at the end of the day:

$\overset{5\ 1}{260}$
$-\ \ 43$
$\overline{217}$ *Number of newspapers sold is 217*

2 A shop bought 200 sweaters at a special price for the sales week. On Monday 27 were sold, on Tuesday 32 were sold, on Wednesday 18 were sold, on Thursday 35 were sold, on Friday 26 were sold and on Saturday 55 were sold. How many were left at the end of the sale?

First, find the total number sold:

Monday	27
Tuesday	32
Wednesday	18
Thursday	35
Friday	26
Saturday	55
Total sold	193

There were 200 sweaters:
$-\ 193$ sold
$\overline{7}$ *Answer 7 left*

3 There are 414 steps to the top of the Giotto tower in Florence. When I have climbed 239 how many more steps are there to the top?

4 In a recent Test Match against Australia, England scored 227 runs in the first innings but Australia scored 416. How many runs were England behind on the first innings?

5 A motoring atlas says that it is 317 miles from London to Paris and 609 miles from London to Lyon. How far is it from Paris to Lyon?

6 A box of matches says that it contains 51 matches. There are 17 left in the box. How many have been used?

7 A book is to contain eighty thousand words. The author has written sixty thousand five hundred and seventy-five. How many words are still to be written?

8 A newsagent starts the day with 300 papers. There are 60 *Express*, 60 *Mirror*, 50 *Sun*, 60 *Mail*, 30 *Telegraph*, 25 *Guardian* and the rest *The Times*. How many *Times* newspapers does he start with? At the end of the day he returns 5 *Express*, 12 *Mirror*, 7 *Sun* and 3 *Times*. How many newspapers were sold in the day?

9 A man won the first prize of one million pounds on a premium bond. He bought a house for one hundred and seventy-five thousand two hundred and fifty pounds and a car for twenty-two thousand three hundred and seventy pounds. How much has he got left? (Give your answer in words.)

10 The table below shows the top four football clubs in the Premier Division, how many goals they have scored, and how many goals have been scored against them. What is the goal difference for each club?

	Goals for	Goals against
Blackburn	81	38
Manchester United	84	39
Liverpool	62	47
Newcastle United	65	54

11 A DIY shop starts the week with 180 tins of white paint. 12 are sold on Monday, 18 on Tuesday, 38 on Wednesday, 20 on Thursday, 37 on Friday and 43 on Saturday. How many tins of white paint are left?

12 A cinema holds 638 people. There are 79 empty seats. How many seats are filled?

5 Multiplication

When multiplying two numbers together, if the sum needs to be worked out on a piece of paper, make sure the units in each number are underneath each other: that is, the last figure of the second number is underneath the last figure of the first number.

As the biggest number in any one column is 9 we are continually asking what is 5 times 5, or 8 times 9, or 4 times 7. If it is this that causes problems and errors you can still cope with multiplication by using a table such as that shown in Figure 1.2.

1	2	3	4	5	6	7	8	9
2	4	6	8	10	12	14	16	18
3	6	9	12	15	18	21	24	27
4	8	12	16	20	24	28	32	36
5	10	15	20	25	30	35	40	45
6	12	18	24	30	36	42	48	54
7	14	21	28	35	42	49	56	63
8	16	24	32	40	48	56	64	72
9	18	27	36	45	54	63	72	81

Figure 1.2 Multiplication table

Being able to multiply together all numbers up to 9 means that any multiplication can now be done, provided the units of both numbers are placed underneath each other when setting out the question. The worked examples now show this.

Worked example 18

Multiply 257 by 3.

$$\begin{array}{r} 257 \\ \times \quad 3 \\ \hline {\scriptstyle 1\ 2} \\ \hline 771 \end{array}$$ *Answer 771*

3 times 7 is 21; write 1 in the answer and carry 2.
3 times 5 is 15, add the 2 carried, making 17.
Write 7 in the answer and carry 1.
3 times 2 is 6, add the 1 carried, making 7
Write 7 in the answer.

Worked example 19

Multiply 38 by 24.

Method 1

Begin by multiplying 38 by 4.

$$\begin{array}{r} 38 \\ \times \quad 24 \\ \hline {\scriptstyle 1\ 3} \\ \hline 152 \\ 760 \\ {\scriptstyle 1} \\ \hline 912 \end{array}$$ *Answer 912*

4 times 8 is 32; write 2 in the answer and carry 3.
4 times 3 is 12, add the 3 carried, making 15. Write 15 in the answer.
Now multiply 38 by 2, which is really 2 tens, so write a 0 in the units column and then you cannot put any tens in the unit column by mistake.
2 times 8 is 16; write 6 in the answer in the tens column and carry 1.
2 times 3 is 6, add the 1 carried, making 7. Add the two results together.

Method 2

Multiply by the 2 first.

$$\begin{array}{r} 38 \\ \times \quad 24 \\ \hline {\scriptstyle 1\ 3} \\ \hline 760 \\ 152 \\ {\scriptstyle 1} \\ \hline 912 \end{array}$$

Use the method with which you are familiar.
The carrying figures can be placed wherever you feel they will not be forgotten.

You will rarely have to do multiplication of numbers with more than two figures in each, except by using a calculator.

But however many figures there are in each number, make sure the units of each number are underneath one another.

Worked example 20

Multiply 567 by 84.

$$\begin{array}{r} 567 \\ \times \quad 84 \\ \hline {\scriptstyle 2\ 2\ ^5\ ^5} \\ \hline 45\ 360 \\ 2\ 268 \\ {\scriptstyle 1} \\ \hline 47\ 628 \end{array}$$ *Answer 47 628*

Exercise 9

Find the value of the following. The first two are completed for you.

1
```
    36
×    9
     5
───
   324        Answer 324
```

2
```
    18
×   34
    3 2
───
   540
    72
     1
───
   612        Answer 612
```

3
```
    32
×    3
───
```

4
```
    54
×    6
───
```

5
```
    83
×    7
───
```

6
```
    49
×    9
───
```

7
```
    27
×    8
───
```

8
```
    48
×    9
───
```

9
```
    97
×   23
───
```

10
```
    35
×   16
───
```

11
```
    74
×   35
───
```

12
```
    87
×   26
───
```

13
```
    52
×   58
───
```

14
```
    73
×   47
───
```

15
```
   354
×    7
───
```

16
```
   278
×    4
───
```

17
```
   748
×   83
───
```

18
```
   484
×   27
───
```

19
```
    36
×  835
───
```

20
```
   638
×  359
───
```

21
```
   367
×    8
───
```

22
```
   205
×   12
───
```

23 69 × 15

24 48 × 24

Exercise 10

The first two are completed for you.

1 A youth earns £46 a week. How much is this per month (4 weeks)?

If he earns £46 a week he will earn 4 times as much in 4 weeks.

```
   £46
×    4
     2
───
   184        Answer £184 per month
```

2 A milk float carries 26 crates of milk and in each crate there are 24 bottles. How many bottles of milk are being carried?

1 crate contains 24 bottles
26 crates will contain 26 times 24 bottles

```
    26
×   24
    21
───
   520
   104
───
   624        Answer Float carries 624 bottles
```

3 A woman puts £4 a week on Littlewoods Pools. How much is this in a 52-week year?

4 A crate of beer holds 24 bottles. A drayman delivers 36 crates. How many bottles of beer are delivered?

5   I earn £148 per week.
   (a)   How much is this per month (4 weeks)?
   (b)   How much is this per year (52 weeks)?

6   Out of a salary of £660 per month a typist saves £535 in the year. How much has she spent in the year?

7   The flight from Manchester to Malaga is usually a Boeing 757, which holds 266 passengers. There are four flights a day. If the planes are full on one particular day, how many passengers are carried on that day?

8   A holiday brochure quotes, for a weekly holiday in Nerja, a cost of £288 per adult, £156 for each child, insurance of £18 per passenger and airport taxes of £12 per passenger. What will be the total cost of this holiday for 2 adults and 2 children?

9   The Council Tax for a house in Band E is £17 per week. How much is this for a 52-week year?

10   A disco and buffet costs £8 per person. How much is taken if 163 people attend?

11   A salesman reckons to travel 384 miles by car each month. How many miles is this in 12 months?

12   A skilled man earns £9 a hour.
   (a)   How much is this in a 34-hour week?
   (b)   How much is this in a 52-week year?

13   The Eurostar train from London to Paris costs £95 for an economy class return at certain times. The train can carry 330 economy class passengers. On a particular journey there were 47 spare seats. How much money did the railway company earn on that journey?

14   A mother arranged to do a buffet party for her teenage daughter for 35 guests, including family. Mother allowed £5 per head for food, £75 for drinks, £45 to cover decorations, £35 for room hire, £130 for a DJ, and £50 for last-minute items. How much was needed to cover the cost of the party?

15   It costs £486 return for a car, including driver, on Motorail from Calais to Nice. The additional adult fare is £106 and the cost for a child is £53. What is the cost for a family of 2 adults and 3 children to travel by Motorail from Calais to Nice?

16   A darts player throws 18, treble 20, double 20 with his first three darts. On his next turn he throws treble 19, 7 and double 17. Next turn he throws 5, treble 20 and double 19. How many more does he need to score to have a total of 501?

6 Division

Worked example 21

Divide 245 by 5 (can also be written 245 ÷ 5).

Method 1   Short division

$$5\overline{)2^2 4^4 5}$$ *Answer 49*

Divide by 5. The small figures show the remainder each time 5 is divided into the figure beginning at the left.

Method 2   Long division

```
     49
 5)245
     20        (5 × 4)
     45
     45        (5 × 9)
     ••        Answer 49
```

5 will not divide into the first figure, 2.
5 will divide into the first two figures (24) 4 times (5 × 4 = 20), leaving a remainder of 4. The next figure, 5, is brought down and 5 is divided into 45. This goes exactly 9 times.

Worked example 22   23 076 ÷ 9

$$
\begin{array}{r}
2564 \\
9\overline{)23076}
\end{array}
$$
    Answer 2564

Worked example 23   8992 ÷ 16

$$
\begin{array}{r}
562 \\
16\overline{)8992} \\
80 \\
\hline
99 \\
96 \\
\hline
32 \\
32 \\
\hline
\bullet\bullet
\end{array}
$$

          (16×5)

          (16×6)

          (16×2)
          Answer 562

Sometimes you have to bring down more than one figure.

Worked example 24   7696 ÷ 37

$$
\begin{array}{r}
208 \\
37\overline{)7696} \\
74 \\
\hline
296 \\
296 \\
\hline
\bullet\bullet\bullet
\end{array}
$$

          (2×37)

          (8×37)
          Answer 208

37 into 76 goes 2 $(2 \times 37 = 74)$.
Bring down 9.
37 will not go into 29.
Put 0 in the answer.
Bring down the next figure, 6.
37 into 296 goes 8 times.

Occasionally there is a remainder, and in this case the answer is shown together with the remainder.

Worked example 25   6430 ÷ 18

$$
\begin{array}{r}
357 \\
18\overline{)6430} \\
54 \\
\hline
103 \\
90 \\
\hline
130 \\
126 \\
\hline
4 \text{ remainder}
\end{array}
$$

          (3×18)

          (5×18)

          (7×18)
                    Answer 357, remainder 4

Exercise 11

Find the value of the following. The first two are completed for you.

1 192 ÷ 8
$$
\begin{array}{r}
24 \\
8\overline{)19^32}
\end{array}
$$

2 322 ÷ 14
$$
\begin{array}{r}
23 \\
14\overline{)322} \\
28 \\
\hline
42 \\
42 \\
\hline
\bullet\bullet
\end{array}
$$

3	$126 \div 7$	**4**	$57 \div 3$	**5**	$216 \div 9$	**6**	$228 \div 6$
7	$882 \div 9$	**8**	$1072 \div 8$	**9**	$1248 \div 6$	**10**	$2380 \div 7$
11	$351 \div 13$	**12**	$836 \div 19$	**13**	$2583 \div 21$	**14**	$3424 \div 32$
15	$6993 \div 27$	**16**	$7820 \div 34$	**17**	$4267 \div 17$	**18**	$8592 \div 48$
19	$3332 \div 49$	**20**	$1849 \div 43$	**21**	$2304 \div 9$	**22**	$6402 \div 11$
23	$5604 \div 12$	**24**	$16\,848 \div 16$				

Exercise 12

The first two are completed for you.

1 An electricity bill is £208 per quarter (13 weeks). How much is this per week?

The electricity is £208 for 13 weeks.
To find how much it is for one week divide £208 by 13.

```
       16
   13)208
       13      (13 × 1)
       ──
       78
       78      (13 × 6)
       ──
       ••
```
Answer £16 per week

2 Daffodil bulbs are delivered to a garden centre in sacks and then they are sold in packets, each one containing 12 daffodils. If a sack contains 3900 bulbs, how many packets can you make up from one sack?

There are 3900 bulbs in one sack,
and there are 12 bulbs in each packet.
To find out how many packets divide 3900 by 12.

```
        325
   12)3900
       36      (12 × 3)
       ──
       30
       24      (12 × 2)
       ──
       60
       60      (12 × 5)
       ──
       ••
```
Answer 325 packets in one sack

3 The Council Tax for a house in Band 3 is £676 per year (52 weeks). How much is this per week?

4 A man pays electricity by monthly payments of £47 each month. At the end of the year the actual electricity bill is £528. By how much has he overpaid?

5 A soldier's marching stride is 33 inches. How many strides does he take in marching 1782 yards? (1 yard is 36 inches.)

6 A typist earns £9100 a year (52 weeks). How much is this per week?

7 A young man earns £135 per week and his sister £7383 per year. Who earns most and by how much per week?

8 A haulier has a lorry that can carry 38 tons of sand. How many lorryloads are required to deliver 722 tons of sand?

9 A 53-seater coach costs £742 for a day's outing. How much is this per person if the coach is full?

10 A garden is 168 feet long. How many 6 foot wooden panels are needed to fence one side? If each panel costs £7, what is the cost of fencing one side?

11 The total cost of a school trip abroad was £2484, with 18 pupils making the trip. How much did it cost each pupil?

12   The second prize in the weekly lottery amount to three million eight hundred and sixty-nine thousand two hundred and thirty-two pounds. Eight people shared this prize. How much did each one receive?

7 Priorities

In an expression such as

$$(4 + 2) \times (9 \div 3)$$

we must decide which parts to deal with first.

A **first priority** is a bracket ( ). Everything in a bracket must be worked out before further calculation.

A **second priority** is multiplication and division, and they are done before addition and subtraction.

Worked example 26   Find the value of $5 + 4 \times 3$.

$$5 + 4 \times 3$$
$$= 5 + 12 \qquad \boxed{\text{Do multiplication first.}}$$
$$= 17$$

Worked example 27   Find the value of $(5 + 4) \times 3$.

$$(5 + 4) \times 3$$
$$= 9 \times 3 \qquad \boxed{\text{Work out bracket before multiplication.}}$$
$$= 27$$

Worked example 28   Find the value of $(5 + 6) \times (2 + 7)$.

$$(5 + 6) \times (2 + 7)$$
$$= (11) \times (9) \qquad \boxed{\text{Work out everything in a bracket before further calculation.}}$$
$$= 99$$

Contrast this with worked example 28a

Worked example 28a   Find the value of $5 + 6 \times 2 + 7$.

$$5 + 6 \times 2 + 7$$
$$= 5 + 12 + 7 \qquad \boxed{\text{Do multiplication before addition.}}$$
$$= 24$$

Worked example 29   Find the value of $10 + 9 \div 3 - 2$.

$$10 + 9 \div 3 - 2$$
$$= 10 + 3 - 2 \qquad \boxed{\text{Do division before addition and subtraction.}}$$
$$= 13 - 2$$
$$= 11$$

Worked example 30   Find the value of $(8 + 7) \div (9 - 4) + 3$.

$$(8+7) \div (9 - 4) + 3$$
$$= 15 \div 5 + 3 \qquad \boxed{\begin{array}{l}\text{Brackets first.} \\ \text{Division before addition.}\end{array}}$$
$$= 3 + 3$$
$$= 6$$

Exercise 13

Find the value of the following. The first two are completed for you.

1   $9 + 6 \div 3$ $= 9 + 2 = 11$

2   $7 - (3 + 2) + 5 = 7 - 5 + 5 = 7$

3 $4 \times 5 + 3$	4 $3 + 5 \times 2$	5 $8 - 2 \times 3$
6 $(4 + 7) \times 5$	7 $8 + (9 - 5)$	8 $(9 \div 3) + 6$
9 $6 + 9 \div 3$	10 $8 - (7 - 4) + 6$	11 $4 \times 3 - 2 \times 5$
12 $16 \div (6 - 2)$	13 $(5 + 7) \div (6 \div 3)$	14 $4 \times (9 - 4) + 4$
15 $12 \div 4 + 2$	16 $8 \times 4 - 2 \times 5$	17 $(9 \div 3) \times (3 + 5)$
18 $24 \div 4 + 2$	19 $34 - (6 + 4) \div 5$	20 $27 - (6 \div 3) \times 8 + 2$
21 $9 \times 7 - 5 \times 3$	22 $28 \div 7 + 7$	23 $4 + 6 \times 10$
24 $15 + 15 \div 3$		

8 Multiplication of Whole Numbers by 10, 100, 1000, etc

This section shows how to multiply whole numbers by 10, 100, etc. To multiply any whole number by 10 simply write 0 after the number.

Worked example 31

$7 \times 10 = 70$ $9 \times 10 = 90$ $15 \times 10 = 150$
$290 \times 10 = 2900$ $107 \times 10 = 1070$ $1237 \times 10 = 12\,370$

To multiply any whole number by 100 simply write 00 after the number.

Worked example 32

$7 \times 100 = 700$ $9 \times 100 = 900$ $15 \times 100 = 1500$
$290 \times 100 = 29\,000$ $107 \times 100 = 10\,700$ $1237 \times 100 = 123\,700$

To multiply any whole number by 1000 simply write 000 after the number.

Worked example 33

$7 \times 1000 = 7000$ $9 \times 1000 = 9000$ $15 \times 1000 = 15\,000$

To multiply by 1 000 000 simply write 000 000 after the number.

9 Multiplication of Numbers Ending in 0

Worked example 34

$30 \times 20 = 3 \times 10 \times 2 \times 10$
$ = 6 \times 10 \times 10$
$ = 6 \times 100$
$ = 600$

There is one 0 in 30 and one 0 in 20.
Multiply 2×3 and then add two 0s.

Worked example 35

$60 \times 70 = 4200$	$6 \times 7 = 42$	Add two 0s
$300 \times 50 = 15\,000$	$3 \times 5 = 15$	Add three 0s
$150 \times 30 = 4500$	$15 \times 3 = 45$	Add two 0s
$300 \times 750 = 225\,000$	$3 \times 75 = 225$	Add three 0s
$400 \times 600 = 240\,000$	$4 \times 6 = 24$	Add four 0s

10 Division of Whole Numbers Ending in 0 by 10, 100, 1000 etc

Where a whole number ends in 0 then to divide by 10 simply take off one 0.

Worked example 36

$40 \div 10 = 4$	4$\cancel{0}$ take off one 0
$370 \div 10 = 37$	37$\cancel{0}$ take off one 0
$37\,000 \div 10 = 3700$	37 00$\cancel{0}$ take off one 0

To divide by 100 take off 00 *provided* there are sufficient 0s at the end of the number.

Worked example 37

$600 \div 100 = 6$	6$\cancel{00}$ take off two 0s
$3500 \div 100 = 35$	35$\cancel{00}$ take off two 0s
$328\,000 \div 100 = 3280$	328 0$\cancel{00}$ take off two 0s

For division by 1000 take off 000 *provided* there are sufficient 0s at the end of the number.

11 Division of Two Whole Numbers Ending in 0

Take off *the same number of 0s from each number* and then divide as usual.

Worked example 38

$2800 \div 70 = 280 \div 7$	Take one 0 off each number.
$\quad\quad\quad\quad = 40$	
$270 \div 90 = 27 \div 9$	Take one 0 off each number.
$\quad\quad\quad\quad = 3$	
$4000 \div 500 = 40 \div 5$	Take two 0s off each number.
$\quad\quad\quad\quad\quad = 8$	

Exercise 14

Find the value of the following. The first two are completed for you.

1 $\quad 40 \times 90 = 4 \times 10 \times 9 \times 10$
$\quad\quad\quad\quad = 36 \times 100$
$\quad\quad\quad\quad = 3600$

2 $\quad 3600 \div 60 = 360 \div 6$
$\quad\quad\quad\quad\quad = 60$

3	12×10	**4**	36×10	**5**	350×10	**6**	30×20
7	14×100	**8**	30×70	**9**	43×100	**10**	340×10
11	70×90	**12**	40×240	**13**	500×30	**14**	250×60
15	80×4000	**16**	$390 \div 10$	**17**	$560 \div 10$	**18**	$3400 \div 100$
19	$27\,000 \div 100$	**20**	$4670 \div 10$	**21**	$8400 \div 100$	**22**	$45\,000 \div 100$
23	$34\,000 \div 1000$	**24**	$400 \div 50$	**25**	$3200 \div 80$	**26**	$230\,000 \div 100$
27	$4400 \div 20$	**28**	$2400 \div 60$	**29**	$25\,500 \div 50$	**30**	$24\,800 \div 40$

12 Approximations

When we have completed a calculation we often wonder whether the answer is right or wrong. To give some idea whether it could be right we can find a **rough estimate** of the answer. For example, there is a big difference between 2 and 200.

There is no hard and fast rule about finding a rough estimate but one method is to 'round off' each number to the nearest 10, or 100, or 1000, etc.

As a general rule, if a figure is 5 or more we round up and if 4 or less we round down.

28 is 30 to the nearest 10   (28 is nearer to 30 than to 20)
22 is 20 to the nearest 10
51 is 50 to the nearest 10

168 is 200 to the nearest 100
1352 is 1000 to the nearest 1000

Using such work may help in multiplication and division in providing a check as to whether an answer may be correct or not.

Worked example 39

79×53 is roughly 80×50 (rounding off each number to the nearest 10), and $80 \times 50 = 4000$, so 79×53 is roughly 4000.
$\approx$ is a symbol that means 'approximately equal'.

$79 \times 53 \approx 4000$

The actual answer is 4187.

Worked example 40

73×47 is roughly $70 \times 50 = 3500$
so $73 \times 47 \approx 3500$ (actual answer is 3431)

Worked example 41

$99 \times 99 \approx 100 \times 100 = 10\,000$
so $99 \times 99 \approx 10\,000$ (actual answer is 9801)

Worked example 42

$3156 \div 79 \approx 3200 \div 80 = 40$
so $3156 \div 79 \approx 40$ (actual answer is 39.9)

Worked example 43

$87\,862 \div 99 \approx 88\,000 \div 100 = 880$
so $87\,862 \div 99 \approx 880$ (actual answer is 887.5)

Exercise 15

Round off the following. The first two are completed for you.

1   64 to the nearest 10 is 60

2   127 to the nearest 100 is 100

3   34 to the nearest 10
4   17 to the nearest 10
5   69 to the nearest 10
6   147 to the nearest 10
7   370 to the nearest 100
8   639 to the nearest 100
9   639 to the nearest 1000
10   639 to the nearest 10
11   498 to the nearest 1000
12   498 to the nearest 100
13   756 to the nearest 1000
14   67 to the nearest 10
15   1845 to the nearest 100
16   307 to the nearest 10
17   2099 to the nearest 1000
18   3503 to the nearest 1000
19   509 to the nearest 10
20   3567 to the nearest 100
21   297 to the nearest 100
22   450 to the nearest 100
23   47 to the nearest 100
24   503 to the nearest 10

Exercise 16

Give approximate answers for the following. The first two are completed for you.

1   $27 \times 32 \approx 30 \times 30 = 900$ $27 \times 32 \approx 900$

2   $3357 \div 82 \approx 3400 \div 80 \approx 42$ $3357 \div 82 \approx 42$

3   17×42
4   29×51
5   48×62
6   21×79
7   154×99
8   321×79
9   44×65
10   49×132
11   26×63
12   199×73
13   $4376 \div 99$
14   $362 \div 29$
15   $56\,742 \div 101$
16   $1357 \div 51$
17   $4684 \div 204$
18   $3505 \div 70$
19   $384 \div 19$
20   $3642 \div 62$
21   $57\,465 \div 99$
22   $8432 \div 32$
23   $56\,846 \div 199$
24   $584\,678 \div 1002$

13 Directed Numbers

All numbers can be represented on a **number line** (even fractions and decimals – see later chapters) such as that below:

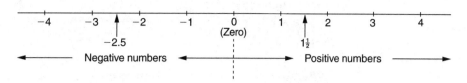

Positive numbers are all greater than zero: they could have a + sign in front of them, such as +2, +4, +27, etc.

Negative numbers are all less than zero and are *always written* with a − sign in front of them, such as −3, −7, −12, −64, etc. Note that with positive numbers 5 is greater than 3, whereas with negative numbers −5 is less than −3.

Negative numbers are used by weather forecasters in the winter; a temperature of −4 °C (Celsius) means 4 degrees below 0 °C (which is freezing point) and, therefore, 4 degrees of frost.

A balance of −£100 in my bank account means I owe the bank £100. In exercise 8, question 10, football teams below the ones mentioned could have scored 42 goals but have had 56 scored against them, a goal difference of $42 - 56 = -14$.

Negative numbers will also be met in Chapter 12 on graphs.

14 Rules for Directed Numbers

Positive numbers have already been covered earlier in this chapter.

Negative numbers

Addition
Add numbers together and put a negative sign in front of the result.

Worked example 44   (a) $-2 - 3 - 4 = -(2 + 3 + 4) = -9$ (b) $-14 - 24 = -(14 + 24) = -38$

Subtraction
When subtracting a negative number change its sign and add.

Worked example 45   (a) $12 - (-5) = 12 + 5 = 17$ (b) $-8 - (-5) = -8 + 5 = -3$
(c) $7 - (-6) - 23 = 7 + 6 - 23 = -10$

Multiplication
When multiplying numbers with **like signs** the answer is **always positive**.

Worked example 46   (a) $5 \times 6 = 30$ (b) $(-5) \times (-6) = 30$ (c) $(-4) \times (-3) = 12$

When multiplying numbers with **unlike signs** the answer is **always negative**.

Worked example 47   (a) $5 \times (-6) = -30$ (b) $-5 \times 6 = -30$
(c) $4 \times (-3) = -12$ (d) $(-4) \times 3 = -12$

Division
When dividing numbers with **like signs** the answer is **always positive**.

Worked example 48

(a) $6 \div 3 = \dfrac{6}{3} = 2$

(b) $(-6) \div (-3) = \dfrac{-6}{-3} = 2$

(c) $24 \div 8 = \dfrac{24}{8} = 3$

(d) $-24 \div -8 = \dfrac{-24}{-8} = 3$

When dividing numbers with **unlike signs** the answer is **always negative**.

Worked example 49

(a) $6 \div (-3) = \dfrac{6}{-3} = -2$

(b) $-6 \div 3 = \dfrac{-6}{3} = -2$

(c) $24 \div (-8) = \dfrac{24}{-8} = -3$

(d) $-24 \div 8 = \dfrac{-24}{8} = -3$

Addition and subtraction together

When there are a lot of positive and negative numbers together, first collect all the positive numbers together and add them, then collect all the negative numbers together and add them, and finally subtract one from the other.

Worked example 50

Find the value of $-4 + 7 + 2 - 1 - 6 + 2 - 1 + 3$.

$$-4 + 7 + 2 - 1 - 6 + 2 - 1 + 3 = (7 + 2 + 2 + 3) - (4 + 1 + 6 + 1)$$
$$= 14 - 12$$
$$= 2$$

Worked example 51

Find the value of $12 - 6 - 4 - 3 + 8$.

$$12 - 6 - 4 - 3 + 8 = (12 + 8) - (6 + 4 + 3)$$
$$= 20 - 13$$
$$= 7$$

Worked example 52

Find the value of $4 - 3 - 5 - 6 + 2 - 5$.

$$4 - 3 - 5 - 6 + 2 - 5 = (4 + 2) - (3 + 5 + 6 + 5) = 6 - 19$$
$$= -13$$

Exercise 17

Find the value of

1 $7 + 4 + 8$	**2** $-5 - 3 - 2$	**3** $-7 + 8 + 2$
4 $-7 - 8 - 2$	**5** $2 - 5 + 6 - 4 + 8 - 3$	
6 $-4 - 3 - 4 - 6 + 7 + 2$	**7** $8 + 3 + 2 - 7 - 6 - 4 - 5 - 3$	
8 5×2	**9** -5×2	**10** $5 \times (-2)$
11 6×7	**12** $6 \times (-7)$	**13** $8 \div 2$
14 $8 \div (-2)$	**15** $(-8) \div (+2)$	**16** $+8 \div (-2)$
17 $-12 \div 3$	**18** $(-12) \div (-3)$	**19** $12 \div (-3)$
20 $-12 \div (-3)$	**21** $2 \times (-2) \times 3$	**22** $-3 \times 2 \times (-3)$
23 $-4 \times -2 \times -1$		

24   Write in order of size, largest first, the numbers $-4, 8, 6, -9, -7, 9$.

25   Write in order of size, smallest first, the numbers $8, 5, -2, 6, -9, -8, 0$.

26 The following table gives the midday temperatures in °C of some cities on
    31 January 1995.

Algiers 20	Chicago −14	Majorca 16	Singapore 24
Barcelona 17	Delhi 26	Melbourne 30	Sydney 31
Belgrade 14	Helsinki −5	Montreal −15	Tokyo 10
Brisbane 32	Kuwait 25	Moscow −18	Wellington 21
Cairo 23	London 5	Paris 2	Zurich 0

(a) Which was the hottest place?
(b) Which was the coldest place?
(c) What was the temperature difference between the hottest and coldest
     places?
(d) What was the difference in temperature between London and Chicago?
(e) What was the temperature difference between Helsinki and Montreal?
(f) What was the temperature difference between Chicago and Singapore?
(g) What was the temperature difference between Delhi and Moscow?
(h) What was the temperature difference between Zurich and Montreal?

15 Number Sequences

You can have fun with numbers. Sequences may provide such fun. A series of
numbers connected in a definite way is a **sequence** of numbers. Each number is
called a **term** of that sequence.

Look at the numbers 1, 3, 5, 7, 9, . . . Can you see how the sequence continues?
Of course you can! It is 11, 13, 15, . . .

Each term in the sequence is formed by adding 2 to the previous term. That was
easy. But you could, perhaps, make up a sequence that would fox even your
teacher.

Here are some more examples.

Worked example 53

Write down the next term of the sequence 2, 7, 12, 17, . . .

Each term is formed by adding 5 to the previous term.
The next term in the sequence would be 22.

Worked example 54

Write down the next term of the sequence 24, 20, 16, 12, 8, . . .

Each term is formed by subtracting 4 from the previous term.
The next term in the sequence would be 4.

Worked example 55

Write down the next term of the sequence 1, 2, 4, 8, 16, . . .

Each term is formed by multiplying the previous term by 2.
The next term in the sequence would be 32.

Worked example 56

Write down the next term of the sequence 729, 243, 81, 27, 9, 3, . . .

Look at the smaller numbers first. Can you see a connection between 27, 9,
3, . . . ? Each term has been divided by 3.
Check the larger numbers to see if this is correct:

$729 \div 3 = 243$
$243 \div 3 = 81$
$81 \div 3 = 27$

Each term is formed by dividing the previous term by 3.
The next term in the sequence would be 1.

Exercise 18

Write down the next term in the following sequences.

1 2, 6, 10, 14, . . .
2 1, 7, 13, 19, . . .
3 22, 19, 16, 13, . . .
4 3, 6, 12, 24, . . .
5 35, 30, 25, 20, . . .
6 162, 54, 18, 6, . . .
7 11, 8, 5, 2, . . .
8 4, 9, 16, . . .
9 2, 5, 3, 6, 4, 7, . . .
10 70, 60, 65, 55, 60, 50, 55, . . .

Exercise 19

Write down the terms, where there is a blank, in the following sequences.

1 5, 10, 15, . . . , 25, . . .
2 2, 4, . . . , 8, . . . , 12,
3 1, 2, 4, 7, 11, . . . , 22, . . . , 37,
4 486, 162, . . . , 18, 6, . . . ,
5 −8, −3, . . . , 5, 8, 13, . . . ,
6 15, 11, . . . , 3, . . . , −5,
7 2, 6, 4, 8, . . . , 10, . . . ,
8 . . . , −5, −3, −1, . . . , 3,
9 . . . , 4, 1, 0, 1, . . . , 9,
10 −20, −15, −17, −12, −14, . . . , . . . ,

Exercise 20 Multiple choice questions

Work out which is the correct answer in the following questions:

1 What is 1842 expressed in words?
   A One thousand and forty-two
   B One hundred and eighty-four
   C Eighteen hundred and twenty
   D One thousand eight hundred and forty-two

2 3469 is added to 323. The answer is
   A Three thousand seven hundred and ninety-two
   B Three thousand one hundred and forty-six
   C Three thousand nine hundred and seventy-two
   D Three thousand seven hundred

3 One thousand five hundred and twenty-five is added to four hundred and six. The answer is
   A 1985   B 1931   C 1119   D 1936

4 If 89 is multiplied by 76 the answer is
   A 6674   B 6764   C 6784   D 6676

5 If 22 100 is divided by 65 the answer is
   A 342   B 346   C 340   D 348

6 A college canteen menu said:
   coffee 21p, tea 19p, sandwich 50p, soup 38p.
   The bill came to 78p. The student bought
   A 4 teas
   B 3 coffees and 1 tea
   C 1 sandwich and 2 teas
   D 1 coffee, 1 tea and 1 soup

7 The answer to $6 + 4 \div 2 + 2$ is
   A 10   B 7   C 6   D 8

8 The answer to $3 + 5 \times 7 − 3$ is
   A 53   B 32   C 60   D 35

9 A salary of £12 480 is
   A £200 a week   B £420 a week   C £240 a week
   D £228 a week

10 A car's mileage at the beginning of a journey was 62 516 and at the end it was 64 032. The car had travelled
   A 526 miles   B 1448 miles
   C 1316 miles   D 1516 miles

11 40×80 is
   A 3200   B 12 000   C 32 000   D 45 320

12 449 to the nearest hundred is
   A 400   B 500   C 450   D 440

13 5201 to the nearest 10 is
   A 52   B 5000   C 521   D 5200

14 69×81 is roughly
   A 150   B 5600   C 4800   D 6300

15 $65 821 \div 101$ is roughly
   A 65   B 621   C 658   D 821

16 The next number in the sequence −7, −2, −5, 0, −3, 2 is
   A 4   B 1   C −1   D 2

2 Fractions

1 Introduction

Everyone knows what we mean when we divide something into two halves, such as a bar of chocolate, or an orange, or a cake – in fact almost anything. In practice, though, it may be difficult to do it exactly.

In mathematics, if something is divided in half then it is divided exactly into two equal pieces.

This line is divided into 2 equal parts.
Bracketed piece = $\frac{1}{2}$ of whole line

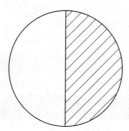

> The fraction $\frac{1}{2}$ means 1 is divided by 2.
> In the fraction $\frac{1}{2}$, 1 is called the **numerator**.
> 2 is called the **denominator**.

This circle is divided into 2 equal parts.
Shaded piece = $\frac{1}{2}$ of whole circle

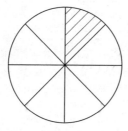

This circle is divided into 8 equal parts.
Shaded piece = $\frac{1}{8}$ of whole circle

Now look at the two examples below.

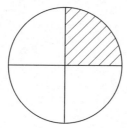

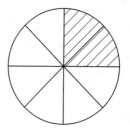

This circle is divided into 4 equal parts.
Shaded piece = $\frac{1}{4}$ of circle

This circle is divided into 8 equal parts.
Shaded piece = $\frac{2}{8}$ of circle

Both shaded pieces are the same fraction of the circle, which means

$$\frac{1}{4} = \frac{2}{8}$$

2 Changing Fractions to Equivalent Fractions

A fraction can be changed to another fraction and yet have exactly the same value; this is said to be changing one fraction to an **equivalent fraction**.

Worked example 1

Change $\frac{3}{4}$ to an equivalent fraction of sixteenths.

We want to make $\frac{3}{4}$ = so many sixteenths = $\frac{}{16}$.

The denominator of the second fraction is 4 times the size of the first. To make the fractions equal the numerator of the second fraction, therefore, has to be 4 times the size of the first.

So $\frac{3}{4} = \frac{12}{16}$

Worked example 2

Complete as equivalent fractions $\frac{3}{5} = \frac{}{25}$.

The denominator of the second fraction is 5 times the size of the first; therefore the numerator of the second fraction has to be 5 times the size of the first:

$$\frac{3}{5} = \frac{15}{25}$$

Exercise 1

Change to equivalent fractions. The first two are completed for you.

1 $\frac{1}{2} = \frac{}{16}$

The denominator has been multiplied by 8 so multiply the numerator by 8.
$1 \times 8 = 8$
$2 \times 8 = 16$

$\frac{1}{2} = \frac{8}{16}$

2 $\frac{4}{3} = \frac{12}{}$

The numerator has been multiplied by 3 so multiply the denominator by 3.
$4 \times 3 = 12$
$3 \times 3 = 9$

$\frac{4}{3} = \frac{12}{9}$

3 $\frac{1}{2} = \frac{}{4}$

4 $\frac{1}{3} = \frac{}{9}$

5 $\frac{1}{4} = \frac{}{16}$

6 $\frac{3}{2} = \frac{}{6}$

7 $\frac{3}{2} = \frac{12}{}$

8 $\frac{3}{4} = \frac{}{12}$

9 $\frac{2}{3} = \frac{12}{}$

10 $\frac{2}{5} = \frac{}{10}$

11 $\frac{4}{5} = \frac{16}{}$

12 $\frac{7}{8} = \frac{}{16}$

13 $\frac{3}{5} = \frac{6}{}$

14 $\frac{11}{8} = \frac{33}{}$

15 $\frac{6}{5} = \frac{24}{}$

16 $\frac{5}{3} = \frac{15}{}$

17 $\frac{3}{8} = \frac{6}{}$

18 $\frac{5}{8} = \frac{}{32}$

19 $\frac{5}{2} = \frac{10}{}$

20 $\frac{3}{4} = \frac{}{8}$

21 Change $\frac{3}{4}$ into sixteenths

22 Change $\frac{4}{5}$ into tenths

23 Change $\dfrac{5}{8}$ into thirty-seconds

24 Change two-thirds into sixths

25 Change three-quarters into twelfths

26 Change five-halves into tenths

27 Change four-thirds into twelfths

28 Change seven-eighths into sixteenths

29 Change sixteen thirty-seconds into eighths

30 Change five-quarters into sixteenths

3 Cancelling Fractions

A fraction should be given in its lowest terms: that is, the denominator and numerator should be looked at to see whether the same number will divide into both of them.

Worked example 3   Reduce $\dfrac{6}{10}$ to its lowest terms.

$$\frac{6}{10} = \frac{3}{5}$$ | Divide numerator and denominator by 2. This is cancelling by 2. |

Note: The cancelling is usually done on the fraction itself: $\dfrac{\cancel{6}^{3}}{\cancel{10}_{5}} = \dfrac{3}{5}$.

Sometimes it is necessary to cancel more than once.

Worked example 4   Give $\dfrac{24}{60}$ as a fraction in its lowest terms.

$$\frac{\cancel{24}^{\cancel{12}^{\cancel{6}^{2}}}}{\cancel{60}_{\cancel{30}_{\cancel{15}_{5}}}} = \frac{2}{5}$$ | Cancel by 2, then 2, and then 3. |

Where both numbers are even you can always cancel by 2.

Exercise 2

Reduce the following fractions to their lowest terms. The first two are completed for you.

1 $\dfrac{6}{8}$ $\dfrac{\cancel{6}^{3}}{\cancel{8}_{4}} = \dfrac{3}{4}$ | Cancel by 2. |

2 $\dfrac{24}{18}$ $\dfrac{\cancel{24}^{\cancel{12}^{4}}}{\cancel{18}_{\cancel{9}_{3}}} = \dfrac{4}{3}$ | Cancel by 2 and then by 3. |

3 $\dfrac{6}{10}$ 4 $\dfrac{8}{12}$ 5 $\dfrac{4}{6}$ 6 $\dfrac{9}{12}$

7 $\dfrac{7}{21}$ 8 $\dfrac{12}{16}$ 9 $\dfrac{8}{14}$ 10 $\dfrac{9}{15}$

11 $\dfrac{14}{20}$ 12 $\dfrac{25}{45}$ 13 $\dfrac{10}{25}$ 14 $\dfrac{16}{24}$

15 $\dfrac{4}{18}$ 16 $\dfrac{15}{35}$ 17 $\dfrac{12}{22}$ 18 $\dfrac{18}{32}$

19 $\dfrac{7}{9}$ 20 $\dfrac{9}{24}$ 21 $\dfrac{3}{8}$ 22 $\dfrac{12}{28}$

23 $\dfrac{32}{48}$ 24 $\dfrac{16}{44}$

4 Comparison of Fractions

A comparison of fractions can be made by making use of equivalent fractions to change all of the fractions to the same denominator.

Worked example 5

Arrange in order of size $\dfrac{1}{3}, \dfrac{3}{4}, \dfrac{5}{8}$.

First, find a denominator into which all three denominators will divide. How do we do this?

A practical way is to look at the largest denominator and see if all the other denominators will divide into it.

- If they will not then double the largest denominator and try again.
- If they will not then multiply the largest denominator by 3.
- If all the other denominators will still not divide into it then multiply by 4, and so on.

For $\dfrac{1}{3}, \dfrac{3}{4}$ and $\dfrac{5}{8}$ a suitable denominator is 24. Now express each fraction with a denominator of 24:

$\dfrac{1}{3} = \dfrac{8}{24}$ $\dfrac{3}{4} = \dfrac{18}{24}$ $\dfrac{5}{8} = \dfrac{15}{24}$

$\dfrac{18}{24}$ is bigger than $\dfrac{15}{24}$, which is bigger than $\dfrac{8}{24}$.

Fractions in order of size are $\dfrac{3}{4}, \dfrac{5}{8}, \dfrac{1}{3}$.

Worked example 6

Arrange in order of size $\dfrac{2}{3}, \dfrac{4}{5}, \dfrac{3}{4}$.

First, look for a denominator into which all three denominators will divide.

A suitable denominator is 60. Change all three fractions to sixtieths:

$\dfrac{2}{3} = \dfrac{40}{60}$ $\dfrac{4}{5} = \dfrac{48}{60}$ $\dfrac{3}{4} = \dfrac{45}{60}$

Fractions in order of size are $\dfrac{4}{5}, \dfrac{3}{4}, \dfrac{2}{3}$.

Exercise 3

Put the following fractions in order of size, smallest first. The first two are completed for you.

1 $\dfrac{1}{4}, \dfrac{1}{3}$

Change each fraction to the same denominator, then place in order. Change each fraction to twelfths:

$\dfrac{1}{4} = \dfrac{3}{12}$ $\dfrac{1}{3} = \dfrac{4}{12}$

Fractions in order of size are $\dfrac{1}{4}, \dfrac{1}{3}$.

2 $\dfrac{3}{8}, \dfrac{3}{4}, \dfrac{1}{2}, \dfrac{7}{10}$

Change each fraction to fortieths:

$$\dfrac{3}{8} = \dfrac{15}{40} \qquad \dfrac{3}{4} = \dfrac{30}{40} \qquad \dfrac{1}{2} = \dfrac{20}{40} \qquad \dfrac{7}{10} = \dfrac{28}{40}$$

Fractions in order of size are $\dfrac{3}{8}, \dfrac{1}{2}, \dfrac{7}{10}, \dfrac{3}{4}$.

3 $\dfrac{1}{4}, \dfrac{1}{3}$

4 $\dfrac{2}{3}, \dfrac{3}{4}$

5 $\dfrac{1}{2}, \dfrac{1}{3}, \dfrac{2}{5}$

6 $\dfrac{2}{3}, \dfrac{1}{2}, \dfrac{3}{5}$

7 $\dfrac{3}{8}, \dfrac{5}{6}, \dfrac{1}{2}$

8 $\dfrac{1}{3}, \dfrac{3}{5}, \dfrac{1}{2}$

9 $\dfrac{5}{8}, \dfrac{7}{16}, \dfrac{1}{2}$

10 $\dfrac{2}{3}, \dfrac{5}{8}$

11 $\dfrac{7}{12}, \dfrac{2}{3}, \dfrac{5}{6}$

12 $\dfrac{11}{24}, \dfrac{5}{8}, \dfrac{2}{3}$

13 $\dfrac{3}{2}, \dfrac{15}{8}, \dfrac{7}{4}$

14 $\dfrac{1}{2}, \dfrac{7}{16}, \dfrac{5}{8}, \dfrac{3}{8}$

15 $\dfrac{3}{4}, \dfrac{2}{3}, \dfrac{13}{16}$

16 $\dfrac{1}{2}, \dfrac{5}{8}, \dfrac{9}{16}, \dfrac{2}{3}$

17 $\dfrac{5}{6}, \dfrac{11}{12}, 1, \dfrac{3}{4}$

18 $\dfrac{3}{4}, \dfrac{17}{24}, \dfrac{5}{8}, \dfrac{2}{3}$

19 $\dfrac{4}{5}, \dfrac{3}{4}$

20 $\dfrac{3}{2}, \dfrac{5}{4}, 1, \dfrac{15}{8}$

21 $\dfrac{3}{4}, \dfrac{23}{32}, \dfrac{5}{8}, \dfrac{15}{16}$

22 $\dfrac{1}{3}, \dfrac{1}{5}, \dfrac{1}{4}$

23 $\dfrac{3}{4}, \dfrac{11}{16}, \dfrac{2}{3}$

24 $\dfrac{9}{16}, \dfrac{17}{24}, \dfrac{5}{8}, \dfrac{2}{3}$

5 Improper Fractions and Mixed Fractions

An **improper fraction** is a fraction in which the numerator is bigger than the denominator.

An improper fraction can be changed into a whole number plus a proper fraction; it is then called a **mixed fraction**.

Worked example 7 Change $\dfrac{15}{8}$ into a mixed fraction

We divide the denominator into the numerator, but instead of finding a remainder we put this remainder over the denominator, so making a proper fraction:

$\dfrac{15}{8} = 1\tfrac{7}{8}$ | 8 into 15 goes 1 with a remainder of 7. Put this 7 over the denominator.

Worked examples 8 $\dfrac{4}{3} = 1\tfrac{1}{3}$ | Divide 4 by 3.

$\dfrac{10}{3} = 3\tfrac{1}{3}$ | Divide 10 by 3.

$\dfrac{15}{4} = 3\tfrac{3}{4}$ | Divide 15 by 4.

Worked example 9 Change $3\tfrac{3}{4}$ to an improper fraction

In changing a mixed fraction to an improper fraction the denominator of the fraction is all-important:

$3\tfrac{3}{4} = 3 + \tfrac{3}{4}$

Now change the 3 whole 1s into quarters, making 12:

$3\tfrac{3}{4} = \tfrac{12}{4} + \tfrac{3}{4}$

$\quad\ = \tfrac{15}{4}$

In other words, multiply the whole number by the denominator and then add the numerator part of the fraction.

Worked examples 10

$1\frac{2}{3} = \frac{5}{3}$ 3×1 and then add 2.

$2\frac{7}{8} = \frac{23}{8}$ 8×2 and then add 7.

$4\frac{3}{4} = \frac{19}{4}$ 4×4 and then add 3.

Exercise 4

Change the improper fractions to mixed fractions. The first two are completed for you.

1   $\frac{5}{4}$

Divide the denominator into the numerator and put any remainder over the denominator.

$\frac{5}{4} = 1\frac{1}{4}$ 4 into 5 goes 1 with a remainder of 1.

2   $\frac{28}{10}$

$\frac{28}{10} = 2\frac{8}{10} = 2\frac{4}{5}$ 10 into 28 goes 2 with a remainder of 8. See if the remaining fraction will cancel.

3	$\frac{3}{2}$	4	$\frac{7}{2}$	5	$\frac{7}{4}$	6	$\frac{9}{2}$
7	$\frac{5}{3}$	8	$\frac{11}{3}$	9	$\frac{16}{6}$	10	$\frac{12}{8}$
11	$\frac{10}{4}$	12	$\frac{17}{5}$	13	$\frac{13}{4}$	14	$\frac{20}{8}$
15	$\frac{12}{5}$	16	$\frac{12}{7}$	17	$\frac{16}{10}$	18	$\frac{17}{7}$
19	$\frac{24}{10}$	20	$\frac{9}{2}$	21	$\frac{16}{9}$	22	$\frac{22}{4}$
23	$\frac{20}{12}$	24	$\frac{8}{2}$				

Exercise 5

Change the mixed fractions to improper fractions. The first two are completed for you.

1   $2\frac{3}{4}$

Multiply the whole number by the denominator of the fraction and then add the numerator part of the fraction.

$2\frac{3}{4} = \frac{11}{4}$ 2×4 and then add 3.

2   $3\frac{5}{6} = \frac{23}{6}$ 3×6 and then add 5.

3	$3\frac{1}{2}$	4	$2\frac{1}{4}$	5	$1\frac{3}{4}$	6	$1\frac{1}{2}$
7	$1\frac{2}{3}$	8	$2\frac{1}{3}$	9	$2\frac{3}{4}$	10	$1\frac{4}{5}$
11	$2\frac{3}{5}$	12	$4\frac{3}{4}$	13	$2\frac{3}{10}$	14	$3\frac{2}{3}$
15	$5\frac{1}{3}$	16	$4\frac{4}{5}$	17	$2\frac{5}{6}$	18	$8\frac{1}{3}$
19	$4\frac{6}{7}$	20	$6\frac{2}{3}$	21	$2\frac{5}{7}$	22	$7\frac{1}{6}$
23	$7\frac{1}{4}$	24	$3\frac{3}{5}$				

6 Addition and Subtraction

Before adding or subtracting it is important to make sure that the denominators of the fractions involved are all the same.

Worked example 11

$$\frac{1}{4} + \frac{3}{8}$$

Change each fraction to eighths (look at worked example 5):

$$\frac{1}{4} + \frac{3}{8} = \frac{2}{8} + \frac{3}{8}$$

$$= \frac{5}{8}$$

$$\boxed{\frac{1}{4} = \frac{2}{8}}$$

Worked example 12

$$\frac{1}{4} + \frac{1}{3}$$

Change each fraction to twelfths:

$$\frac{1}{4} + \frac{1}{3} = \frac{3}{12} + \frac{4}{12}$$

$$= \frac{7}{12}$$

$$\boxed{\frac{1}{4} = \frac{3}{12}, \frac{1}{3} = \frac{4}{12}}$$

It is usual to use only one line when the common denominator has been chosen, so

$$\frac{1}{4} + \frac{1}{3} = \frac{3+4}{12}$$

$$= \frac{7}{12}$$

Worked example 13

$$\frac{1}{4} + \frac{1}{3} + \frac{1}{5} = \frac{15 + 20 + 12}{60}$$

$$= \frac{47}{60}$$

$$\boxed{\frac{1}{4} = \frac{15}{60}, \frac{1}{3} = \frac{20}{60}, \frac{1}{5} = \frac{12}{60}}$$

When adding mixed fractions, add together the whole numbers first followed by the fractions.

Worked example 14

$$2\frac{1}{4} + 3\frac{5}{8} = 5 + \frac{1}{4} + \frac{5}{8}$$

$$= 5\frac{2+5}{8}$$

$$= 5\frac{7}{8}$$

$$\boxed{\text{Add whole numbers first.}}$$

Worked example 15

$$\frac{2}{3} - \frac{1}{4} = \frac{8-3}{12}$$

$$= \frac{5}{12}$$

More care may have to be taken when subtracting mixed fractions.

Worked example 16

$$3\frac{1}{2} - 2\frac{1}{3} = 1\frac{3-2}{6}$$

$$= 1\frac{1}{6}$$

$$\boxed{\text{This example is straightforward.}}$$

Worked example 17

$$4\frac{1}{2} - 2\frac{2}{3} = 2\frac{3-4}{6}$$

Care is needed because 4 cannot be taken from 3. Use one of the whole numbers and change it into sixths:

$$= 1\frac{6+3-4}{6}$$

$$= 1\frac{9-4}{6}$$

$$= 1\frac{5}{6}$$

Exercise 6

Add together the following fractions. The first two are completed for you.

1   $\dfrac{1}{3} + \dfrac{1}{5}$

Change each fraction to the same denominator, in this case fifteenths:
$\frac{1}{3} + \frac{1}{5} = \frac{5}{15} + \frac{3}{15} = \frac{8}{15}$

2   $1\frac{1}{2} + \frac{3}{4} + 1\frac{1}{8}$
Add whole numbers together. Change fractions to the same denominator, in this case eighths:

$1\frac{1}{2} + \frac{3}{4} + 1\frac{1}{8} = 2\frac{4+6+1}{8}$

$\qquad\qquad\qquad = 2\frac{11}{8}$

$\qquad\qquad\qquad = 3\frac{3}{8}$ $\boxed{\dfrac{11}{8} = 1\frac{3}{8}}$

3 $\frac{1}{10} + \frac{3}{10}$	4 $\frac{1}{2} + \frac{1}{4}$	5 $\frac{2}{3} + \frac{1}{6}$	6 $\frac{3}{8} + \frac{1}{4}$
7 $\frac{1}{2} + \frac{3}{8}$	8 $\frac{1}{2} + \frac{1}{4} + \frac{3}{8}$	9 $\frac{1}{8} + \frac{1}{4} + \frac{5}{16}$	10 $1\frac{1}{3} + 1\frac{2}{3}$
11 $\frac{3}{4} + \frac{2}{3} + \frac{1}{5}$	12 $3\frac{2}{3} + 2\frac{1}{4}$	13 $\frac{3}{4} + 2 + \frac{2}{5}$	14 $2\frac{1}{3} + 3\frac{3}{8}$
15 $1\frac{1}{4} + 2\frac{2}{3} + \frac{2}{5}$	16 $\frac{3}{16} + 2\frac{7}{8} + 3\frac{3}{8}$	17 $1\frac{4}{5} + 2\frac{2}{3} + 2\frac{1}{2}$	18 $2\frac{3}{8} + 3\frac{1}{2} + 3\frac{3}{4}$
19 $2\frac{1}{4} + 3\frac{2}{3} + 1\frac{2}{3}$	20 $1\frac{1}{2} + 3\frac{3}{4} + 2\frac{5}{8}$	21 $\frac{1}{3} + 2\frac{1}{5} + 2\frac{3}{4}$	22 $2\frac{1}{2} + 3\frac{5}{16} + 1\frac{3}{8}$
23 $\frac{3}{4} + \frac{2}{3} + 2\frac{7}{24}$	24 $\frac{1}{2} + \frac{7}{10} + 1\frac{2}{5}$		

Exercise 7

Subtract the following fractions. The first three are completed for you.

1   $\dfrac{3}{4} - \dfrac{2}{3}$
Change each fraction to the same denominator, in this case 12:
$\frac{3}{4} - \frac{2}{3} = \frac{9-8}{12} = \frac{1}{12}$

2   $2\frac{1}{2} - 1\frac{1}{8}$
Subtract the whole numbers first, and then subtract one fraction from the other:

$2\frac{1}{2} - 1\frac{1}{8} \qquad = 1\frac{4-1}{8}$

$\qquad\qquad\qquad = 1\frac{3}{8}$

3   $3\frac{1}{4} - 1\frac{5}{8}$
Subtract the whole numbers first, and put the fractions over the same denominator:

$3\frac{1}{4} - 1\frac{5}{8} = 2\frac{2-5}{8}$

But 5 cannot be taken from 2, so use one of the whole numbers and change to eighths (8 is the denominator):

$\qquad\qquad = 1\frac{8+2-5}{8}$

$\qquad\qquad = 1\frac{5}{8}$

4 $\frac{2}{3} - \frac{1}{4}$	5 $1\frac{3}{4} - \frac{2}{3}$	6 $\frac{3}{4} - \frac{1}{3}$
7 $1\frac{3}{4} - 1\frac{2}{5}$	8 $3\frac{7}{8} - 1\frac{1}{3}$	9 $2\frac{5}{8} - 1\frac{1}{3}$
10 $3\frac{1}{2} - 1\frac{1}{3}$	11 $1\frac{2}{3} - \frac{3}{4}$	12 $1\frac{2}{5} - \frac{3}{4}$
13 $3\frac{7}{16} - \frac{3}{4}$	14 $3\frac{1}{8} - 1\frac{7}{16}$	15 $2\frac{2}{3} - 1\frac{3}{4}$
16 $5\frac{1}{4} - 2\frac{7}{16}$	17 $2\frac{3}{8} - 1\frac{4}{5}$	18 $2\frac{1}{2} + 1\frac{3}{4} - 3\frac{5}{8}$
19 $1\frac{3}{4} + 2\frac{2}{3} - 3\frac{3}{8}$	20 $1\frac{1}{2} - 2\frac{1}{4} + 2\frac{1}{3}$	21 $3\frac{1}{2} - 1\frac{7}{8} + \frac{2}{3}$
22 $5\frac{1}{4} - 7\frac{1}{3} + 2\frac{2}{5}$	23 $1\frac{11}{16} + 2\frac{3}{8} + \frac{3}{4}$	24 $2\frac{3}{5} + 3\frac{8}{15} - 4\frac{13}{15}$

7 Multiplication   For proper fractions multiply all the numerators together and all the denominators together; if mixed fractions are involved convert them to improper fractions before multiplying.

The working can be made easier by cancelling, and you can cancel any number in a numerator with any number in a denominator.

Worked example 18 $\dfrac{1}{3} \times \dfrac{4}{5} = \dfrac{4}{15}$

Numerators: $1 \times 4 = 4$
Denominators: $3 \times 5 = 15$

Worked example 19 $\dfrac{3}{4} \times \dfrac{4}{9} = \dfrac{12}{36} = \dfrac{1}{3}$

or $\dfrac{\cancel{3}^1}{\cancel{4}_1} \times \dfrac{\cancel{4}^1}{\cancel{9}_3} = \dfrac{1 \times 1}{1 \times 3} = \dfrac{1}{3}$

Worked example 20 $\dfrac{\cancel{2}^1}{\cancel{3}_1} \times \dfrac{\cancel{9}^3}{\cancel{10}_5} = \dfrac{3}{5}$

Cancel by 3 for 3 and 9.
Cancel by 2 for 2 and 10.

Worked example 21 $2\frac{1}{2} \times 1\frac{1}{3}$

These are mixed fractions; change to improper fractions.

$2\frac{1}{2} \times 1\frac{1}{3} = \dfrac{5}{\cancel{2}_1} \times \dfrac{\cancel{4}^2}{3} = \dfrac{10}{3} = 3\frac{1}{3}$.

Exercise 8

Multiply the following fractions. The first three are completed for you.

1 $\dfrac{3}{4} \times \dfrac{2}{3} = \dfrac{6}{12}$
$= \dfrac{1}{2}$

or $\dfrac{\cancel{3}^1}{\cancel{4}_2} \times \dfrac{\cancel{2}^1}{\cancel{3}_1} = \dfrac{1}{2}$

Multiply the numerators together.
Multiply the denominators together.
Cancel by 6.
Cancel before multiplying.

2 $2\frac{1}{8} \times 1\frac{1}{3} = \dfrac{17}{\cancel{8}_2} \times \dfrac{\cancel{4}^1}{3}$
$= \dfrac{17}{6}$
$= 2\frac{5}{6}$

Change mixed fractions to improper fractions and then cancel.

3 Find $\frac{3}{4}$ of 120

In this context, 'of' means multiply.

$\dfrac{3}{4}$ of $120 = \dfrac{3}{\cancel{4}_1} \times \cancel{120}^{30}$
$= 90$

4 $\frac{4}{7} \times \frac{3}{4}$	5 $\frac{2}{3} \times \frac{3}{4}$	6 $\frac{5}{6} \times \frac{12}{25}$
7 $\frac{3}{4} \times \frac{10}{13}$	8 $\frac{3}{4} \times \frac{6}{11}$	9 $2\frac{1}{4} \times 1\frac{1}{3}$
10 $3\frac{2}{3} \times 2\frac{1}{11}$	11 $1\frac{3}{4} \times 1\frac{1}{3}$	12 $2\frac{5}{8} \times 2\frac{2}{3}$
13 $3\frac{1}{3} \times 1\frac{3}{5}$	14 $2\frac{1}{3} \times 2\frac{5}{7}$	15 $2\frac{1}{2} \times 3\frac{3}{5}$
16 $\frac{2}{3}$ of $3\frac{1}{3}$	17 $\frac{3}{4}$ of $4\frac{2}{3}$	18 $\frac{7}{8}$ of $5\frac{1}{3}$

19 Find $\frac{4}{5}$ of 240   20 Find $\frac{2}{3}$ of 120

21 What is $\frac{3}{4}$ of 64?   22 Find $\frac{3}{5}$ of £90

23 How much is $\frac{5}{9}$ of 45? 24 How much is $\frac{3}{7}$ of 105?

8 Division

To divide by a fraction, whether a proper or an improper fraction, all we have to do is invert the fraction and then multiply. (A mixed fraction should first be changed to an improper fraction.)

Worked example 22

$$\frac{3}{4} \div \frac{1}{2} = \frac{3}{\cancel{4}_2} \times \frac{\cancel{2}^1}{1}$$

$$= \frac{3}{2} = 1\frac{1}{2}$$

> Invert $\frac{1}{2}$ and then multiply.

Worked example 23

$$1\frac{1}{5} \div 1\frac{1}{10} = \frac{6}{5} \div \frac{11}{10}$$

$$= \frac{6}{\cancel{5}_1} \times \frac{\cancel{10}^2}{11}$$

$$= \frac{12}{11} = 1\frac{1}{11}$$

> Change to improper fractions.
>
> Invert $\frac{11}{10}$ and then multiply.

Exercise 9

Divide the following fractions. The first two are completed for you.

1   $2\frac{3}{4} \div 1\frac{1}{4} = \frac{11}{4} \div \frac{5}{4}$

$$= \frac{11}{\cancel{4}_1} \times \frac{\cancel{4}^1}{5}$$

$$= \frac{11}{5} = 2\frac{1}{5}$$

> Change to improper fractions.
> Invert divisor and multiply.

2   $2\frac{1}{4} \div \frac{2}{3} = \frac{9}{4} \div \frac{2}{3}$

$$= \frac{9}{4} \times \frac{3}{2}$$

$$= \frac{27}{8} = 3\frac{3}{8}$$

3 $\frac{3}{4} \div \frac{1}{3}$	4 $\frac{5}{6} \div \frac{2}{3}$	5 $1\frac{1}{5} \div 1\frac{2}{5}$	6 $1\frac{3}{4} \div \frac{1}{2}$
7 $3\frac{1}{2} \div 1\frac{1}{4}$	8 $2\frac{5}{6} \div 1\frac{1}{3}$	9 $2\frac{3}{4} \div 1\frac{1}{4}$	10 $4\frac{3}{4} \div 2\frac{1}{4}$
11 $4\frac{2}{3} \div 1\frac{5}{6}$	12 $2\frac{1}{2} \div 5$	13 $6 \div \frac{2}{3}$	14 $\frac{3}{4} \div \frac{2}{3}$
15 $\frac{4}{7} \div 1\frac{3}{7}$	16 $3\frac{1}{2} \div 4\frac{1}{2}$	17 $\frac{4}{7} \div 1\frac{3}{4}$	18 $6\frac{1}{2} \div 2\frac{2}{3}$
19 $4 \div 1\frac{2}{3}$	20 $3 \div \frac{3}{4}$	21 $1\frac{7}{8} \div 1\frac{1}{4}$	22 $2\frac{5}{6} \div 1\frac{1}{4}$
23 $3\frac{2}{5} \div 1\frac{2}{15}$	24 $4\frac{1}{2} \div 3\frac{1}{4}$		

9 Priorities

If we are asked to work out an expression such as

$$(1\frac{2}{3} + \frac{3}{4}) \times (\frac{1}{2} + 1\frac{1}{4})$$

then we must know the order in which to work out the different parts of the expression.

The order of priorities for fractions is exactly the same as that used for numbers.

- First, complete work in the brackets.
- Second, complete multiplication and division.
- Finally, complete addition and subtraction.

Worked example 24

$$1\frac{3}{4} \times (1\frac{1}{2} - \frac{1}{6})$$

$$= 1\frac{3}{4} \times (1\frac{3-1}{6})$$

$$= 1\frac{3}{4} \times 1\frac{2}{6}$$

$$= \frac{7}{\cancel{4}_1} \times \frac{\cancel{4}^1}{3} = \frac{7}{3} = 2\frac{1}{3}$$

> Complete work in brackets first.
> $(1\frac{2}{6} = 1\frac{1}{3})$

Exercise 10

Priorities:

- First, complete work in the brackets.
- Second, do multiplication and division.
- Third, do addition and subtraction.

Answer the following questions. The first three are completed for you.

1 $\quad \dfrac{1}{2} + \dfrac{3}{4}$ of $\dfrac{2}{3} = \dfrac{1}{2} + \dfrac{\cancel{3}^{1}}{\cancel{4}_{2}} \times \dfrac{\cancel{2}^{1}}{\cancel{3}_{1}}$

> Do multiplication first.

$$= \dfrac{1}{2} + \dfrac{1}{2}$$

$$= 1$$

2 $\quad \left(\dfrac{1}{2} + \dfrac{3}{4}\right)$ of $\dfrac{2}{3} = \left(\dfrac{1}{2} + \dfrac{3}{4}\right) \times \dfrac{2}{3}$

> Complete work in brackets first.

$$= \left(\dfrac{2+3}{4}\right) \times \dfrac{2}{3}$$

$$= \dfrac{5}{\cancel{4}_{2}} \times \dfrac{\cancel{2}^{1}}{3}$$

$$= \dfrac{5}{6}$$

3 $\quad 4 \div \dfrac{2}{3} + 3 = \cancel{4}^{2} \times \dfrac{3}{\cancel{2}_{1}} + 3$

> Do division first.

$$= 6 + 3$$

$$= 9$$

4 $\left(\tfrac{1}{2} + \tfrac{2}{3}\right) \times 4$ **5** $\left(\tfrac{3}{4} - \tfrac{1}{3}\right) \times 6$ **6** $\left(\tfrac{3}{8} + \tfrac{5}{16}\right) \times 1\tfrac{5}{11}$

7 $\tfrac{1}{2} \times \left(\tfrac{4}{5} + \tfrac{2}{3}\right)$ **8** $\tfrac{3}{8} \times \left(1\tfrac{1}{2} + \tfrac{1}{3}\right)$ **9** $\tfrac{2}{3} \times \left(1\tfrac{3}{4} + 2\tfrac{1}{2}\right)$

10 $\tfrac{3}{4}$ of $\left(1\tfrac{1}{2} + 2\tfrac{3}{4}\right)$ **11** $\tfrac{3}{4}$ of $(8 - 4)$ **12** $\tfrac{1}{2}$ of $\left(2\tfrac{1}{2} + 1\tfrac{1}{4}\right)$

13 $1\tfrac{3}{4} \times \left(1\tfrac{1}{4} - \tfrac{2}{3}\right)$ **14** $2\tfrac{1}{2} + 1\tfrac{1}{2} + \tfrac{2}{3}$ **15** $1\tfrac{1}{4} - \tfrac{1}{4} \div \tfrac{3}{8}$

16 $2\tfrac{1}{2} \div \tfrac{3}{4} \times 1\tfrac{1}{3}$ **17** $2\tfrac{1}{4} + \tfrac{1}{2} \times 1\tfrac{1}{3} + \tfrac{1}{3}$ **18** $1\tfrac{3}{4} \div \tfrac{3}{4}$ of $1\tfrac{1}{5}$

19 $\tfrac{3}{4}$ of $20 - 12$ **20** $1\tfrac{2}{3} \times 1\tfrac{5}{6} \div \tfrac{3}{4}$ **21** $\left(\tfrac{2}{3} + \tfrac{3}{4}\right) \times 1\tfrac{1}{2} + 2\tfrac{1}{2}$

22 $3\tfrac{1}{4} \times 2 \div 1\tfrac{5}{8}$ **23** $1\tfrac{3}{4} + 1\tfrac{1}{5} \times \left(\tfrac{1}{3} + 1\tfrac{3}{4}\right)$ **24** $2\tfrac{1}{2} \times 3\tfrac{2}{3} \div 1\tfrac{2}{9}$

Exercise 11

Answer the following questions. The first four are completed for you.

1 How much is $\tfrac{2}{3}$ of £60?

In this context 'of' means multiply.

The question now becomes $\dfrac{2}{\cancel{3}_{1}} \times \cancel{£60}^{\,20}$

> Don't forget the £ symbol.

$$= £40$$

2 Find the cost of $1\tfrac{1}{2}$ lb of ham at 180p per lb.

You are given the cost of 1 lb.

To find the cost of $1\tfrac{1}{2}$ lb multiply the cost of 1 lb by $1\tfrac{1}{2}$:

Cost of $1\tfrac{1}{2}$ lb $= 1\tfrac{1}{2} \times 180$p

$$= \dfrac{3}{\cancel{2}_{1}} \times \cancel{180}^{\,90} \text{p}$$

> Don't forget the p symbol.

$$= 270\text{p}$$

3 $\frac{2}{3}$ of a sum of money is £100. How much is $\frac{3}{5}$ of it?

In question 1 of this exercise it was said that 'of' means multiply; the question now asked can therefore be rewritten as

$\frac{2}{3} \times$ sum of money = £100

First, find the sum of money.
This can be done as follows:

$\frac{2}{3} = £100$

$\frac{1}{3} = £50$

$\frac{3}{3} = 3 \times £50 = £150$

Having found the sum of money £150 now find $\frac{3}{5}$ of £150:

$$= \frac{3}{\underset{1}{\cancel{5}}} \times £\cancel{150}^{\,30}$$

$= £90$

Don't forget the £ symbol.

4 $\frac{1}{3}$ of a pole is red, $\frac{5}{12}$ is blue and the remaining 6 ft is white. How long is the pole and what length is painted red?

First, find what fraction of the pole is painted red and blue:

$= \frac{1}{3} + \frac{5}{12} = \frac{4+5}{12} = \frac{9}{12} = \frac{3}{4}$

This means that $\frac{1}{4}$ $(1 - \frac{3}{4})$ is painted white.

We are told the white-painted piece is 6 ft long, which means $\frac{1}{4}$ of the pole is 6 ft.

The length of the whole pole is 24 ft.
The red portion is $\frac{1}{3}$ of pole = $\frac{1}{3} \times 24$ ft
$\qquad\qquad\qquad\qquad\qquad = 8$ ft

5 What needs to be added to $1\frac{1}{2}$ to make it $2\frac{5}{6}$?

6 What needs to be taken from $4\frac{1}{4}$ to make it $2\frac{2}{3}$?

7 How much is $\frac{2}{3}$ of £60?

8 How much is $\frac{5}{9}$ of £54?

9 $\frac{2}{3}$ of a sum of money is £60. How much is $\frac{1}{2}$ of it?

10 $\frac{3}{4}$ of a sum of money is £27. How much is $\frac{1}{3}$ of it?

11 I have £84. How much is $\frac{5}{12}$ of it?

12 A horse-jumping cross-pole is 20 ft long and is painted black and white. $\frac{2}{5}$ is painted white. What length of pole is painted black?

13 First prize in a raffle was £12 and this was half of the total prize money. Second prize was one third of the total and third prize was the rest. How much was
(a) second prize
(b) third prize?

14 A car took $2\frac{1}{2}$ minutes to cover a mile but another car took $1\frac{4}{5}$ minutes. What was the difference in time to cover a mile?

15 A survey of 120 teenagers found that $\frac{1}{4}$ were heavy smokers, $\frac{1}{3}$ smoked occasionally and the rest were non-smokers. How many were non-smokers?

16 The same survey of 120 teenagers found that $\frac{1}{15}$ had never tried beer. How many had tried beer?

17 A pub manager said that of 288 customers on one night $\frac{1}{2}$ drank beer, $\frac{1}{3}$ drank spirits and the rest drank soft drinks. How many were on soft drinks?

18 An audience were asked whether they liked red, blue or green. $\frac{2}{3}$ liked red, $\frac{1}{4}$ liked blue and the rest liked green. What fraction of this audience liked green?

19 In 1994 it was found that 260 million pounds (£260 million) was spent on corn flakes. Kellogg's accounted for $\frac{3}{5}$ of this total. How much was spent on Kellogg's corn flakes?

20 A man left money in his will as follows: he left $\frac{1}{2}$ to the National Trust, $\frac{5}{12}$ to other charities, and the rest (£1500) to his local church. How much did he leave to the National Trust?

Exercise 12 Multiple choice questions

Work out which is the correct answer in the following questions:

1 $\frac{3}{4}$ is equal to
A $\frac{4}{3}$ B $\frac{9}{14}$ C $\frac{12}{16}$ D $\frac{6}{10}$

2 $\frac{2}{5}$ is equal to
A $\frac{8}{20}$ B $\frac{6}{10}$ C $\frac{12}{25}$ D $\frac{5}{2}$

3 Five sixteenths is equal to
A $\frac{16}{15}$ B $16 \div 5$ C 5×16 D $\frac{5}{16}$

4 $3\frac{3}{4}$ is equal to
A $\frac{9}{4}$ B $\frac{15}{4}$ C $\frac{11}{4}$ D $\frac{6}{4}$

5 $\frac{3}{4}$ is bigger than
A $\frac{2}{3}$ B $\frac{5}{6}$ C $\frac{11}{12}$ D 1

6 $\frac{22}{7}$ is equal to
A 22×7 B $3\frac{3}{7}$ C $22 \div 7$ D 3

7 $1\frac{1}{4} + \frac{2}{3}$ is equal to
A $1\frac{3}{7}$ B $1\frac{3}{4}$ C $1\frac{11}{12}$ D $1\frac{5}{6}$

8 $2\frac{1}{2} \div \frac{1}{2}$ is equal to
A $1\frac{1}{4}$ B 2 C $1\frac{3}{4}$ D 5

9 $1\frac{3}{8} \div \frac{3}{8}$ is equal to
A 1 B $3\frac{2}{3}$ C $\frac{9}{64}$ D $1\frac{7}{8}$

10 $\frac{1}{3}$ of $\frac{1}{3}$ is equal to
A $\frac{2}{3}$ B 1 C $\frac{1}{9}$ D $\frac{1}{3}$

11 $\frac{5}{12}$ of a class smoke. 14 do not smoke. How many are in the class?
A 19 B 24 C 26 D 30

12 $2\frac{1}{4} \times \frac{4}{9}$ is equal to
A 1 B 9 C 2 D $1\frac{3}{4}$

13 In a college, $\frac{1}{2}$ of the staff are lecturers, $\frac{1}{3}$ are in administration and the remaining total 42. The number of lecturers is
A 84 B 108 C 126 D 166

14 A team won $\frac{5}{12}$ of its matches, drew $\frac{1}{3}$ and lost 9. The number of matches played was
A 42 B 27 C 45 D 36

15 $1\frac{1}{2} + \frac{1}{2} \times 2$ is
A 4 B $3\frac{3}{4}$ C $2\frac{1}{2}$ D 3

16 A family holiday cost £1200. $\frac{3}{5}$ was spent on accommodation. All other items cost a total of
A £720   B £3600   C £480   D £240

17 $\frac{3}{4}$ of $24 - 12$ is
A 6 B 9 C 12 D 10

18 $(1\frac{1}{4} + \frac{3}{4}) \div \frac{1}{2}$ is
A 2 B 1 C 4 D 0

19 Money was shared so that Sarah received $\frac{1}{2}$ of it, John received $\frac{1}{6}$ of it and Susan $\frac{1}{3}$ of it. The fraction of money left over was
A $\frac{1}{12}$ B None   C $\frac{1}{3}$ D $\frac{1}{24}$

20 One quarter of six hundred and forty pounds is
A £150   B £10   C £180   D £160

3 Decimals

1 Place Value

Decimal fractions are usually called **decimals**, and are separated from the whole numbers by a dot called the **decimal point**.

The numbers to the right of the decimal point are a special way of writing fractions whose denominators are 10, 100, 1000, etc.

The place value table showing the relationship between whole numbers and decimals is:

Decimal point
↓

Thousands Hundreds Tens Units . Tenths Hundredths Thousandths

Worked example 1

Four point three (4.3) means 4 units and 3 tenths.
Six point three five (6.35) means 6 units, 3 tenths and 5 hundredths.
Thirty-six point nought eight seven (36.087) means 3 tens, 6 units, 0 tenths, 8 hundredths and 7 thousandths.

You may find a whole number written with the decimal point followed by 0, such as 4.0.

It is usual to put 0 in front of the decimal point if there are no whole numbers: for example 0.53, 0.824.

Exercise 1

Write down the following words in decimals, and decimals in words. The first two are completed for you.

1 Two point six four = 2.64

2 3.065 = three point nought six five

3 Five point six

4 Three point five

5 Two point six three

6 Eight point four one

7 Twenty-four point nine three

8 Sixty-two point five nine

9 Seven point nought four

10 Nought point six seven

11 Ninety-eight point four

12 One hundred and thirty point nine two

13 Forty point nought six

14 Thirteen point two four

15	2.5	16	3.8
17	2.65	18	1.87
19	45.34	20	24.06
21	37.80	22	28.03
23	146.48	24	4.07

25   What does the 5 in 3.5 mean?   26   What does the 1 in 24.14 mean?

27   What does the 4 in 34.65 mean?   28   What does the 2 in 4.52 mean?

2 Converting Simple Fractions to Decimals and Decimals to Fractions

If a fraction is expressed in tenths, hundredths, thousandths, it can be written as a decimal immediately.

Worked example 2

Look at the place value table as these are written out:

$\frac{1}{10} = 0.1 \quad \frac{4}{10} = 0.4$

$\frac{36}{100} = 0.36$

$\frac{95}{100} = 0.95 \quad \frac{195}{100} = 1.95$

> This is 36 hundredths and the 6 must go in the hundredths column.

$\frac{387}{1000} = 0.387 \quad \frac{37}{1000} = 0.037$

Look at the place value table and remember that

0.4 is 4 tenths or $\frac{4}{10}$

0.09 is 9 hundredths or $\frac{9}{100}$

0.36 is 36 hundredths or $\frac{36}{100}$

0.012 is 12 thousandths or $\frac{12}{1000}$

0.268 is 268 thousandths or $\frac{268}{1000}$

Remember to cancel these fractions to their lowest terms.

Exercise 2

Change these fractions to decimals. The first two are completed for you.

1   $\frac{3}{10} = 0.3$

2   $\frac{182}{1000} = 0.182$

3	$\frac{3}{10}$	4	$\frac{7}{10}$	5	$\frac{5}{10}$	6	$\frac{1}{10}$
7	$\frac{12}{100}$	8	$\frac{34}{100}$	9	$\frac{62}{100}$	10	$\frac{69}{100}$
11	$\frac{6}{100}$	12	$\frac{48}{100}$	13	$\frac{60}{100}$	14	$\frac{46}{1000}$
15	$\frac{48}{1000}$	16	$\frac{123}{1000}$	17	$\frac{83}{100}$	18	$\frac{6}{100}$
19	$\frac{24}{10}$	20	$\frac{31}{10}$	21	$\frac{4}{10}$	22	$\frac{324}{100}$
23	$\frac{476}{1000}$	24	$\frac{5}{1000}$	25	$\frac{75}{10}$	26	$\frac{456}{100}$
27	$\frac{305}{1000}$	28	$\frac{509}{100}$				

Exercise 3

Change these decimals to fractions and reduce to lowest terms. The first three are completed for you.

1   $0.6 = \frac{\cancel{6}^{3}}{\cancel{10}_{5}} = \frac{3}{5}$

> Cancel by 2.

2   $0.35 = \frac{\cancel{35}^{7}}{\cancel{100}_{20}} = \frac{7}{20}$

> Cancel by 5.

3 $0.375 = \dfrac{\cancel{375}}{\cancel{1000}} = \dfrac{3}{8}$ | Cancel by 5, and then 5, and then 5. |

4	0.2	**5**	0.6	**6**	0.7	**7**	0.3
8	0.15	**9**	0.25	**10**	0.65	**11**	0.64
12	0.75	**13**	0.24	**14**	0.4	**15**	0.88
16	0.28	**17**	0.96	**18**	0.72	**19**	0.40
20	0.45	**21**	0.125	**22**	0.625	**23**	0.94
24	0.324	**25**	0.390	**26**	0.555	**27**	0.42
28	0.464	**29**	0.95	**30**	0.286		

3 Addition and Subtraction

The method is exactly the same as that for whole numbers (Chapter 1, Sections 2 and 4), but remember to keep all the decimal points underneath one another; this ensures that all the units, all the tenths, all the hundredths, and so on will be underneath one another.

Worked example 3

Add together 8.24, 26.84, 7.3 and 2.625.

Place the numbers in columns with the decimal points underneath one another:

```
    8.24
   26.84
    7.3
+   2.625
   ₂ ₂ ₁
   45.005        Answer 45.005
```

Worked example 4

Add together 3.72, 46, 0.294, 100.04 and 92.5

Place the numbers in columns with the decimal points underneath one another. Note how a decimal point is placed behind the units of a whole number:

```
    3.72
   46.0
    0.294
  100.04
+  92.5
   ₁ ₁ ₁ ₁
  242.554        Answer 242.554
```

Exercise 4

Find the value of the following. The first two are completed for you.

1   4.3 + 7.52 + 3.7
Add like ordinary numbers but make sure the decimal points of each number are underneath one another:

```
    4.3
    7.52
+   3.7
   ₁ ₁
   15.52        Answer 15.52
```

2   27.9 + 0.056 + 8.94 + 108.5

         27.9
         0.056
         8.94
   + 108.5
         ₂ ₂
   ‾‾‾‾‾‾‾
     145.396   *Answer 145.396*

3	2.4 + 1.2	4	3.1 + 4.7	5	7.8 + 2.1
6	1.3 + 2.4 + 5.1	7	3.5 + 4.8	8	4.8 + 3.6
9	3.43 + 2.35	10	4.41 + 3.27	11	5.9 + 6.5
12	4.3 + 6.7 + 4.2	13	0.35 + 0.42	14	7.64 + 0.84
15	4.46 + 7.35 + 8.9	16	7.5 + 0.74 + 6.49	17	9.06 + 4.86 + 0.47
18	0.63 + 6.7 + 8.43	19	2.08 + 6.85 + 4.07	20	4.98 + 6.74 + 0.08
21	4.657 + 3.632	22	86.45 + 35.36	23	5.86 + 53.97 + 0.876
24	5.74 + 0.007 + 65.73				

In subtraction, again keep the decimal points underneath one another.

Worked examples 5   **48.96 − 26.42**

       48.96
   − 26.42
   ‾‾‾‾‾‾‾
       22.54   *Answer 22.54*

8.3 − 3.7

     ⁷ ¹
     8.3
   − 3.7
   ‾‾‾‾‾
     4.6   *Answer 4.6*

Worked example 6   **45.4 − 18.26**

     ³¹ ³¹
     45.40
   − 18.26
   ‾‾‾‾‾‾
     27.14   *Answer 27.14*

Exercise 5

Find the value of the following. The first two are completed for you.

1   8.7 − 5.9

   Subtract like ordinary numbers but make sure the decimal points of each
   number are underneath one another:

   ⁷ ¹   2   20 − 12.74
   8.7
   − 5.9   ¹ ⁹ ⁹¹
   ‾‾‾‾   20.00
   2.8   *Answer 2.8*   − 12.74
                                      ‾‾‾‾‾
                                       7.26   *Answer 7.26*

3	7.8 − 3.6	4	8.9 − 5.6	5	8.6 − 4.0
6	6.75 − 4.34	7	5.87 − 3.62	8	7.86 − 4.56
9	45.87 − 32.65	10	89.74 − 74.61	11	7.28 − 5.39
12	5.4 − 2.9	13	6.3 − 4.8	14	8.4 − 6.8
15	34.27 − 17.57	16	65.43 − 38.72	17	35.24 − 28.69
18	29.05 − 5.58	19	16.05 − 4.08	20	10.07 − 5.76
21	435.67 − 65.48	22	72.34 − 38.59	23	28.04 − 17.46
24	45.25 − 20.78				

4 Multiplication

Ignore the decimal point and multiply the numbers as if they were whole numbers. Place the decimal point in the answer after multiplying.

How to place the decimal point?

Count how many figures, including 0s, there are to the right of the decimal point in each number and add together. This total gives the number of figures that must be to the right of the decimal point in the answer.

Worked example 7 2.4×4

$$\begin{array}{r} 24 \\ \times \quad 4 \\ \hline {\scriptstyle 1} \\ 96 \end{array}$$ | Multiply as if whole numbers. |

There is 1 figure to the right of the decimal point in 2.4.
There are no figures to the right of the decimal point in 4 (4.0).
There has to be $1 + 0 = 1$ figure to the right of the decimal point in the answer.
Count 1 figure from the right: *Answer 9.6*

Worked example 8 3.8×5.2

$$\begin{array}{r} 38 \\ \times \quad 52 \\ {\scriptstyle 4\ 1} \\ \hline 1900 \\ 76 \\ \hline 1976 \end{array}$$ | Multiply as if whole numbers. |

There is 1 figure to the right of the decimal point in 3.8.
There is 1 figure to the right of the decimal point in 5.2.
There must be $1 + 1 = 2$ figures to the right of the decimal point (decimal places) in the answer.
Answer 19.76

Exercise 6

Multiply the numbers given. The first three are completed for you.

1   8.6×2.4
     Multiply as if whole numbers:

$$\begin{array}{r} 86 \\ \times \quad 24 \\ \hline 1720 \\ 344 \\ \hline 2064 \end{array}$$ *Answer 20.64*

| Add together the number of decimal places in each number: $1 + 1 = 2$. There have to be 2 decimal places in the answer. |

2   39.5×7.64
     Multiply as if whole numbers:

$$\begin{array}{r} 395 \\ \times \quad 764 \\ \hline 276\,500 \\ 23\,700 \\ 1\,580 \\ \hline 301\,780 \end{array}$$ *Answer 301.780*

| Add the number of decimal places in each number: $1 + 2 = 3$. There have to be 3 decimal places in the answer. |

3 0.37×4.8

Multiply as if whole numbers:

$$\begin{array}{r} 37 \\ \times\ \ 48 \\ \hline 1480 \\ 296 \\ \hline 1776 \end{array}$$

Answer 1.776

There have to be $2 + 1 = 3$ decimal places in the answer.

4	3.1×2	**5**	3.2×3	**6**	3.2×4
7	4.2×6	**8**	2.7×5	**9**	3.8×7
10	2.3×1.4	**11**	4.3×2.2	**12**	4.3×9
13	4.3×5.5	**14**	3.7×4.2	**15**	4.8×3.4
16	8.6×0.6	**17**	4.7×0.4	**18**	5.43×8
19	45.3×6	**20**	32.6×4.3	**21**	6.5×0.5
22	0.45×0.26	**23**	6.7×0.47	**24**	5.34×14
25	0.67×5.48	**26**	56.7×37.2	**27**	8.45×0.63
28	6.07×5.4	**29**	5.07×6.3	**30**	8.05×5.06

5 Multiplication and Division by Powers of 10

$$\begin{aligned} 10 \times 1 &= 10 &&= 10^1 \\ 10 \times 10 &= 100 &&= 10^2 \\ 10 \times 10 \times 10 &= 1000 &&= 10^3 \\ 10 \times 10 \times 10 \times 10 \times 10 &= 100\,000 &&= 10^5 \end{aligned}$$

The small figures 1, 2, 3 and 5 are said to be the **powers** of 10; the power gives the number of times the base number (10) is multiplied to itself. The power of 10 corresponds to the number of 0s after the figure 1.

Any decimal number can be multiplied by a power of 10 by moving the decimal point to the right – the number of places corresponds to the power of 10.

Worked examples 9

$$\begin{aligned} 1.3 \times 10 &= 13 \\ 1.3 \times 100 &= 130 \\ 1.3 \times 1000 &= 1300 \\ 1.3 \times 10^5 &= 130\,000 \end{aligned}$$

Move decimal point in 1.3 one place to the right.
Move decimal point 2 places to the right.

Any decimal number can be divided by a power of 10 by moving the decimal point to the left – the number of places to correspond to the power of 10.

Worked examples 10

$$\begin{aligned} 12.62 \div 10 &= 1.262 \\ 12.62 \div 100 &= 0.1262 \\ 12.62 \div 1000 &= 0.012\,62 \\ 12.62 \div 10^5 &= 0.000\,126\,2 \end{aligned}$$

Move decimal point 1 place to the left.
Move decimal point 2 places to the left.

Exercise 7

Find the value of the following. The first two are completed for you.

1 $3.7 \times 100 = 370$

2 $3.7 \div 100 = 0.037$

3	3.4×10	**4**	5.7×10	**5**	34.3×10
6	5.67×10	**7**	0.84×10	**8**	5.04×10
9	34.56×100	**10**	4.83×100	**11**	8.37×100
12	0.46×100	**13**	3.06×100	**14**	12.065×1000
15	0.65×1000	**16**	5.25×1000	**17**	8.067×1000
18	$34.5 \div 10$	**19**	$38.56 \div 10$	**20**	$56.45 \div 10$
21	$3.678 \div 10$	**22**	$456.5 \div 10$	**23**	$0.87 \div 10$

24 $4.56 \div 10$	25 $0.64 \div 10$	26 $456.5 \div 100$
27 $4.35 \div 100$	28 $0.75 \div 100$	29 $56.45 \div 100$
30 $3.876 \div 10$	31 $6.078 \div 100$	32 4.64×10^3
33 0.576×10^2	34 $45.67 \div 10^2$	35 $546.08 \div 10^3$
36 $45.067 \div 10^3$		

6 Division

Division of a decimal number by a whole number is similar to the method shown in Chapter 1, Section 6, but care has to be taken in placing the decimal point.

Worked example 11

$76.8 \div 8$

If we are dividing by a number less than 10 then we do it similarly to worked example 21 in Chapter 1:

$$\begin{array}{r} 9.6 \\ 8\overline{)7\,6.8} \end{array}$$

Answer 9.6

Put a decimal point in the answer immediately above the one in the number being divided.

Worked example 12

$737.1 \div 7$

$$\begin{array}{r} 105.3 \\ 7\overline{)737.1} \end{array}$$

Answer 105.3

Put decimal point in answer.
7 into 7 goes 1.
7 into 3 won't go.
Put 0 in the answer and carry 3.

If dividing by a large number then use long division as in worked examples 23, 24 and 25 in Chapter 1.

Worked example 13

$849.42 \div 27$

$$\begin{array}{r} 31.46 \\ 27\overline{)849.42} \\ \underline{81} \\ 39 \\ \underline{27} \\ 124 \\ \underline{108} \\ 162 \\ \underline{162} \\ \bullet\bullet\bullet \end{array}$$

3×27
1×27
4×27
6×27

Answer 31.46

Put decimal point in answer.

When dividing by a decimal number, move its decimal point to make it into a whole number and adjust the position of the decimal point of the other number in the same direction.

Worked example 14

$75.66 \div 0.6$

Make 0.6 into a whole number by moving the decimal point 1 place to the right.

If this is done then 75.66 also has to have the decimal point moved one place to the right.

$75.66 \div 0.6$ is exactly the same as $756.6 \div 6.0$

Now that we are dividing by a whole number continue as in the previous examples:

$$\begin{array}{r} 126.1 \\ 6\overline{)756.6} \end{array}$$

Answer 126.1

Worked example 15   4.158 ÷ 0.18

Make 0.18 a whole number by moving the decimal point 2 places to the right. 4.158 becomes 415.8 when the decimal point is moved 2 places to the right.

4.158 ÷ 0.18 is the same as 415.8 ÷ 18

$$
\begin{array}{r}
23.1 \\
18\overline{)415.8} \\
\end{array}
$$

Put the decimal point in the answer.

$$
\begin{array}{rl}
36 & \quad 2 \times 18 \\
\overline{55} & \\
54 & \quad 3 \times 18 \\
\overline{18} & \\
18 & \quad 1 \times 18 \\
\overline{\bullet\bullet} & \\
\end{array}
$$

                                        Answer 23.1

Exercise 8

Find the value of the following. The first three are completed for you.

1 95.2 ÷ 7

$$
\begin{array}{r}
13.6 \\
7\overline{)9 5.^2 2^4} \\
\end{array}
$$
        Answer 13.6

2 8.64 ÷ 2.4
Change the divisor (2.4) into a whole number 24 by moving the decimal point 1 place to the right.

Now move the decimal point 1 place to the right, in the dividend, changing 8.64 to 86.4: 8.64 ÷ 2.4 is the same as 86.4 ÷ 24.

$$
\begin{array}{rl}
3.6 & \\
24\overline{)86.4} & \\
72 & \quad 3 \times 24 \\
\overline{14.4} & \\
14.4 & \quad 6 \times 24 \\
\overline{\bullet\bullet\bullet\bullet} & \\
\end{array}
$$
                    Answer 3.6

3 5.6 ÷ 0.4 is the same as 56 ÷ 4.

$$
\begin{array}{r}
14.0 \\
4\overline{)56.0} \\
\end{array}
$$
        Answer 14.0

4	4.8 ÷ 2	**5**	9.6 ÷ 3	**6**	12.8 ÷ 4
7	32.2 ÷ 7	**8**	28.2 ÷ 6	**9**	41.4 ÷ 9
10	17.92 ÷ 7	**11**	37.12 ÷ 8	**12**	19.85 ÷ 5
13	64.08 ÷ 12	**14**	7.84 ÷ 1.4	**15**	8.14 ÷ 2.2
16	22.8 ÷ 2.4	**17**	25.74 ÷ 3.3	**18**	207.9 ÷ 7
19	129.6 ÷ 4	**20**	373.6 ÷ 8	**21**	340.2 ÷ 9
22	3.44 ÷ 0.4	**23**	6.79 ÷ 0.7	**24**	25.41 ÷ 0.3
25	0.576 ÷ 0.8	**26**	1.3386 ÷ 0.23	**27**	93.6 ÷ 2.4
28	0.648 ÷ 0.9	**29**	36.16 ÷ 0.8	**30**	58.08 ÷ 1.6

7 Corrected Decimals

In Chapter 1, section 12 we saw how numbers can be rounded off. For most decimals it is usual to work to only 2 or 3 decimal places and give an answer to a certain degree of accuracy.

Giving a **corrected** answer means giving an answer to a specified number of decimal places.

Worked example 16   4.31 is 4.3 correct to one decimal place
4.37 is 4.4 correct to one decimal place

As in rounding off, if the last figure is a 5 or more put the previous figure up by 1; if the last figure is 4 or less leave the previous figure as it was.

- When correcting to one decimal place look at the figure in the second decimal place.
- When correcting to two decimal places look at the figure in the third decimal place.
- When correcting to three decimal places look at the figure in the fourth decimal place.

Worked example 17

3.26 is 3.3 correct to one decimal place
3.264 is 3.26 correct to two decimal places
3.2645 is 3.265 correct to three decimal places

Exercise 9

Write the following correct to one decimal place. The first three are completed for you.

1   7.68 = 7.7 correct to one decimal place

2   2.97 = 3.0 correct to one decimal place

3   3.549 = 3.5 correct to one decimal place

4	2.44	5	5.32	6	3.67	7	8.58
8	4.29	9	4.13	10	5.65	11	3.17
12	0.68	13	1.96	14	45.58	15	5.79
16	37.83	17	0.74	18	0.49	19	26.97
20	3.06	21	7.05	22	42.94	23	22.96
24	0.06	25	5.345	26	3.763	27	0.87
28	0.95	29	2.45	30	67.05		

Exercise 10

Write the following correct to two decimal places. The first three are completed for you.

1   2.928 = 2.93 correct to two decimal places

2   0.7249 = 0.72 correct to two decimal places

3   7.996 = 8.00 correct to two decimal places

4	4.543	5	5.678	6	2.065	7	43.427
8	21.684	9	5.489	10	3.064	11	3.065
12	45.507	13	8.008	14	4.077	15	3.997
16	0.305	17	31.004	18	5.068	19	7.471
20	56.796	21	3.995	22	42.505	23	5.099
24	31.706	25	31.239	26	8.477	27	99.999
28	1.4036	29	4.7629	30	4.675		

8 Significant Figures

A number may have a lot of figures, but some of the figures may not be important in relation to the others, and we may be asked to express the number to so many significant figures, i.e. important figures.

For example, a person winning one million and three pounds on the football pools can afford to ignore the three pounds.

The number of significant figures must be stated for an answer to be given.

Significant figures include all figures in a number except noughts at the beginning and end.

Worked example 18   800 and 0.08 each have 1 significant figure; ignore noughts at beginning and end.
370 and 0.0037 each have 2 significant figures; ignore noughts at beginning and end.
A nought between figures is significant.
4060 and 0.0406 each have 3 significant figures.
3008 and 0.030 08 each have 4 significant figures.

Worked example 19   2324 is 2300 when given to 2 significant figures.
171 is 170 to 2 significant figures.
103 is 100 to 2 significant figures.
0.0152 is 0.015 to 2 significant figures.
0.0104 is 0.010 to 2 significant figures.

9 Corrected Significant Figures

Most questions ask for an answer 'correct to so many significant figures', and so we have to combine the knowledge of sections 7 and 8.

Worked example 20   What is 42.53 correct to 3 significant figures?

We want only 3 figures in the answer, including any in-between noughts, and as the fourth figure is less than 5 the answer is 42.5

What is 42.765 correct to 3 significant figures?

The fourth figure is 6; in 'rounding up' the 7 becomes 8, and so the answer is 42.8

What is 6038 correct to 3 significant figures?

The answer is 6040

Exercise 11

Write the following numbers correct to two significant figures. The first three are completed for you.

1   6520 = 6500 correct to two significant figures

2   503 = 500 correct to two significant figures

3   0.0767 = 0.077 correct to two significant figures

4	356	5	358	6	7463	7	492
8	1856	9	15.3	10	35.7	11	25.85
12	4.07	13	3.027	14	777	15	4.63
16	6.045	17	31.73	18	3060	19	5.463
20	47 390	21	6.83	22	457.8	23	4.007
24	2.065	25	45.9	26	0.0567	27	0.0707
28	0.0583	29	60 006	30	0.605		

Exercise 12

Write the following numbers correct to three significant figures. The first four are completed for you.

1   72.835 = 72.8 correct to three significant figures

2   72.875 = 72.9 correct to three significant figures

3 7004 = 7000 correct to three significant figures

4 0.023 86 = 0.0239 correct to three significant figures

5	45.76	6	4.543	7	56.75	8	3784
9	4798	10	5.962	11	8.006	12	45.03
13	5003	14	4.448	15	6.807	16	356.45
17	357.27	18	4.004	19	36.72	20	40 763
21	0.003 45	22	6.75	23	4.906	24	9.006
25	3599	26	41.036	27	6.798	28	0.000 548 5
29	0.060 73	30	6.0006				

10 Changing Any Fraction to a Decimal

The denominator is divided into the numerator to give the decimal equivalent of the fraction.

Worked example 21

Find $\frac{3}{4}$ as a decimal.

The fraction $\frac{3}{4}$ means $3 \div 4$.
Divide 3 by 4 as in worked example 21 in Chapter 1:

$$\begin{array}{r} 0.75 \\ 4\overline{)3.00} \end{array} \qquad \textit{Answer 0.75}$$

Worked example 22

Change $\frac{1}{8}$ to a decimal.

$\frac{1}{8}$ means $1 \div 8$

$$\begin{array}{r} 0.125 \\ 8\overline{)1.0\overset{2}{0}\overset{4}{0}0} \end{array} \qquad \textit{Answer 0.125}$$

Exercise 13

Change the following fractions to decimals. The first three are completed for you.

1 $\frac{3}{5} = 3.0 \div 5 = 0.6$ — Divide 5 into 3.

2 $\frac{3}{8} = 3.0 \div 8 = 0.375$ — Divide 8 into 3.

3 $\frac{2}{3} = 2.0 \div 3 = 0.6666\ldots = 0.\dot{6}$ or 0.67 — This is a **recurring decimal**.
correct to 2 significant figures

4	$\frac{1}{2}$	5	$\frac{1}{4}$	6	$\frac{3}{4}$	7	$\frac{2}{5}$
8	$\frac{7}{10}$	9	$\frac{3}{20}$	10	$\frac{2}{3}$	11	$\frac{1}{5}$
12	$\frac{9}{10}$	13	$\frac{1}{3}$	14	$\frac{3}{8}$	15	$\frac{7}{20}$
16	$\frac{5}{8}$	17	$\frac{7}{4}$	18	$\frac{13}{20}$	19	$\frac{3}{2}$
20	$\frac{5}{3}$	21	$\frac{11}{20}$	22	$\frac{7}{8}$	23	$\frac{5}{4}$
24	$\frac{9}{5}$	25	$\frac{1}{6}$	26	$\frac{4}{3}$	27	$\frac{4}{5}$
28	$\frac{1}{10}$	29	$\frac{6}{5}$	30	$\frac{17}{20}$		

11 Standard Form

Standard form is a neat way in which we write very large or very small numbers (such as those used in astronomy, physics or engineering, for example).

To put a number into standard form we rewrite the number to have a value between 1 and 10 and then make the necessary adjustments by multiplying by a power of 10 so that the value of the number remains the same.

Look again at section 5 as a reminder:

1000 is 10^3

100 is 10^2

10 is 10^1

and, continuing the sequence,

$$1 \text{ is } 10^0$$
$$0.1 \quad \text{is } 10^{-1}$$
$$0.01 \quad \text{is } 10^{-2}$$
$$0.001 \text{ is } 10^{-3}$$

and so on.

Now we use this to write any number in standard form:

$38 = 3.8 \times 10$	$= 3.8 \times 10^1$	This is standard form.
$380 = 3.8 \times 100$	$= 3.8 \times 10^2$	Standard form.
$3800 = 3.8 \times 1000$	$= 3.8 \times 10^3$	Standard form.

Remember that the power of 10 coincides with the number of places the decimal point has been moved in order for the number to be written between 1 and 10.

If the number is originally less than 1, the decimal point has to be moved the other way, hence producing a negative power of 10.

Worked example 23   Write 4685.0 in standard form.

To rewrite 4685.0 as a number between 1 and 10 the decimal point has to be after the 4 and so we get 4.685.

But this has meant moving the decimal point of the original number 3 places to the *left*.

4685.0 is the same as 4.685×1000
$1000 = 10^3$
$4685.0 = 4.685 \times 1000 = 4.685 \times 10^3$
Answer 4.685×10^3

Worked example 24   Write 39 600.0 in standard form.

$39\,600.0 = 3.96 \times 10\,000 = 3.96 \times 10^4$

Answer 3.96×10^4

Worked example 25   Write 0.0582 in standard form.

Rewrite 0.0582 as a number between 1 and 10 to give 5.82.

The decimal point has been moved 2 places, but this time to the *right*. So this time use a negative power of 10:

$0.0582 = 5.82 \times 10^{-2}$

(In effect this is the same as saying $5.82 \div 100$.)

Worked example 26   Write 0.007 25 in standard form.

$0.007\,25 = 7.25 \times 10^{-3}$ | Decimal point was moved 3 places to right. |

Exercise 14

Write the following numbers in standard form. The first two are completed for you.

1 $3725 = 3.725 \times 10^3$

2 $0.003\,725 = 3.725 \times 10^{-3}$

3 46.0	**4** 63.0	**5** 87
6 4845.0	**7** 3865.0	**8** 2831

9	37.8	**10**	374.9	**11**	4178.7
12	3968.0	**13**	578.65	**14**	37 468.0
15	273.8	**16**	90 696.0	**17**	3856
18	0.56	**19**	67.87	**20**	0.876
21	0.007 45	**22**	0.0089	**23**	61.86
24	0.0135	**25**	0.000 647	**26**	8976.45
27	365 700	**28**	0.0631	**29**	869.65
30	0.000 086				

Exercise 15

Write the following as ordinary numbers. The first two are completed for you.

1 $2.3 \times 10^3 = 2300$

2 $4.64 \times 10^{-4} = 0.000\,464$

3 3.5×10^1		**4** 5.8×10^1		**5** 6.4×10^2	
6 4.87×10^2		**7** 5.63×10^2		**8** 5.85×10^3	
9 5.654×10^3		**10** 5.49×10^1		**11** 8.765×10^1	
12 4.3×10^4		**13** 4.987×10^4		**14** 5.4286×10^2	
15 3.76×10^1		**16** 5.275×10^4		**17** 6.2057×10^2	
18 5.654×10^{-1}		**19** 9.3065×10^{-1}		**20** 6.47×10^{-1}	
21 2.7×10^{-2}		**22** 6.843×10^{-3}		**23** $5.890\,56 \times 10^{-1}$	
24 2.76×10^{-3}		**25** 4.6957×10^{-2}		**26** 4.1847×10^{-4}	
27 4.795×10^{-1}		**28** 1.907×10^{-2}		**29** $3.007\,08 \times 10^2$	
30 1.4835×10^3					

Exercise 16 Multiple choice questions

Work out which is the correct answer in the following questions:

1 5.3 is
 A Five point nought three
 B Five point three
 C Five three
 D Fifty-three

2 23.62 is
 A Twenty-three and sixty-two
 B Two three six two
 C Twenty-three point six two
 D Two thousand three hundred and sixty-two

3 The 5 in 31.51 means
 A Five   B Fifty
 C Five hundred   D Five tenths

4 The 1 in 5.216 means
 A One hundred   B One
 C One hundredth   D One thousandth

5 $\frac{7}{10}$ as a decimal is
 A 7.0   B 0.7   C 0.17   D 0.71

6 $\frac{35}{1000}$ as a decimal is
 A 35.00   B 351.00   C 0.035   D 0.0135

7 If you change 0.45 to a fraction the answer is
 A 45   B $\frac{45}{10}$ C $\frac{9}{100}$ D $\frac{9}{20}$

8 If you change 0.12 to a fraction the answer is
 A 12   B $\frac{3}{25}$ C $\frac{12}{10}$ D $\frac{3}{10}$

9 2.96 + 3.04 + 7.8 is
 A 13.80   B 12.88   C 13.08   D 13.88

10 9.08 taken from 18.91 leaves
 A 27.99   B 9.93   C 9.83   D 10.53

11 5.94 taken from 10 leaves
 A 15.94   B 5.06   C 5.94   D 4.06

12 What needs to be added to 16.62 to make 25.24?
 A 8.62   B 41.86   C 9.86   D 9.62

13 Which of the following is nearest to 99.5×8?
 A 100   B 800   C 400   D 900

14 5.7×7 is
 A 577   B 57.7   C 39.9   D 38.7

15 $167.4 \div 9$ is
 A 18.6   B 20   C 17.4   D 19

16 4031 correct to 2 significant figures is
 A 4030   B 4000   C 4100   D 4031

17 276.8 in standard form is
 A 2.7×10^1 B 2.768×10^3
 C 2.768×10^{-2} D 2.768×10^2

18 0.27×10^{-3} is
 A 270   B 0.000 27   C 2.7   D 0.0027

19 $\frac{7}{8}$ as a decimal is
 A 0.7   B 0.16   C 0.78   D 0.875

20 $2.5 + 1.5 \times 7 + 3.5$ is
 A 31.5   B 42   C 16.5   D 21

4 Money

1 Money and Decimals

All operations on decimals (addition, subtraction, multiplication and division) can be applied to our money system. Note that there will be only two places of decimals.

£4.12 means 4 pounds and 12 pence
£15.03 means 15 pounds and 3 pence
£0.42 means 42 pence

Exercise 1

Complete the following. The first two are completed for you.

1   Find the total of £27, £16.49 and £25.46.

    £
27.00
16.49
<u>25.46</u>
<u>68.95</u>   *Answer £68.95*

2   From £50 take £23.47.

    £
 50.00
<u>−23.47</u>
<u>26.53</u>   *Answer £26.53*

3	£1.23 + £2.54	4	£4.21 + £5.68
5	£8.57 + £1.42	6	£6.54 + £7.42
7	£13.75 + £8.57	8	£32.86 + £0.64
9	£20.86 + £7.47	10	£39.28 + £18.09
11	£30.27 + £1.53	12	£25.75 + £20.84 + £7.94
13	£8.37 + £73.29 + £62.75	14	£38.65 + £7.06 + £425.45
15	£82.38 + £7.05 + £52.94	16	£524.08 + £47.84 + £83.21
17	£32.11 + £48.79 + £107.37	18	£54.93 + £104.09 + £36.50
19	£78.46 + £30.08 + £124.07	20	£45.38 + £4.07 + £547.07
21	£8.76 − £4.24	22	£9.74 − £5.73
23	£10 − £4.75	24	£20 − £10.74
25	£13.56 − £9.64	26	£17.42 − £12.86
27	£43.47 − £35.59	28	£100 − £48.37
29	£16.00 − £8.48	30	£148.47 − £64.78
31	£27.62 − £17.97	32	£4.32 − £3.69
33	£102.34 − £46.74	34	£84.04 − £57.36
35	£16.84 − £5.97	36	£21.62 − £14.48
37	£50.06 − £36.47	38	£25 − £17.46
39	£53.47 − £36.57	40	£41.36 − £34.77

Complete the following. The first four are completed for you.

1 How much is £12.85 × 4?
(This could be how much you pay in a four-week month if you pay £12.85 a week.)

£12.85 × 4

Multiply without the decimal point (see Chapter 3, section 4):

1285 × 4 = 5140

Total number of decimal places in the original question was 2: therefore there have to be 2 places in the answer.
Answer £51.40

2 How much is £33.40 × 12?
(This could be a payment of £33.40 a month and you are trying to find the cost per year.)

£33.40 × 12

Multiply without the decimal point:

Either   3 340 × 12 = 40 080 | (if you know your 12 times table) |
or
$$\begin{array}{r} 3\,340 \\ \times \quad 12 \\ \hline 33\,400 \\ 6\,680 \\ \hline 40\,080 \end{array}$$

There were 2 decimal places in the original question so there must be 2 decimal places in the answer.
Answer £400.80

3 £1667.82 ÷ 7
(This could be trying to find the cost per day if £1667.82 is the cost for a week.)

£1667.82 ÷ 7

Divide as for ordinary decimals:

$$\begin{array}{r} 238.26 \\ \hline 7)1667.82 \end{array}$$

| Place decimal point in answer; see Chapter 3, section 6. |

Answer £238.26

4 £82.42 ÷ 13
(This could be finding how much electricity costs per week if £82.42 is the cost per quarter, i.e. 13 weeks.)

£82.42 ÷ 13

Divide as for ordinary decimals:

$$\begin{array}{r} 6.34 \\ \hline 13)82.42 \\ 78 \\ \hline 44 \\ 39 \\ \hline 52 \\ 52 \\ \hline \end{array}$$

6 × 13

3 × 13

4 × 13

Answer £6.34

5	£1.21 × 3	6	£2.31 × 4	7	£2.47 × 3
8	£2.13 × 7	9	£4.34 × 6	10	£0.64 × 7
11	£4.85 × 8	12	£22.32 × 4	13	£17.74 × 11
14	£27.03 × 12	15	£0.48 × 24	16	£46.83 × 24
17	£18.49 × 36	18	£25.46 × 12	19	£18.34 × 24
20	£74.05 × 36	21	£32.09 × 12	22	£0.74 × 24
23	£9.69 ÷ 3	24	£8.44 ÷ 4	25	£15.75 ÷ 5
26	£18.06 ÷ 3	27	£24.36 ÷ 7	28	£21.04 ÷ 8
29	£44.77 ÷ 11	30	£57.78 ÷ 9	31	£87.84 ÷ 12
32	£180.96 ÷ 8	33	£161.64 ÷ 12	34	£224.64 ÷ 24
35	£18.72 ÷ 24	36	£49.68 ÷ 36	37	£38.88 ÷ 36
38	£84.48 ÷ 24	39	£414.96 ÷ 24	40	£432.96 ÷ 24

Exercise 3

The following items were offered on a college menu board:

Coffee, cup	32p	Tea, cup	27p
Coffee, mug	45p	Tea, mug	40p
Chocolate	32p	Fruit juice	28p
Crisps	24p	Toast (2 slices)	32p
Cheese sandwich	65p	Ham sandwich	65p
Ham and cheese toastie	68p	Curry and rice	£1.10
Cheese and onion sandwich	68p	Fish and chips	£1.40
Turkey and salad sandwich	68p	Sausage and chips	£1.35
Sausage roll	45p	Pizza	95p
Cornish pasty	54p	Chips	40p
Steak and kidney pie	£1.15	Baked potato	30p
Soup and roll and butter	62p	Mars bar	26p
KitKat	26p	Twix	28p
Ice cream	50p	Apple pie	64p
Sticky toffee pudding	64p	Apple	25p
Cheese and biscuits	44p	Orange	28p

From the menu find the cost of the following:

1 Cup of coffee, crisps and cheese sandwich

2 Toast and 2 cups of tea

3 Fruit juice, fish and chips, mug of coffee

4 Chocolate, sausage and chips, apple pie

5 Cornish pasty, sticky toffee pudding, mug of coffee

6 Turkey sandwich, Mars bar, cup of tea

7 Sausage and chips, cheese and biscuits, cup of coffee

8 Ham and cheese toastie, Twix, mug of coffee

9 Curry and rice, baked potato, Mars, ice cream, 2 mugs of coffee

10 Soup and roll, pizza, chips, 2 cups of tea

11 2 mugs of tea, 2 sausage rolls, 3 Mars bars, 2 KitKats

12 Cheese and onion sandwich, crisps, 2 cups of coffee

13 Chocolate, crisps, fish and chips, orange, cup of tea

14 Chips, ham sandwich, apple pie, 2 cups of coffee

15 Toast, chips, Mars bar, apple, cup of tea

16 Sausage roll, ham sandwich, apple pie, 2 cups of coffee

17   3 crisps, 2 KitKats, chocolate, fruit juice, mug of tea

18   Cornish pasty, chips, Twix, cup of tea, mug of coffee

19   Cup of tea, curry and rice, cheese and biscuits, Mars bar

20   3 mugs of coffee, 2 sausage rolls, cornish pasty, Twix

Exercise 4

1   I pay a bill for £2.24 and buy a book of stamps for £1.90. How much change do I get from a £5 note?

2   The daily paper is 28p, the Saturday paper 55p, and the Sunday paper is 90p. How much is paid for newspapers in a week?

3   I went to Marks & Spencer and bought a pullover for £19.99 and a shirt for £16.75. How much change did I get from two £20 notes?

4   A four-pack set of video tapes was £9.76. How much was each tape?

5   A cheap day return fare by rail from Preston to London was £38.64. On the train to London £3.38 was spent and £5.27 was spent on the way back. What was the total amount spent?

6   The running costs of a car for a year are petrol £765.68, car tax £140, insurance £376.46, and repairs and servicing £488.42. What are the total running costs for a year?

7   A Sony Walkman can be bought with 12 payments of £4.75 each. How much will it cost?

8   A man earns £8.75 an hour for a 32-hour week. How much does he earn in a week?

9   A woman earns £742 per calendar month. What is her annual salary?

10   The rent of a house is £2925 per year. How much is this per month?

11   Sale items were advertised at half normal price. Normal price for trousers was £24.66, pullover £31, shirt £19.50 and socks £3.20. What did it cost to buy one item of each in the sale?

12   A video recorder can be bought with 24 payments, each one £13.44. How much does the video recorder cost?

13   The council tax can be paid monthly. The council tax per year for Band A is £463.92 and for Band E is £976.80. How much council tax per month do you pay for a house in (a) Band A (b) Band E?

14   The annual electricity bill was £513.96. How much was this per month?

15   A teenager went 'shop browsing' one Saturday. The bus journey cost £1.20 each way. She spent £5.65 on make-up, £2.48 on a snack and coffee, and £1.85 on a magazine. How much did she spend? She left the house with £18.34. How much did she have left?

16   The gas bill was paid monthly for the year 1994/95 and was £54.36 per month. What was the gas bill for the year?

17   A standard entry on Littlewoods Pools is £2.24. How much is this per year (52 weeks)?

18   A one-week holiday in Benidorm is £284 for adults, £224 for children aged between 11 and 16, and half price for children under 11. What is the total cost of a holiday for 2 adults and 2 children, one aged 14 and one 9?

19   The George & Dragon offers pub lunches as follows:

Soup, with roll and butter	£1.95
Paté, with toast and butter	£1.75
Prawns	£1.55
Beefburger, chips and vegetables	£2.85
Fish, chips and peas	£3.60
Ham, turkey or chicken salad	£3.30
Any sweet	£1.65
Coffee	75p

How much is the bill for 2 soups, 1 paté, 1 prawns, 2 fish, chips and peas, 2 salads, 3 sweets, and 4 coffees?

20   The local supermarket sells the following items:

pkt cornflakes	£1.99	1 kg sugar	£1.15
250 g butter	78p	1 pint milk	34p
80 tea bags	£1.69	8 oz cheese	£1.48
1 doz eggs	£1.45	1 kg bacon	£2.99
100 g coffee	£2.86	1 pkt biscuits	99p
500 g oat bran flakes	£1.99	500 g fibre cereal	£1.45

How much does it cost for
(a)   1 kg sugar, 250 g butter, 1 doz eggs and 100 g coffee?
(b)   1 pint milk, 1 pkt biscuits, 500 g fibre cereal, and 80 tea bags?
(c)   500 g bran flakes, 8 oz cheese, 1 kg bacon, 1 pint milk, 1 doz eggs, 100 g coffee, and 80 tea bags?
(d)   one of each item?

Exercise 5 Multiple choice questions

Work out which is the correct answer in the following questions:

1   I spend £2.87. How much change is there from £10?
   A £8.13   B £7.00   C £7.13   D £6.23

2   £2.50 is changed to 5p pieces. How many are there?
   A 100   B 250   C 50   D 5

3   The total of £2.49, £3.26 and 89p is
   A £6.64   B £7.44   C £5.76   D £10

4   From a £20 note I receive £9.24 in change. How much have I spent?
   A 76p   B £11.00   C £10.76   D £10

5   12 × £4.09 is
   A £48.18   B £48.02   C £49.02   D £49.08

6   £41.52 ÷ 12 is
   A £3.46   B £4.00   C £3.52   D £3.66

7   Electricity costs £432 per year. How much is this per quarter?
   A £180   B £81   C £112   D £108

8   Vinyl flooring costs £4.99 per metre. 8 metres will cost
   A £12.99   B £32   C £39.92   D £5.07

9   Stacking chairs are £96 a dozen. How much will fifty cost?
   A £400   B £500   C £480   D £520

10   The salary per week of £7592 per year (52 weeks) is
   A £152   B £142   C £146   D £156

11   Petrol costs 54.3p a litre. 40 litres will cost
   A £21.72   B £20.30   C £44.30   D £25.43

12   A quote for seven identical double glazed windows is £1307.25. How much is this for one window?
   A £175.65   B £195.75   C £186.75   D £187.95

13   How much is 0.3 of £1200?
   A £360   B £312   C £123   D £400

14   A bag of sugar costs £1.12 and a jar of jam £1.24. The bill came to £5.84. I bought
   A 2 sugars and 3 jams   B 5 sugars
   C 4 jams and 1 sugar   D 3 sugars and 2 jams

15   A set of nine golf clubs costs £338.85. Each club costs the same. How much is each club?
   A £29.95   B £36.75   C £37.65   D £34.50

16   A table is £290. A chair is £36.50. How much is a table and six chairs?
   A £499   B £526   C £509   D £409

17 A sale gave ⅓ off all normal prices. The normal price of a coat was £87. The sale price was
    A £29   B £116   C £68   D £58

18 A taxi driver charged a total of £27 for a journey. Six people shared the taxi. Each one paid
    A £4   B £4.75   C £5   D £4.50

19 A man gives away one half of everything over £100. He gives away £24.75. He started with
    A £149.50   B £124.75   C £75.25   D £49.50

20 A set 3-course lunch was £5.95. 8 friends all had lunch. The change from £50 was
    A £2.00   B £2.40   C £0.40   D £3.20

5 | Introducing the Calculator

1 Introduction

Figure 5.1 shows the figures and symbols that you are likely to find on a simple, cheap, electronic calculator.

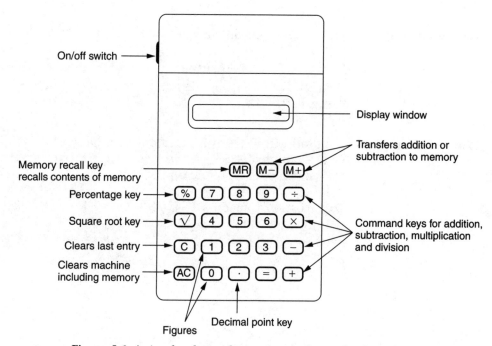

On/off switch

Display window

Transfers addition or subtraction to memory

Memory recall key recalls contents of memory

Percentage key

Square root key

Clears last entry

Clears machine including memory

Command keys for addition, subtraction, multiplication and division

Decimal point key

Figures

Figure 5.1 A simple, cheap electronic calculator, the Casio SL 450

Check how your calculator face differs from this. Read the instructions that were given with your calculator and make yourself familiar with what it can do.

- What happens when you switch on? 0. appears: that is, nought followed by a decimal point.
- What happens when you press the figure 6? 6. appears in the display window.
- When you press 6 and 4? 64. appears.
- When you press 6 and then 4 and then 2 and then 5? 6425. appears.
- When you press 6, then decimal point key, then 5? 6.5 appears.
- When you press 6, then decimal point key, then 0, then 4? 6.04 appears.

2 Use of a Calculator

A calculator will do what you tell it to do. It will not think for you, you have to do the thinking; but it will do calculations in a fraction of the time that you normally take.

Switch on. Check that '0.' appears in the display window.
Remember to CLEAR the calculator before beginning a new calculation.

Note: All calculations and operations in this chapter are done on the Casio SL 450, unless stated otherwise.

3 Addition

Worked example 1

38 + 19

Press key 3, then 8, then ⊞ then 1, then 9.
Press ⊟ key.
Answer 57 Easy!

Get into the habit of looking in the display window after each number or
operation to check that you have recorded the correct figure or instruction. Any
mistake is yours; the calculator does not make mistakes.

Worked example 2

302 + 87 + 194

Press key 3, then 0, then 2, then ⊞, then 8, then 7, then ⊞, then 1, then 9,
then 4. Press ⊟ key.
Answer 583

Worked example 3

Add 27.2, 48.6, 3.54, 5.09 and 16.9

Press keys 27 ⊡ 2, then ⊞, then 48 ⊡ 6, then ⊞, then 3 ⊡ 54, then ⊞ ,
then 5 ⊡ 09, then ⊞, then 16 ⊡ 9. Press ⊟ key.
Answer 101.33

Worked example 4

A motorist finds that his car in one year has cost £1309.60 in petrol and oil,
£642.38 in repairs, £324.84 in insurance, £110 in tax, and £38.50 for an AA fee.
How much does he spend on the car?

Total cost = £1309.60 + £642.38 + £324.84 + £110 + £38.50
Using a calculator
1309 ⊡ 60 ⊞ 642 ⊡ 38 ⊞ 324 ⊡ 84 ⊞ 110 ⊡ ⊞ 38 ⊡ 50 ⊟ 2425.32
Answer £2425.32

Exercise 1

Use a calculator to do the following additions:

1	65 + 49	**2**	132 + 88
3	64 + 29 + 75	**4**	347 + 205 + 47
5	97 + 306 + 33	**6**	3206 + 594 + 6075
7	496 + 24 + 5007 + 687	**8**	74.63 + 9.09
9	156.82 + 60.66	**10**	25.07 + 72.84 + 7.06
11	7.27 + 296.04 + 84.77	**12**	392.1 + 4090.84 + 30.08 + 591.40

13 The distances for the first nine holes of a golf course are 132 m, 347 m,
465 m, 402 m, 361 m, 153 m, 474 m, 289 m, and 331 m. What is the total
length of the first nine holes?

14 A motorist drives 296.2 miles, 87.4 miles, 350.8 miles, 160.7 miles and 98.7
miles on successive days. What total mileage did he do in these five days?

15 Shopping for the weekend cost £18.62, £56.24, £2.05, £14.27, £27.43 and
£3.95. How much was spent?

4 Subtraction   This is carried out as instructed in the question.

Worked example 5 $2734 - 1857$

Press keys 2734, then $\boxed{-}$, then 1857. Press $\boxed{=}$ key.
Answer 877

Worked example 6 $924 - 85 - 293$

$924 \boxed{-} 85 \boxed{-} 293 \boxed{=} 546.$
Answer 546

Worked example 7 $100 - 28.7 - 30.65$

$100 \boxed{-} 28 \boxed{.} 7 \boxed{-} 30 \boxed{.} 65 \boxed{=} 40.65.$
Answer 40.65

Worked example 8 $-32 - 56 - 94$

$\boxed{-} 32 \boxed{-} 56 \boxed{-} 94 \boxed{=} -182.$
Answer -182

5 Addition and Subtraction   This can be done by the calculator in one operation, provided you press the $\boxed{+}$ key or $\boxed{-}$ key as directed.

Worked example 9 $46 - 296 + 385 - 15$

$46 \boxed{-} 296 \boxed{+} 385 \boxed{-} 15 \boxed{=} 120$
Answer 120

Worked example 10 $35.6 + 7.08 - 8.29 - 15.74$

$35 \boxed{.} 6 \boxed{+} 7 \boxed{.} 08 \boxed{-} 8 \boxed{.} 29 \boxed{-} 15 \boxed{.} 74 \boxed{=} 18.65$
Answer 18.65

Exercise 2

1 $427 - 89$	**2** $105 - 68$
3 $183 - 87$	**4** $3025 - 764$
5 $46 - 124$	**6** $175 - 256$
7 $75.2 - 18.6 - 34.5$	**8** $175.4 - 73.2 - 19.4 - 10.7$
9 $34.7 - 72.9 + 185.4 - 97.3$	**10** $8.24 + 15.65 - 9.06 - 7.48$
11 $-15.26 - 17.08 + 58.24$	**12** $100.09 - 70.06 + 3.67 - 8.6$

13 $3275.4 - 609.08 - 217.42 - 1107.64 + 5.08$

14 $95.73 + 108.76 - 50.07 + 3.79 - 120.06$

15 $-0.07 - 28.04 - 5.64 - 357.21$

16 $-85.76 + 378.4 + 20.26 - 193.07$

17 $200.82 - 50.08 - 3.80 - 0.49 - 31.06$

18 $3.159 + 18.62 - 2.006 - 5.108$

19 $-180.07 + 573.74 - 0.09 - 30.76$

20 $5978 - 82.68 - 308.07 - 200.04$

6 **Multiplication**   Simply press the appropriate command keys.

Worked example 11 24×47

Press keys 24, then ×, then 47. Press = key.
Answer 1128

Worked example 12 134×86

134 × 86 = 11524
Answer 11 524

Worked example 13 57.6×138.2

57 . 6 × 138 . 2 = 7960.32
Answer 7960.32

Worked example 14 $42.7 \times 581.6 \times 65.1$

42 . 7 × 581 . 6 × 65 . 1 = 1616714.2
Answer 1 616 714.2

The calculator can show only 8 figures, so if the answer contains more than 8 figures (and worked example 14 should contain 10 figures), then the calculator will show only the first 8 significant figures. Any figures after the eighth are 'lost'.

For multiplication of large numbers, where is the decimal point? This is crucial. If the number of figures before the decimal point exceeds 8 then most calculators will show an 'E' in the display window.

Worked example 15 $568 \times 568 \times 568$

568 × 568 × 568 = 1.8325043 E
Obviously, the three numbers multiplied together give an answer greater than 1.8.

What is the answer?

The answer is found by moving the decimal point 8 places to the right from that shown in the display window.

The true value of 1.832 504 3 E is 183 250 430.

Worked example 16 $1584 \times 592 \times 403$

1584 × 592 × 403 = 3.7790438 E
'E' occurs in the display window, and so to get the true value of the multiplication sum move the decimal point 8 places to the right.
Answer 377 904 380

Worked example 17   Repeat the question above: $1584 \times 592 \times 403$

Now try and multiply or divide by any other number. What happens? Nothing.

When an 'E' is shown in the display window the calculator will not perform any other function until this 'E' has been cleared.

Press C (or CE on some calculators) and 'E' disappears. Further calculations can continue, but *remember* that the decimal point has to be moved 8 places to the right.

Worked example 18 | 83 742 × 4691 × 6.43

83742 ☒ 4691 ☒ ... When the second multiplication command is pressed the 'E' appears.

Clear 'E' by pressing C (or CE on some calculators) and then multiply by 6.43. The operation now becomes

83742 ☒ 4691 ☒ C ☒ 6 ⊡ 43 ▭ 25.259208

Remember the *true position* of the decimal point.
Answer 2 525 920 800

Exercise 3

Use your calculator to find

1	32×18	**2**	27×59
3	283×43	**4**	8.25×39.08
5	47.54×17.29	**6**	$13.4 \times 75.9 \times 12.7$
7	£7.95×18	**8**	£215.49×35
9	£1327.08×47	**10**	$394 \times 15.8 \times 47.07$
11	$28.07 \times 19.25 \times 36$	**12**	$0.08 \times 36.93 \times 0.42$
13	$9.08 \times 246.43 \times 39.76$	**14**	$82.59 \times 0.018 \times 5.075$
15	$4964 \times 3825 \times 758$	**16**	406.06×78.68
17	$0.007 \times 5975.47 \times 83.2$	**18**	787×778
19	5296×4849	**20**	$9.068 \times 525.09 \times 0.0753$
21	$3784 \times 94 \times 7475$	**22**	$96.24 \times 159.06 \times 27.65$
23	578.32×49.076	**24**	$758 \times 415 \times 297 \times 901$
25	$8205 \times 57.29 \times 94.83$	**26**	$52\,785 \times 48\,096$
27	$180.07 \times 7.68 \times 15.09$	**28**	$3796 \times 59\,476 \times 67$
29	305.62×965.08		

30 Out of the 29 previous questions, how many answers are exact and how many are approximate?

7 Division

Simply press the appropriate command keys.

Worked example 19 | 12 312 ÷ 27

Press keys 12312, then ⊟, then 27. Press ▭ key.
Answer 456

Worked example 20 | 53 118 ÷ 78

53118 ⊟ 78 ▭ 681
Answer 681

Worked example 21 | 295.1289 ÷ 5.23

295 ⊡ 1289 ⊟ 5 ⊡ 23 ▭ 56.43
Answer 56.43

Worked example 22 $387.6 \div 27$

387 $\boxed{.}$ 6 $\boxed{\div}$ 27 $\boxed{=}$ 14.355555
The question, in this case, would probably ask for the answer to be given to two decimal places or correct to two decimal places.
Answer to 2 decimal places 14.35
Answer correct to 2 decimal places 14.36

Exercise 4

1	$4864 \div 19$	2	$13\,301 \div 47$	3	$13\,409 \div 23$
4	$113\,652 \div 132$	5	$34\,352 \div 76$	6	$183.6 \div 2.7$
7	$366.6 \div 3.9$	8	$114.54 \div 8.3$	9	$324.198 \div 6.51$
10	$6088.8 \div 11.8$	11	$6822.14 \div 24.7$	12	$549.594 \div 0.57$
13	$2402.48 \div 5.9$	14	$228.5976 \div 2.64$	15	$6011.556 \div 0.92$

Exercise 5

Give answers correct to 2 decimal places.

1	$88 \div 10.3$	2	$97 \div 8$	3	$35 \div 6$
4	$98.4 \div 7.2$	5	$496 \div 12.4$	6	$397.9 \div 13$
7	$0.87 \div 14$	8	$7.92 \div 39.04$	9	$3924 \div 127.8$
10	$0.27 \div 7.5$	11	$82.08 \div 13.68$	12	$75\,241 \div 587.6$
13	$0.065 \div 0.0074$	14	$100 \div 17.27$	15	$8 \div 35.06$
16	$15.83 \div 215.83$	17	$46.2 \div 0.075$	18	$13 \div 207.4$
19	$3078 \div 85.9$	20	$24 \div 476.4$		

8 Mixed Operations

The calculator will do only what you tell it to do, and so in questions involving more than one different operation you have to know what is meant by the arithmetical part of the question.

Worked example 23 $3 + 8 \times 4$

If you cannot remember how to work this out look at section 7 in Chapter 1 on priorities. The answer is 35. (3 has to be added to 8×4.)

Put this question on the calculator, *as it stands*, and you would have

3 $\boxed{+}$ 8 $\boxed{\times}$ 4 $\boxed{=}$ 44

The calculator adds 3 to 8 and then multiplies the result by 4.

The priorities of an arithmetical calculation are brackets, multiplication and division, addition and subtraction, in that order.

This example can be done on the calculator as follows:

8 $\boxed{\times}$ 4 $\boxed{+}$ 3 $\boxed{=}$ 35

Look carefully to see what must be done first.

Worked example 24 $54 + 16 \div 4 - 32$

Division is first, and then the rest on the calculator:

16 $\boxed{\div}$ 4 $\boxed{+}$ 54 $\boxed{-}$ 32

(No sign in front of 54 implies it is $+$.)

16 $\boxed{\div}$ 4 $\boxed{+}$ 54 $\boxed{-}$ 32 $\boxed{=}$ 26

Worked example 25 $(11 + 7) \div 4$

Brackets are first, with the result divided by 4:

11 $\boxed{+}$ 7 $\boxed{\div}$ 4 $\boxed{=}$ 4.5

Worked example 26 $86 - 32 \div 8 - 24$

Division first, but note the $-$ sign in front of 32:

$\boxed{-}$ 32 $\boxed{\div}$ 8 $\boxed{+}$ 86 $\boxed{-}$ 24 $\boxed{=}$ 58

Worked example 27 $\dfrac{48.2 \times 39.7}{24.92}$

The line means divide:

48 $\boxed{.}$ 2 $\boxed{\times}$ 39 $\boxed{.}$ 7 $\boxed{\div}$ 24 $\boxed{.}$ 92 $\boxed{=}$ 76.78

Worked example 28 $\dfrac{18.96 \times 7.65}{3.06 \times 23.87}$

Try this question without further reading. What is your answer? 1131.438? Wrong.

The question asks, what is the result of multiplying 18.96 by 7.65 and then dividing by 3.06 and then by 23.87.

The calculation is

18 $\boxed{.}$ 96 $\boxed{\times}$ 7 $\boxed{.}$ 65 $\boxed{\div}$ 3 $\boxed{.}$ 06 $\boxed{\div}$ 23 $\boxed{.}$ 87 $\boxed{=}$ 1.99

Think what the question is asking before using the calculator.

Exercise 6

Give answers correct to 2 decimal places.

1 $58 \div 8 + 9$	**2** $24 + 10 \div 8$
3 $(16 + 8) \div 7$	**4** $24 + 10 \div 5 - 6$
5 $38 \div 6 + 7$	**6** $20.6 + 3.4 \div 6 + 10$
7 $(15 - 8.2) \div 5.4$	**8** $14.7 + (8.52 \times 7.5)$
9 $\dfrac{21}{9}$	**10** $\dfrac{11.23}{7.16}$
11 $\dfrac{41.75 + 8.31}{12.65}$	**12** $\dfrac{39.41 - 18.45}{9.03}$
13 $\dfrac{12.56 \times 18.62}{74.07}$	**14** $\dfrac{34.17 \times 1.86}{0.054}$
15 $\dfrac{87.08 \div 9.26}{5.08}$	**16** $\dfrac{125.26 \times 91.48}{15.79 \times 99.06}$
17 $\dfrac{5287}{11.94 \times 84.01}$	**18** $\dfrac{145.6 + 32.94}{111.07}$
19 $\dfrac{5.96 \times 4.24}{0.06 \times 0.014}$	**20** $\dfrac{94.32 \times 2.47}{11.25 \times 18.61 \times 0.04}$

6 Measurement

1 Imperial and Metric Measures

You should try and remember the various weights, lengths and capacities in imperial and metric units. The following are the most common units in use.

Metric measure

Weight
1000 milligrams (mg) = 1 gram (g)
1000 grams   = 1 kilogram (kg)
1000 kilograms   = 1 tonne (t)

Length
10 millimetres (mm) = 1 centimetre (cm)
100 centimetres   = 1 metre (m)
1000 metres   = 1 kilometre (km)

Capacity
10 millilitres (ml) = 1 centilitre (cl)
1000 millilitres   = 1 litre (ℓ)

Imperial measure

(remember 1 dozen = 12)

Weight
16 ounces (oz)   = 1 pound (lb)
14 pounds   = 1 stone (st)
112 pounds   = 1 hundredweight (cwt)
20 hundredweights = 1 ton

Length
12 inches (in) = 1 foot (ft)
3 feet   = 1 yard (yd)
1760 yards   = 1 mile

Capacity
2 pints (pt) = 1 quart (qt)
8 pints   = 1 gallon (gal)

Also, there are 20 fluid ounces (fl oz) in 1 pint.

For products such as butter, coffee, cereals, biscuits, sugar and crisps, the weight is usually given in grams or kilograms.

A milligram is a very small weight, and is likely to be used in a laboratory, a hospital, or for prescriptions such as eye-drops, or small amounts of healing cream.

Vegetables are often given in lb and oz.

Weights of cars or lorries are often in cwt or tons and cwt.

Bottles of liquid such as wine, cooking oil and vinegar usually have contents measured in cl, though some small bottles may also give fluid ozs as well.

For an approximate comparison between units:

1 metre is a little more than 1 yard
1 kg is a little more than 2 lb
100 g is just less than 4 oz
1 tonne is just less than 1 ton
5 litres is a bit more than 1 gallon
1 gallon of water weighs 10 lb
A good striding pace is about 1 yd
1 km is about $\frac{3}{5}$ of a mile

Here are a few simple questions using the comparisons already given (more accurate comparisons are given later in the chapter).

1   You know your own weight. (a) If you know it in lb what is it roughly in kg? (b) If you know it in kg what is it roughly in lb?

2   A 4-door Golf car weighs 2348 lb. How many people of your weight weigh the same as the Golf car?

3   A large cornflake packet is 750 g. About how much is this in oz?

4   A pint of milk is 20 fl oz. About how much is this in cl? (Look at 5 litres and 1 gallon.)

5   Stride across the room. About how far is this in metres?

6   What is your estimate for the height of the ceiling?

7   A jar of coffee holds 200 g. About how many oz is this?

8   A car petrol tank holds 12 gal. About how many litres is this?

9   Paris to Calais is 300 km. About how many miles is this?

10   London to Plymouth is 210 miles. About how many km is this?

11   A bottle of wine is 75 cl. About how much is this in oz if you assume wine weighs the same as water?

12   Bring a lot of bottle or tin labels to the class. Change the weight or volume given on the labels to another unit.

From October 1995 the European Commission decreed that **pre-packed** produce, including meat, vegetables and milk, sold in supermarkets should have its weight given in kilograms, grams or litres only, with the price given per kg or litre. Items sold loose can be sold in pounds and ounces and priced accordingly. Also, evidence in court after that date has to be in metres, centimetres, litres, kilograms and grams: for example, a knife would have to be described as being fifteen centimetres long, not six inches.

2 Changing Units

To change units in imperial or metric measure multiply or divide by the appropriate figure.

Worked example 1

Change 3 kg to g.

What is the relation between kg and g?
1 kg = 1000 g.
Then 3 kg = 3 × 1000 g
            = 3000 g
Answer 3000 g

Worked example 2

Change 2800 g to kg.

Again, 1000 g = 1 kg

Then 2800 g = $\dfrac{2800}{1000}$ kg

$\qquad\qquad$ = 2.8 kg

Answer 2.8 kg

Worked example 3

Change 100 in to ft.

12 in = 1 ft

So 100 in = $\dfrac{100}{12}$ ft

$\qquad\qquad$ = 8 remainder 4

The 4 units left over are inches.

Answer 8 ft 4 in or $8\frac{1}{3}$ ft

3 Changing Imperial Units to Metric Units

Where you have to change from one set of units to another you will be given the relationship between the two; this is called the **conversion factor**.

Worked example 4

Change 3 km to miles, given that 1 km = 0.62 miles.

1 km = 0.62 miles. This is the conversion factor.

Then 3 km = 3 × 0.62 miles

$\qquad\qquad$ = 1.86 miles

Answer 1.86 miles

Worked example 5

Change 5 miles to km given that 1 km = 0.62 miles.

0.62 miles = 1 km

Then 1 mile = $\dfrac{1}{0.62}$ km

5 miles $\quad$ = $5 \times \dfrac{1}{0.62}$ km

$\qquad\qquad$ = $\dfrac{5}{0.62}$

$\qquad\qquad$ = 8.06 km

Answer 8.06 km

Worked example 6

Change 200 litres to gallons given that 1 gallon = 4.54 litres.

4.54 litres = 1 gallon

Then 1 ℓ = $\dfrac{1}{4.54}$ gal

So 200 ℓ = $200 \times \dfrac{1}{4.54}$ gal

$\qquad\qquad$ = $\dfrac{200}{4.54}$

$\qquad\qquad$ = 44.05 gal

Answer 44.05 gal

Sometimes you have to multiply by the conversion factor and at other times divide by it. If you are not sure whether to multiply or divide, then think whether you are looking for a bigger answer or a smaller answer.

Exercise 1

Use the measures at the beginning of the chapter.

1   Change to m: (a) 2 km (b) 6 km (c) 5 km (d) 20 km

2   Change to m: (a) 1.6 km (b) 4.8 km (c) 5.2 km (d) 3.4 km

3   Change to m: (a) 1.56 km (b) 2.34 km (c) 3.06 km (d) 1.80 km

4   Change to km: (a) 3000 m (b) 8000 m (c) 12 000 m (d) 50 000 m

5   Change to km: (a) 2500 m (b) 5600 m (c) 4250 m (d) 1800 m

6   Change to km: (a) 1250 m (b) 880 m (c) 60 m (d) 240 m

7   Change to m and cm: (a) 25.40 m (b) 8.3 m (c) 48.75 m (d) 4.5 m

8   Change to m and cm: (a) 5.24 m (b) 9.09 m (c) 82.18 m (d) 0.62 m

9   Change to kg: (a) 3000 g (b) 8000 g (c) 24 000 g (d) 120 000 g

10   Change to kg: (a) 1500 g (b) 2900 g (c) 7850 g (d) 4250 g

11   Change to kg: (a) 900 g (b) 450 g (c) 248 g (d) 70 g

12   Change to g: (a) 2 kg (b) 5 kg (c) 15 kg (d) 21 kg

13   Change to g: (a) 1.6 kg (b) 2.5 kg (c) 0.82 kg (d) 2.04 kg

14   Change to kg and g: (a) 1.28 kg (b) 1.062 kg (c) 3.59 kg (d) 3.059 kg

15   Change to ml: (a) 4 ℓ (b) 9 ℓ (c) 2 ℓ (d) 13 ℓ

16   Change to ml: (a) 2.5 ℓ (b) 3.44 ℓ (c) 0.4 ℓ (d) 5.09 ℓ

17   Change to ℓ: (a) 3000 ml (b) 8000 ml (c) 15 000 ml (d) 120 000 ml

18   Change to ℓ: (a) 2800 ml (b) 1750 ml (c) 3070 ml (d) 8008 ml

19   Change to ℓ and ml: (a) 3.06 ℓ (b) 52.3 ℓ (c) 2.95 ℓ (d) 1.082 ℓ

20   $1\frac{1}{4}$ litres is added to 30 cl. What is the total?

21   A cask of wine holds 168 litres. How many bottles, each of 75 cl, can be filled from the cask?

22   2 kg of potatoes cost 52p. What is the cost of 5 kg?

23   From 2 kg is taken 0.2 kg, 0.5 kg, and 750 g. What weight is left?

24   In a 1500 m race a man reckons to run 200 m in 48 seconds. In what time does he run the 1500 m at that pace?

25   A panel is 1 m 60 cm long. How many such panels placed side by side will cover a length of 38 m 40 cm?

Exercise 2

Use the measures at the beginning of the chapter.

1   Change to in: (a) 2 ft (b) 6 ft (c) 12 ft (d) 20 ft

2   Change to in: (a) 1 ft 9 in (b) 3 ft 4 in (c) 5 ft 2 in (d) 8 ft 6 in

3   Change to ft and in: (a) 40 in (b) 58 in (c) 76 in (d) 35 in

4   Change to ft: (a) 2 yd (b) 7 yd (c) 9 yd (d) 14 yd

5   Change to ft: (a) 3 yd 1 ft (b) 5 yd 2 ft (c) 7 yd 2 ft (d) 6 yd 1 ft

6   Change to yd and ft: (a) 13 ft (b) 8 ft (c) 19 ft (d) 15 ft

7   How many cwt are there in (a) 3 tons (b) 5 tons (c) 8 tons (d) 10 tons?

8   How many cwt are there in (a) 2 ton 10 cwt (b) 4 ton 5 cwt (c) 0.5 ton (d) 3 ton 15 cwt?

9   How many oz are there in (a) 3 lb (b) 5 lb (c) 4 lb 7 oz (d) 2 lb 9 oz?

10   How many pints are there in (a) 3 gal (b) 2 gal 3 pt (c) 1 gal 7 pt (d) 3 gal 3 pt?

11   How many fluid ounces are there in (a) 3 pt (b) 1 pt 10 fl oz (c) 2 pt 4 fl oz (d) 5 pt 10 fl oz?

12   A packet weighs 5 oz. How many packets can you get from 4 lb 1 oz?

13   An empty lorry weighs 15 ton 7 cwt. When loaded it is 33 ton 2 cwt. What is the weight of the load?

14   A kerbstone is 4 ft long and costs £3.60. How much does it cost to put kerbstones to cover a length of 12 yd?

15   Beer is sold at £1.80 a pint. A pub sells a barrel containing 36 gal in one night. How much cash is taken from the sale of this barrel?

16   A woman weighs 10 st 4 lb and after going on a diet she weighs 8 st 12 lb. How much weight has she lost?

17   A 5 gallon drum of oil is used to sell oil at £1.35 a pint. How much cash is taken from selling the oil in this way?

18   A house brick is 22 cm long. How many bricks are needed in one row, neglecting mortar, to cover a length of 11 metres?

19   100 g of coffee are in a jar. The jar and the coffee weigh 0.384 kg. What is the weight of the jar?

20   Hazelnuts are sold loose from a sack containing 8 kg of nuts. How many 200 g packets of nuts can be sold from the sack?

Exercise 3

For the purpose of this exercise assume the following approximate conversion factors:

1 ft = 30 cm; 1 gal = 4.5 ℓ; 1 kg = 2.2 lb

1   How many gallons are there in a 225 litre drum?

2   How many gallons of petrol are needed to fill a car's petrol tank that holds 63 litres?

3   A concrete flag is 3 ft long. How many cm is this?

4   A room is 7 ft 6 in high. How high is this in m and cm?

5   A bag of coal weighs 25 kg. What is the weight in lb?

6   A man weighs 13 st 9 lb. What is his weight in kilograms?

7   Petrol is 55p a litre. How much is this per gallon?

8   A garden is 28 yd long. How long is this in metres and cm?

9   By how much is a ton heavier than one thousand kilograms?

10   A 75 cl bottle of wine costs £5.75. How much does each wine glass cost if a glass holds 15 cl?

11 A small barrel of beer holds 9 gallons. How many litres is this?

12 A piece of glass is 6 ft by 4 ft 6 in. What are these measurements in cm?

13 How many fluid ounces are there in 4 pt?

14 A soldier's stride is 33 in. What is it in cm?

15 A gallon of water weighs 10 lb. What does it weigh in grams? (Give your answer to the nearest whole number.)

16 A church steeple is 300 ft high. How high is this in metres and cm? (Give your answer to the nearest cm.)

17 A cricket pitch is 22 yd long. How long is this in metres and cm? (Give your answer to the nearest cm.)

18 A hot water tank holds 25 gallons. What does it hold in litres?

19 A golf course measures 7350 yd. How long is this in km? (Give your answer correct to 2 decimal places.)

20 A wooden fencing post is £4.50 per metre. How much is this per ft?

4 Time

All countries use the same measurement: seconds, minutes, hours, days and years.

Time of day can be given as morning (a.m.) or afternoon (p.m.), but a more usual way is to use the 24-hour clock, which runs from 0000 hours to 2400 hours midnight, and 1200 hours is midday (noon). The abbreviation for hour is h.

Thus for example:

0600 hours is 6 a.m.   1100 hours is 11 a.m.
1300 hours is 1 p.m.   1800 hours is 6 p.m.
2030 hours is 8.30 p.m.   2210 hours is 10.10 p.m.

Note: 8.30 p.m. means 8 hours 30 minutes after noon, or it might be called half-past eight at night. It does not mean 8 point 30, as in the decimal system.

Worked example 7

Change ten past five in the morning to a 24-hour clock time.

What is meant by ten past five?
It means ten minutes past five o'clock: that is, 5.10.
We are told it is a morning time, so it becomes 5.10 a.m.
On the 24-hour clock this is 0510 hours.

Worked example 8

What is a quarter past one in the afternoon as a 24-hour clock time?

A quarter past one means a quarter of an hour past one o'clock: that is, 15 minutes past one or 1.15.
It is an afternoon time, which means 1.15 p.m. or 1.15 after noon (midday).
1200 hours is midday.
1.15 after midday is 1315 hours.

Worked example 9

How long is it, in hours and minutes, from 8.20 a.m. until 4.30 p.m.?

Work out in easy stages:
From 8.20 a.m. to 9.00 a.m. =   40 min
From 9.00 a.m. to 12 noon = 3 h
From 12 noon to 4.30 p.m. = 4 h 30 min
Total time   = 8 h 10 min
Answer 8 h 10 min

Worked example 10   A flight is due to take off at 2130 hours, but owing to fuelling problems it does not take off until 0120 hours the following day. How long is the delay?

From 2130 hours until 2200 hours =   30 min
From 2200 hours until 2400 hours = 2 h
From 2400 hours until 0120 hours = 1 h 20 min
Total delay   = 3 h 50 min
Answer 3 h 50 min
Note: After midnight 2400 hours you begin another day.

Exercise 4

Change the following times to those of a 24-hour clock:

1	5 o'clock in the morning	**2**	11 o'clock in the morning
3	6 o'clock in the afternoon	**4**	9 o'clock at night
5	3.00 a.m.	**6**	11.30 a.m.
7	4 p.m.	**8**	10 p.m.
9	8.30 p.m.	**10**	7.25 a.m.
11	Half past two in the morning	**12**	A quarter past four in the afternoon
13	Six thirty in the morning	**14**	Ten minutes to nine at night

15 8.45 p.m.
16 Twenty-four minutes past nine in the morning
17 Eighteen minutes past midnight
18 Thirty minutes past midday
19 Half-past ten at night
20 A quarter to seven at night

Exercise 5

Change these 24-hour clock times to morning or afternoon time:

1	0700 hours	**2**	1000 hours	**3**	1400 hours
4	1900 hours	**5**	0330 hours	**6**	1430 hours
7	1945 hours	**8**	0420 hours	**9**	1116 hours
10	2150 hours	**11**	0040 hours	**12**	2315 hours
13	0942 hours	**14**	1250 hours	**15**	1715 hours
16	2130 hours	**17**	0408 hours	**18**	1030 hours
19	0640 hours	**20**	1527 hours		

Exercise 6

How long is it between these times? (Give answers in minutes or hours and minutes.)

1 7.00 a.m. to 11.00 a.m. on the same day.

2 8.30 a.m. to 10.30 a.m. on the same day.

3 4.30 a.m. to 2.00 p.m. on the same day.

4 5.25 a.m. to 3.15 p.m. on the same day.

5 10.15 a.m. to 9.25 p.m. on the same day.

6 9.40 a.m. to 10.04 a.m. on the same day

7 8.25 p.m. to 2.15 a.m. on the next day

8 11.15 a.m. to 1.05 a.m. on the next day

9 Twenty past nine in the morning until five to eight at night on the same day

10 Seven fifteen a.m. until four twenty p.m. on the same day

11 0600 hours to 1430 hours on the same day

12 0930 hours to 1215 hours on the same day

13 1020 hours to 0200 hours on the next day

14 1640 hours to 1910 hours on the same day

15 1150 hours to 0024 hours on the next day

16 1850 hours to 0640 hours on the next day

17 1120 hours to 0010 hours on the next day

18 1410 hours to 1905 hours on the same day

19 1920 hours to 0310 hours on the next day

20 0230 hours to 1320 hours on the same day

7 | Ratio and Proportion

1 Ratio as a Comparison

Ratio is a comparison of quantities; it can be written in a special way or as a fraction.

Proportion is one part expressed as a fraction of the whole.

Worked example 1

In the garden there are 3 apple trees and 2 pear trees.

- The ratio of apple trees to pear trees is said to be $3 : 2$ (three to two) or $\frac{3}{2}$.

- The number of trees in the whole garden is 5.

- The proportion of apple trees in the garden is $\frac{3}{5}$ and that of pear trees is $\frac{2}{5}$.

Worked example 2

In a class there are 15 boys and 18 girls. What is the ratio of boys to girls? What is the proportion of girls in the class?

There are 15 boys, 18 girls.

Ratio of boys : girls = 15 : 18
= 5 : 6

Ratios can be simplified in the same way as fractions.

In the class there are 15 boys and 18 girls, making a total of 33.
There are 18 girls out of a total of 33.

$$\text{Proportion of girls} = \frac{18}{33} = \frac{6}{11}$$

Note: The proportion of boys is $\frac{15}{33}\left(\frac{5}{11}\right)$.

Ratios, like fractions, can be put in their simplest or lowest terms, or if they are in fractional form can be simplified.

Worked example 3

A ratio of $6 : 4$ is the same as $3 : 2$, dividing both parts by 2.

$4 : 12$ is the same as $1 : 3$.

$9 : 15$ is the same as $3 : 5$.

$\frac{3}{4} : 1$ is the same as $3 : 4$, multiplying both parts by 4.

$\frac{2}{3} : 1$ is the same as $2 : 3$, multiplying both parts by 3.

$\frac{1}{2} : \frac{3}{4} = \frac{2}{4} : \frac{3}{4} = 2 : 3$.

$\frac{2}{3} : \frac{3}{4} = \frac{8}{12} : \frac{9}{12} = 8 : 9$.

70

Worked example 4   Flaky pastry is made by mixing fat and flour in the ratio of 3 : 4. How much fat is required to 12 oz of flour?

Fat to flour is in ratio of 3 : 4. This must always be maintained.

If 12 oz of flour are used then we have multiplied the second part of the ratio by 3 oz (4×3 oz = 12 oz).

The first part of the ratio, which is fat, must also be multiplied by 3 oz in order to keep the same ratio.

Fat to flour is 3 : 4
Fat to flour is 9 oz : 12 oz
Fat required is 9 oz

Worked example 5   A garden compost is made up of loam, peat and coarse sand in the ratio of 7 : 3 : 2. If I use 4 bucketfuls of sand how much loam and peat is required?

Loam to peat to coarse sand is 7 : 3 : 2.

Write down 4 buckets in place of the sand figure and the ratio then becomes

loam to peat to coarse sand:

7	:	3	:	2
14 buckets	:	6 buckets	:	4 buckets
				(each figure doubled)

Answer 14 bucketfuls of loam and 6 bucketfuls of peat

Exercise 1

Simplify the following ratios:

1	2 : 4	2	4 : 6	3	8 : 10
4	6 : 9	5	15 : 10	6	12 : 4
7	10 : 4	8	15 : 20	9	12 : 8
10	25 : 40	11	14 g : 20 g	12	6 ft : 10 ft
13	12 kg : 6 kg	14	4 ft : 2 ft 6 in	15	1 ft 6 in : 3 ft 6 in
16	10 km : 16 km	17	4 miles : 6 miles	18	50 g : 150 g
19	45 min : 3 h	20	15 litres : 9 litres	21	15 g : 25 g
22	$1\frac{1}{2}$: 2	23	$2\frac{1}{2}$: $1\frac{1}{2}$	24	3 : $2\frac{1}{2}$
25	4 : 6 : 10	26	12 : 8 : 4	27	15 : 10 : 10
28	70 : 50 : 30	29	18 : 12 : 9	30	$4\frac{1}{2}$: $2\frac{1}{2}$: 2

Exercise 2

1   An adult French class has 6 men and 9 women. (a) What is the ratio of men to women? (b) What is the proportion of women in the class? (c) What is the proportion of men in the class?

2   A rose bed has 12 red roses and 8 white ones. (a) What is the ratio of red roses to white ones? (b) What is the proportion of red roses in the bed? (c) What is the proportion of white roses in the bed?

3   The junior section of a tennis club has 24 boys and 16 girls. (a) What is the ratio of girls to boys? (b) What is the proportion of boys in the section?

4   In a carpark there are 42 hatchbacks and 56 cars with a boot. (a) What is the ratio of hatchbacks to cars with a boot? (b) What is the proportion of hatchbacks in the car park?

5   A hotel, on a Wednesday, had 18 men and 4 women all staying overnight. (a) What was the ratio of men to women staying overnight? (b) What was the proportion of women staying overnight?

6   On a Barratt development there are 32 houses and 12 bungalows. (a) What is the ratio of houses to bungalows? (b) What is the proportion of bungalows on the estate?

7   A bookseller on one day sold 115 paperbacks and 25 hardbacks. (a) What was the ratio of paperbacks to hardbacks sold? (b) What was the proportion of paperbacks sold?

8   A small tree-planting exercise had evergreens and deciduous trees in the ratio 3 : 2. The number of evergreens planted was 360. How many deciduous trees were planted?

9   A concrete can be made using 5 parts sand to 2 parts cement. 35 cwt of sand was used. How much cement is used?

10   A garden dressing was made from loam and peat in the ratio 3 : 2. 36 litres of peat was used. How much loam was used?

11   A main fertiliser used chemicals to release nitrogen, phosphate and potash in the ratio 3 : 2 : 2. 1500 g of chemical releasing nitrogen was used. What weight of the chemical releasing phosphate was used?

12   A pastry can be made by mixing flour and fat in the ratio $2\frac{1}{2} : 1\frac{1}{2}$. How much flour is needed to 240 g of fat?

2 Proportional Parts

This section looks at how to calculate the parts of a whole quantity when the proportions are given as a ratio. The method is to add up all the individual parts of the ratio. The answer becomes the denominator of a fraction in which each individual part is the numerator. Examples will show this clearly.

Worked example 6

The ratio of fat to flour in shortcrust pastry is 1 : 2. How much of each is needed to make 450 g of pastry?

Ratio of fat to flour = 1 : 2
Add the parts of the ratio together, 1 + 2 = 3
This means there are going to be 3 parts altogether, with 1 part fat and 2 parts flour.
Fat is $\frac{1}{3}$ of whole; flour is $\frac{2}{3}$; 450 g of pastry required
1 part = $\frac{450}{3}$ g = 150 g
Fat is 1 part = 150 g
Flour is 2 parts = 2 × 150 g = 300 g
Answer 150 g fat, 300 g flour

Worked example 7

Divide £30 in the ratio 7 : 3.

Ratio of 7 : 3 means there are 10 parts (7 + 3).
Divide £30 by 10 to find each part.

Each part = £$\frac{30}{10}$ = £3

7 parts = 7 × £3 = £21
3 parts = 3 × £3 = £9
Answer £21 and £9

Worked example 8 | An alloy is made of copper and tin in the ratio 3 : 2. How much copper and tin is there is 2 kg of alloy?

Ratio of 3 : 2 means there are 5 parts (3 + 2).
2 kg = 2000 g
Now divide 2000 g by 5 to find each part:

$$\text{Each part} = \frac{2000}{5}\,\text{g} = 400\,\text{g}$$

Copper is 3 parts = 3 × 400 g = 1200 g
Tin is 2 parts   = 2 × 400 g =   800 g
Answer 1200 g of copper, 800 g of tin

The method works for any number of figures in the ratio.

Worked example 9 | Bandages are available in three sizes – large, medium and small – and they are ordered in the ratio 3 : 4 : 5. How many of each size are ordered in a total of 1800 bandages?

Ratio of 3 : 4 : 5 means there are 12 parts (3 + 4 + 5).
Divide 1800 by 12 to find each part:

$$\text{Each part} = \frac{1800}{12} = 150\,\text{bandages}$$

Large bandages = 3 parts = 3 × 150 = 450 bandages
Medium bandages = 4 parts = 4 × 150 = 600 bandages
Small bandages = 5 parts = 5 × 150 = 750 bandages
Answer 450 large bandages, 600 medium and 750 small

Worked example 10 | Divide £300 in the ratio $1\frac{1}{2} : 2 : 2\frac{3}{4}$.

With fractional ratios, first multiply to remove the fractions. In this case multiply each part of the ratio by 4.
$1\frac{1}{2} : 2 : 2\frac{3}{4}$ is the same as 6 : 8 : 11.
6 : 8 : 11 means there are 25 parts (6 + 8 + 11)
Divide £300 by 25 to find each part:

$$\text{Each part} = £\frac{300}{25} = £12$$

6 parts = £72
8 parts = £96
11 parts = £132
Answer £72, £96, £132

Exercise 3

1 Divide £5 in the ratio 3 : 2
2 Divide £12 in the ratio 2 : 1
3 Divide £20 in the ratio 3 : 7
4 Divide £14 in the ratio 4 : 3
5 Divide £3.50 in the ratio 3 : 2
6 Divide £25 in the ratio 2 : 3
7 Divide 1 metre in the ratio 7 : 3
8 Divide 125 g in the ratio $1 : 1\frac{1}{2}$
9 Divide 300 ml in the ratio $1\frac{1}{2} : 3\frac{1}{2}$
10 Divide £80 in the ratio 2 : 3 : 3
11 Divide £1500 in the ratio 3 : 8 : 4
12 Divide £60 in the ratio $1\frac{1}{2} : 2\frac{1}{2} : 1$

13 A screenwash is made up of water and chemical in the ratio 4 : 1 by volume. There are two litres of screen wash. How much water and chemical is there?

14 The mixture for a car radiator is water and antifreeze in the ratio 6 : 4. How much water is required for 2 litres of antifreeze?

15 1200 g of bronze are made from copper and brass in the ratio 3 : 2. How much brass is needed?

16 A box of chocolates has hard and soft centres in the ratio 3 : 4. A box had 21 chocolates. How many soft-centred chocolates were there?

17 A concrete can be made from cement, sand and gravel in the ratio 1 : 3 : 6. How much sand is required for 5 tons of concrete?

18 An alloy of copper and tin is made in the ratio 4 : 3. How much copper is there in 210 g of alloy?

19 The ratio of flour to fat in shortcrust pastry is 2 : 1. How much of each is needed to make 360 g of pastry?

20 In a newsagents, papers are sold as tabloids and broadsheets in the ratio 5 : 1. Out of 300 newspapers sold, how many tabloids are sold?

21 A drink is made of white wine and cassis in the ratio 7 : 2. How much cassis is used in a drink of 18 cl?

22 The ratio of rented houses and owned houses has changed in the last ten years from 2 : 3 to 3 : 2. Ten years ago there were 24 rented houses on an estate. How many are rented now?

23 An alloy of tin and copper is in the ratio 4 : 7. There is 3025 g of alloy. How much copper is in the alloy?

24 A display of red, blue and green sweaters was in the ratio 4 : 3 : 2. In the display of 36 sweaters how many were blue?

3 Scales and Maps

Maps, models and diagrams are often reduced in size in a fixed ratio. This reduction is then stated.

- An Ordnance Survey map may show 1 : 50 000.
- A drawing of a house may show 1 : 125.
- A model may show 1 : 10.

Worked example 11

An Ordnance Survey map has a scale of 1 : 50 000. The distance between two towns on the map is measured as 2 cm. What is the actual distance between the two towns?

Scale is 1 : 50 000
This means that 1 unit on the map represents 50 000 units on the ground.

2 cm on the map represents 50 000 × 2 cm on the ground
= 100 000 cm
= 1000 m
= 1 km
Answer 1 km

Worked example 12

A walker is in Keswick and using an Ordnance Survey map of scale 1 : 25 000. He wants to walk to Buttermere, which he finds, by using a piece of cotton, is 50 cm on the map. How far does he walk to get to Buttermere?

Scale is 1 : 25 000.
1 unit of the map is 25 000 units on the ground.

50 cm on the map = 25 000 × 50 cm on the ground
= 1 250 000 cm
= 12 500 m
= 12.5 km
Answer 12.5 km

Worked example 13   A map of the British Isles is on a scale of 1 : 5 000 000. The straight-line distance between London and Edinburgh is approximately 650 km. How far does this appear on the map?

Scale is 1 : 5 000 000.
1 unit on the map is 5 000 000 units on the ground,
or 5 000 000 units on the ground is 1 unit on the map.

1 unit on the ground = $\dfrac{1}{5\,000\,000}$ units on the map.

650 km on the ground = $\dfrac{650}{5\,000\,000}$ km on the map.

Change km into m and then cm:

$= \dfrac{650 \times 1000 \times 100}{5\,000\,000}$ cm

$= \frac{65}{5}$ cm
$= 13$ cm
Answer 13 cm

Worked example 14   A map of the British Isles is on a scale of 1 : 5 000 000. The straight-line distance between Land's End and John o' Groats is approximately 600 miles. How far apart are Land's End and John o' Groats on the map in inches (to 1 decimal place?)

Scale is 1 : 5 000 000.
This means that 1 unit on the map is 5 000 000 units on the ground.
5 000 000 units on the ground is 1 unit on the map.

1 unit on the ground = $\dfrac{1}{5\,000\,000}$ units on the map.

600 miles on the ground = $\dfrac{600}{5\,000\,000}$ miles on the map.

Now change 600 miles to yards and then to inches:

$= \dfrac{600 \times 1760}{5\,000\,000}$ Change 600 miles to yd (1 mile = 1760 yd).

$= \dfrac{600 \times 1760 \times 36}{5\,000\,000}$ Change yd to in (1 yd = 36 in).

$= \dfrac{6 \times 176 \times 36}{5000}$ in

$= \dfrac{38\,016}{5000}$ in

$= \dfrac{38.016}{5}$ in

$= 7.6$ in
Answer 7.6 in

Worked example 15   An aeroplane has a wingspan of 150 ft. A model of it is made on a scale 1 : 100. How big is the wingspan on the model?

Scale is 1 : 100.
1 unit on the model is 100 units on the aeroplane,
or 100 units on the aeroplane = 1 unit on the model.

$$1 \text{ unit on the aeroplane} = \frac{1}{100} \text{ unit on the model}$$

$$150 \text{ ft on the aeroplane} = \frac{150}{100} \text{ ft on the model}$$

$$= 1.5 \text{ ft on the model}$$

Answer 1.5 ft

Exercise 4

1   A cupboard is drawn on a scale of 1 : 10. The cupboard is 6 ft 8 in long. How long will this be on the drawing?

2   A yacht is drawn on a scale of 1 : 30. The yacht is 25 ft long. How long will this be on the drawing?

3   A boat is drawn on a scale of 1 : 50. It is shown as 14 in on the drawing. What is the length of the boat in feet and inches?

4   A walking map has a scale of 1 : 25 000. How much does 1 cm on the map represent? (Answer in metres.)

5   A map has a scale of 1 : 50 000. How much does 4 cm on the map represent? (Answer in km.)

6   A map has a scale of 1 : 25 000. From Keswick to Borrowdale on the map is 20 cm. How far is it, in km, from Keswick to Borrowdale?

7   An aeroplane has a wingspan of 60 metres. A model is made of it using a scale of 1 : 100. How big is the wingspan of the model? (Answer in cm.)

8   A Michelin map has a scale of 1 : 200 000. Calais to St Omer is 18 cm on the map. How far is it, in km, from Calais to St Omer?

9   On the same Michelin map, Calais to Boulogne is 15 cm on the map. How far is it, in km, from Calais to Boulogne?

10   Walkers using a map of scale 1 : 25 000 reckon a distance on the map is 25 cm. What distance is this to walk in km?

11   On an Ordnance Survey map of 1 : 50 000 two towns are 8 in apart. How far apart are they in miles? (Answer to nearest mile.)

12   A house plan is drawn to a scale of 1 : 20. The kitchen in the drawing is 9 in long and 6 in wide. What are (a) the length (b) the width of the kitchen in feet and inches?

13   A garden plan is drawn to a scale of 1 : 50. The length is 14 in on the plan. What is the length of the garden?

14   A map scale is given as 1 : 50 000. How far is it, in km, between two towns that are 12 cm apart on the map?

15   A Michelin map is 1 : 200 000. Le Havre to Paris on the map is 105 cm. How far is it from Le Havre to Paris?

16   On the same Michelin map Paris to Nice is measured as 461 cm. How far is it, in km, from Paris to Nice?

17   A map of Europe is on a scale of 1 : 3 000 000. How far, in km, does 10 cm on the map represent?

18   By what length on a map of scale 1 : 25 000 will a distance of 20 km be shown?

19   A map has a scale of 1 : 50 000. The distance between two towns is 150 km. How far will this be on the map?

20   An Ordnance Survey map of 1 : 50 000 shows two villages 8 km apart. What distance is this on the map itself?

4 Direct Proportion

Two quantities are said to be in direct proportion if an increase (or decrease) in one quantity makes the second quantity increase (or decrease) in the same ratio.

Worked example 16

I pay 40p for 4 oz of sweets. How much will 8 oz cost?

In this case the weight is doubled and so the cost has to be doubled. But the best method for working out is as follows:

4 oz of sweets cost 40p

1 oz of sweets cost $\dfrac{40}{4}$ p = 10p.   Find what 1 unit costs.

8 oz of sweets cost 8 × 10p = 80p
Answer 80p

Worked example 17

The cost of a holiday is £63 for a week. How much would it cost for 10 days?

7 days cost £63

1 day costs £ $\dfrac{63}{7}$ = £9

10 days will cost 10 × £9 = £90
Answer £90

Worked example 18

7 empty barrels weigh 336 lb. What will 5 empty barrels weigh?

7 barrels weigh 336 lb

1 barrel weighs $\dfrac{336}{7}$ lb = 48 lb

5 barrels weigh 5 × 48 = 240 lb
Answer 240 lb

After some practice you may not want to divide at the second line but proceed directly to the third line.

Worked example 19

35 kg of tomatoes cost £55. How much will 21 kg cost?

35 kg of tomatoes cost £55

1 kg cost £ $\dfrac{55}{35}$

21 kg cost 21 × £ $\dfrac{55}{35}$ = £33

Answer £33

5 Inverse Proportion

Two quantities are said to be in inverse proportion if an increase in one quantity makes the second quantity decrease in the same ratio, or a decrease in one quantity makes the second quantity increase in the same ratio.

Quite often we have to make certain assumptions: that all men (or women) work at the same rate, that conditions do not change, that there are no breakdowns, and so on.

Worked example 20

If two men can load a lorry in 4 h, how long will it take 4 men?

We assume the men all work at the same rate.
2 men take 4 h
1 man will take 2×4 h $= 8$ h

4 men will take $\dfrac{8}{4}$ h $= 2$ h

Answer 2 h
As the workforce is doubled, the time taken is halved. This is **inverse proportion**.

Worked example 21

Two mechanical diggers can move 200 tons of earth in 6 h. How long will it take three diggers to shift the same amount?

We assume the diggers work at the same rate and that they don't hinder one another.
2 diggers take 6 h
1 digger will take $2 \times 6 = 12$ h

3 diggers will take $\dfrac{12}{3}$ h $= 4$ h

Answer 4 h

Hints: Ask yourself a series of questions: If I employ more people will it take less time or more time to complete the work? If I have more work to do will it take longer or less time to complete? Will it cost more or cost less to employ more people?

Worked example 22

4 women in a factory make 2400 components in a 6 hour shift. How long will it take 6 women to do the same work?

The time taken is 6 h to make 2400 components.
Will 6 women take longer or less time than 4 women to make the same amount?
They will take less time.

Then decrease 6 h in the ratio $\dfrac{4 \text{ women}}{6 \text{ women}}$

Time taken $= 6 \times \dfrac{4}{6}$

$= 4$ h
Answer 4 h

Worked example 23

If 6 bricklayers can build a wall in 8 days working 7 h a day, how long would you expect 8 bricklayers to take working 6 h a day?

Will it take 8 bricklayers less or more time than 6 bricklayers? Less. Then

decrease 8 days in ratio $\dfrac{6}{8}$:

$$= 8 \times \frac{6}{8}$$

$= 6$ days

If they work 6 h a day instead of 7 h a day will it take more or less time?
More.

Then increase 6 days in the ratio $\frac{7}{6}$:

$6 \text{ days} \times \frac{7}{6} = 7 \text{ days}$

Answer 7 days

Exercise 5

1   2 Mars bars cost 26p. How much will 5 cost?

2   3 coffees cost £2.25. How much will 2 cost?

3   5 scones cost £1.65. How much will 3 cost?

4   It costs £84 to hire a car for 4 days. What will it cost for 7 days at the same rate?

5   A hotel charges £50 for a two-night stay. How much will the cost be for 7 nights?

6   2 books are on offer for £9.50. How much will 6 books cost?

7   A recipe for 4 people shows 100 g of sugar. How much sugar will be required for 7 people?

8   6 flags cover a length of 18 ft. How many flags are required to cover 30 ft?

9   Loose sweets are £2.25 for 450 g. How much will 100 g cost?

10   A recipe quotes 4 oz of flour to 3 oz of fat. How much flour is required for 9 oz of fat?

11   A 7 day holiday costs £301. How much will 10 days cost?

12   3 whisky tumblers hold 81 cl. What will 5 hold?

13   4 oz of concentrated fertiliser should be added to 5 pints of water. How much fertiliser needs to be added to 2 gal of water?

14   For good results 5 ml of a washing up liquid should be added to 2 litres of water. How much washing up liquid would be needed for 7 litres of water?

15   It costs £40 to hire a large lawnmower for 3 days. How much would it cost for 12 days?

16   $2\frac{1}{2}$ kg of potatoes cost 60p. How much will 40 kg cost?

17   3 chairs cost £49.50. How much will 5 cost?

18   There is twice as much tonic as gin in a gin and tonic. How much gin is there in a drink of 21 cl?

19   15 kg of chemical fertiliser costs £20.40. How much does 28 kg cost?

20   Petrol costs £2.75 for 5 litres. How much do 24 litres cost?

Exercise 6 Multiple choice questions

Work out which is the correct answer in the following questions:

1   A ratio of 4 : 6 is the same as
    A 1 : 10   B $1\frac{1}{2}$: 1   C 2 : 3   D 2 : 1
2   A ratio of $2\frac{1}{2}$: $3\frac{1}{2}$ is the same as
    A 10 : 14   B $2\frac{1}{2}$: 6   C 5 : 3   D 2 : 3

3   A club has 24 men and 18 women. The ratio of men to women is
    A 24 : 42   B 18 : 42   C 2 : 1   D 4 : 3

4   £20 divided in the ratio of 3 : 2 gives the bigger share as
    A £10   B £15   C £11.50   D £12

5   650 g of an alloy made from copper and tin in a ratio of 3 : 2 means the amount of tin is
    A 390 g   B 260 g   C 130 g   D 280 g

6   £80 is divided in the ratio 3 : $2\frac{1}{2}$: $2\frac{1}{2}$. The biggest share is
    A £50   B £40   C £45   D £30

7   A map has a scale of 1 : 50 000. 2 cm on the map represents
    A 1 km   B 50 000 cm
    C 2 km   D 10 km

8   A map has a scale of 1 : 25 000. 10 km is represented on the map by
    A 25 cm   B 40 cm   C 10 cm   D 250 cm

9   The Michelin map scale of 1 : 200 000 means that 2 cm on the map represents
    A 2 km   B 1 km   C 4 km   D 20 km

10   5 litres of petrol cost £2.95. 28 litres cost
    A £24   B £19.40   C £16.52   D £14.70

8 | Averages

1 Arithmetic Mean

An average in mathematics can mean any kind of representative number, but in everyday language the word 'average' usually refers to the arithmetic mean. To find the average (that is, the arithmetic mean) we add all the quantities together (money, weights, runs, people, etc.) and then divide by the number of quantities.

Worked example 1

Find the average of 9, 6, 5, 12, and 8.

First, add all the numbers together:
$9 + 6 + 5 + 12 + 8 = 40$
There are 5 numbers.
To find the average divide the total by 5:

Average $= \dfrac{40}{5} = 8$

Answer 8

Worked example 2

Six sacks are found to contain 52 kg, 48 kg, 49 kg, 53 kg, 52 kg and 58 kg. What is the average weight in each sack?

Total weight $= 52 + 48 + 49 + 53 + 52 + 58$ kg
$\qquad\qquad\quad = 312$ kg
Number of sacks $= 6$

Average weight $= \dfrac{312}{6}$ kg $= 52$ kg

Answer 52 kg

Worked example 3

Of six teenagers starting work, two earn £42 a week, two earn £46 a week, one earns £38 and the other earns £44. What is their average weekly pay?

In a question like this we find the total and divide by the number of quantities.
2 earn £42 a week = £84 in total
2 earn £46 a week = £92 in total
1 earns $\qquad\qquad$ £38
1 earns $\qquad\qquad$ £44
Total earnings $\quad = $ £258

Average pay $= £\dfrac{258}{6} = £43$

Answer £43

Worked example 4

A garage sold an average of 32 cars per month over a year. How many did it sell in a year?

The average of 32 cars a months means it is the equivalent of selling 32 cars every month.

1 month's average is 32 cars
Total over 12 months $= 12 \times 32$
$\qquad\qquad\qquad\qquad\quad = 384$ cars

Answer 384 cars

Note: The garage may not have sold 32 cars in any one month.

Worked example 5 A mother gives an average of £1.20 pocket money a week to her 3 children. What is the total she gives per week?

Average is £1.20 for each child
There are 3 children
Total = 3 × £1.20 = £3.60
Answer £3.60

Worked example 6 A garage has average sales of 42 cars a month for 11 months but in the 12th month it sells 78 cars. What is the average over 12 months?

Average for 11 months is 42 cars a month.

Total sold over this period = 11 × 42
$\qquad\qquad\qquad\qquad\quad$ = 462 cars
In the 12th month it sells 78 cars.
Total sold = 462 + 78
$\qquad\qquad$ = 540 cars

Average over 12 months $= \dfrac{540}{12} = 45$ cars

Answer 45 cars

Worked example 7 An exam consists of three papers, and to pass the exam a student needs an average of 50 marks over the three papers. After two papers the average is only 43 marks. What mark is required on the third paper?

To average 50 marks over 3 papers needs 3 × 50 marks = 150 marks
Average of 2 papers is 43 marks = 2 × 43 = 86 marks
Mark required on third paper = 150 − 86
$\qquad\qquad\qquad\qquad\qquad\qquad$ = 64 marks

Answer 64 marks

Worked example 8 4 lb of coffee at £4.50 per lb is blended with 5 lb at £5.40 per lb. At what average price per lb should the mixture be sold to cover the cost?

4 lb at £4.50 per lb cost 4 × £4.50 = £18.00
5 lb at £5.40 per lb cost 5 × £5.40 = £27.00
$\qquad\qquad\qquad\qquad\qquad$ Total cost = £45.00
There are 9 lb altogether.

Average cost $= £\dfrac{45}{9} = £5$

Answer £5

Worked example 9 A salesman has average sales over three weeks of £1300. What does he need to sell in the 4th week to increase this average by £200 over the four-week period?

Sales over 3 weeks = 3 × £1300 = £3900
He wants the average to be £1500 over 4 weeks.
Sales over 4 weeks = 4 × £1500 = £6000
Sales needed in 4th week = £6000 − £3900
$\qquad\qquad\qquad\qquad\qquad\qquad$ = £2100

Answer £2100

Worked example 10

The ratio of men to women in an office is 1 : 4. The men's average earnings were £160 while those of the women averaged £180. What was the average earnings of all the office staff?

The ratio of men to women is 1 : 4, and it doesn't matter how many there are altogether; the ratio remains the same.
Ratio of 1 : 4 means 5 parts, 1 part being men, 4 parts being women.
Earnings of the men: 1 part at £160 = £160
Earnings of the women: 4 parts at £180 = £720
                                                            Total = £880
Average of the 5 parts = £$\frac{880}{5}$ = £176
Answer £176

Exercise 1

1 Find the average of
   (a) 7, 11   (b) 3, 9   (c) 1, 13   (d) 7, 15

2 Find the average of
   (a) 2, 8, 8   (b) 7, 11, 12   (c) 1, 13, 10   (d) 8, 15, 4

3 Find the average of
   (a) 5, 9, 6, 4   (b) 14, 3, 19, 8   (c) 12, 1, 22, 13   (d) 3, 8, 9, 8

4 Find the average of
   (a) £14, £22   (b) £8, £32   (c) £2, £22   (d) £7, £29

5 Find the average of
   (a) £5, £18   (b) £24, £7   (c) £11.50, £10   (d) £5.50, £9.50

6 Find the average of
   (a) £17, £8, £22, £13
   (b) £38, £115, £92, £43
   (c) £68, £9, £141, £170
   (d) £39, £17, £109, £143

7 Find the average of
   (a) £4.64, £7.07, £12.48, £8.53
   (b) £21.32, £49.51, £127.06, £65.31
   (c) £7.09, £15.83, £18.24, £30.04
   (d) £112.71, £38.09, £74.61, £27.83

8 Find the average of
   (a) 4 ft 6 in, 7 ft, 8 ft 4 in, 9 ft 6 in
   (b) 7 in, 2 ft 3 in, 5 ft 2 in, 1 ft 4 in
   (c) 2 yd 1 ft, 2 ft, 3 yd 2 ft, 1 yd 1 ft
   (d) 5 yd, 4 yd 2 ft, 8 yd 1 ft, 2 yd

9 Find the average of
   (a) 3.2 km, 76 km, 9.8 km, 0.6 km
   (b) 325 m, 706 m, 924 m, 173 m
   (c) 450 g, 1.3 kg, 5.08 kg, 1 kg 242 g
   (d) 12 cm, 7 mm, 15 cm 2 mm, 4 cm 5 mm

10 Find the average of
   (a) 2 h 15 min, 5 h 28 min, 37 min, 1 h 32 min
   (b) 3 yr 2 months, 10 yr 1 month, 7 yr 5 months, 2 yr 8 months
   (c) 4 ton 2 cwt, 1 ton 16 cwt, 19 cwt, 2 ton 11 cwt
   (d) 2 litres, 8 cl 8 ml, 9 cl, 1 litre 2 cl 4 ml

11   The price of petrol per litre at 5 garages in the town was 55.2p, 55.0p, 56.2p, 52.3p, and 54.3p. What was the average price per litre?

12   A car covered a journey on different occasions in the following times: 1 h 32 min, 1 h 56 min, 1 h 12 min, 2 h 24 min. What was the average time for the journey?

13   Four men earn an average of £290 per week. Three of them earn an average of £284 per week. What does the fourth man earn?

14   Three anglers catch an average of 7 lb 6 oz of fish. One catches 9 lb 10 oz. What is the average catch of the other two?

15   A book contains 232 pages, and the number of words on each page averages 370. How many words are in the book?

16   The maximum daily temperatures for one week last July were 21.2 °C, 22.3 °C, 21.7 °C, 20.4 °C, 19.5 °C, 20.6 °C and 19.2 °C. What was the average maximum daily temperature?

17   A garage reckons to sell in a year an average of 36 cars per month. After 10 months the average is only 33 cars. How many cars, on average, have to be sold in the remaining two months?

18   Of 10 people in an office, 2 earn an average of £340 per week, 3 earn an average of £310 per week, 4 earn an average of £282 per week and one earns £382 a week. (a) What is the total wage bill for the office and (b) what is the average wage per person per week?

19   3 kg of tea at £2.60 per kg is blended with 2 kg of tea at £3.20 per kg. At what price per kg should the blended tea be sold to cover the cost?

20   2 kg of coffee at £6.40 per kg is blended with 4 kg of coffee at £7.00 per kg. At what price per kg should the blended coffee be sold to cover the cost?

21   A student has 4 end-of-term exams and has to average 75 marks to pass overall. After 3 exams her average is 72 marks. What is needed in the final exam to pass overall?

22   On a coast-to-coast walk a hiker wishes to average 15 miles a day over 8 days. For the first 4 days he averages 12 miles. He then has a rest day. What does he need to average over the last 3 days to keep to his target?

23   A grass seed is a mixture of ryegrass and fescue in the ratio 3 : 2. If ryegrass is £2.64 per kg and fescue is £3.29 per kg, what is the average price per kg of the mixture?

24   The ratio of men to women in an office is 2 : 5. The men's average earnings were £311 per week while those of the women averaged £220. What were the average earnings per week of all the office staff?

2 Median

Median is sometimes used, instead of arithmetic mean, in connection with a set of figures.

The median is the middle figure of a set of figures after they have been arranged in ascending or descending order. When there is an even number of figures the median is the average of the two middle figures.

Worked example 11   Find the median of the numbers 10, 4, 8, 9, 3, 5, 2.

Arrange the numbers in ascending order:

2, 3, 4, 5, 8, 9, 10

The middle number is 5. The median is 5.

Note: the average of the number is $\dfrac{41}{7}$, which is about 6.

Worked example 12   Find the median of the numbers 18, 5, 15, 4, 2, 9, 16, 14.

Arrange the numbers in ascending order:

2, 4, 5, 9, 14, 15, 16, 18

The middle two numbers are 9 and 14

$$\text{Median} = \frac{9 + 14}{2} = \frac{23}{2} = 11\frac{1}{2}$$

Note: The mean of the numbers $= \frac{83}{8}$, which is just over 10.

Worked example 13   The number of lambs and ewes slaughtered for each month of 1994, January to December, in thousands, was 186, 160, 159, 188, 164, 151, 195, 195, 199, 260, 212, and 194. Find the mean and the median.

Arrange in ascending order:

151, 159, 160, 164, 186, 188, 194, 195, 195, 199, 212, 260

The middle two numbers are 188 and 194

$$\text{Median} = \frac{188 + 194}{2} = \frac{382}{2} = 191$$

i.e. median = 191 thousand or 191 000

$$\text{Mean (average)} = \frac{\text{addition of all numbers}}{12 \text{ months}} = \frac{2263}{12} = 188.58$$

Mean = 188.58 thousand = 188 580

Worked example 14   Look at the figures 32, 32, 34, 34, 34, 36, 36, 36, 38, 38, 38, 38, 38, 40, 40, 40, 42, 42, 44, 46.

$$\text{Median} = \frac{38 + 38}{2} = 38 \qquad \text{Mean} = \frac{758}{20} = 37.9$$

The number that occurs most is 38 (5 times). 38 is called the **mode**, because it occurs more often than any other number in this set of figures.

The figures range from 32 to 46. The **range** is 14.

The figures were sales of different sizes of pullovers in a high street shop on a particular Thursday. The median is obviously of more value than the mean. 38 would be the modal size.

Exercise 2

Find the median of the following sets of numbers:

1   12, 10, 2, 6, 5, 8, 5, 10, 9

2   4, 11, 10, 2, 3, 12, 7, 7

3   3, 7, 1, 14, 12, 13, 9, 7

4   18, 9, 2, 14, 0, 13, 8, 9, 7

5   What is the mode of the numbers 3, 7, 4, 3, 5, 5, 3, 7, 8, 3?

6   The number of recorded sexual offences in England and Wales, in thousands, for each quarter since 1992 was 7.2, 7.4, 7.8, 7.1, 6.7, 7.9, 8.8, 7.8, 7.8, 8.9.
    Find the mean and median of sexual offences for a quarter.

7   The number of goods vehicles, in thousands, registered for each month of 1994 was 3.2, 2.7, 3.7, 2.9, 3.1, 3.2, 1.4, 5.9, 4.0, 4.2, 4.6, 3.0.
Find the mean and median of goods vehicles registered for one month.

8   A shop sells 2 shirts size 14, 4 size 14½, 6 size 15, 7 size 15½, 5 size 16, 3 size 16½, and 1 size 17.
What are the mean, median and modal sizes?

9   The net receipts by HM Customs & Excise (£million) from beer in the years 1990–1994 were 2226, 2282, 2376, 2230, 2500.
Find the mean and median for beer duty in a year.

10   The number of season ticket holders (millions) on London Underground for the years 1988–1994 was 452, 385, 376, 383, 359, 364.
Find the mean and median number of season ticket holders a year on London Underground.

Exercise 3 Multiple choice questions

Work out which is the correct answer in the following questions:

1   The average of 5.8, 9.6, 15, 12.3 and 0.3 is
   A 8.6   B 3.55   C 7.5   D 15

2   Four men have an average age of 65. Three have an average age of 66. The age of the fourth man is
   A 65   B 67   C 62   D 66

3   The average of 640 g, 1 kg 30 g, 842 g and 1.308 kg is
   A 1.012 kg   B 0.955 kg
   C 940 g   D 1.008 kg

4   The average of 4 yr 5 months, 5 yr 2 months, and 4 yr 2 months is
   A 4 yr 3½ months   B 4 yr 7 months
   C 4 yr 8 months   D 4 yr 11 months

5   A gardener mixes sand and loam in the ratio 1:2. Sand costs £2.50 per cwt and loam costs £4.40 for 2 cwt. The cost of the mixture per cwt is
   A £3.40   B £2.50   C £2.30   D £3.70

6   Five women earn an average of £220 a week. one earns £248 a week. The average of the other four is
   A £188   B £213   C £248   D £195

7   The average of 4 cl, 5 ml, 8 cl 4 ml, 9 cl, and 7 cl 6 ml is
   A 5 cl 4 ml   B 5 cl 2 ml
   C 5 cl 9 ml   D 5 cl 63 ml

8   4 kg of tea at £2.80 per kg are blended with 3 kg of tea at £3.43 per kg. The blended tea, to cover cost, is sold per kg at
   A £3.10   B £2.80   C £3.07   D £3.43

9   A wine merchant blends Bordeaux red wine with Languedoc red wine in the ratio 3 : 7. The Bordeaux is £6.40 a litre and the Languedoc wine is £2.60 a litre. To blend 1000 litres the average price per litre is
   A £4.45   B £3.74   C £4.00   D £2.60

10   The wine merchant blends white wine with a sweeter white wine in the ratio 2 : 5. The white wine is £7.36 per litre and the sweeter wine £2.46 per litre. The average price per litre is
   A £4.91   B £3.50   C £3.95   D £3.86

11   The difference between the median and the mean of the numbers 5, 4, 8, 12, 6, 5, 9 is
   A 0.5   B 1.0   C 1.3   D 0.8

9 Speed, Distance and Time

1 Average Speed

Speed describes how far is travelled in a unit of time, the most common speeds being expressed in miles per hour or km per hour.

20 mile/h is 20 miles per hour or 20 miles in an hour.
20 km/h is 20 km per hour or 20 km in an hour.

$$\text{Average speed} = \frac{\text{distance}}{\text{time}} \quad (\text{distance} \div \text{time})$$

Worked example 1

A car travels 120 miles in 4 hours. What is its average speed?

Speed is how far it travels in a unit of time (1 h):
120 miles in 4 hours
is 30 miles in 1 hour
Average speed is 30 mile/h;

or Average speed $= \dfrac{\text{distance}}{\text{time}} = \dfrac{120 \text{ miles}}{4 \text{ hours}} = 30$ miles per hour

Answer 30 mile/h

Worked example 2

An express coach leaves Leeds at 0930 hours and arrives in London at 1330 hours, which includes a short break. The distance is 180 miles. What is the average speed of the coach?

Time taken is 1330 hours − 0930 hours = 4 h

Average speed $= \dfrac{\text{distance}}{\text{time}} = \dfrac{180 \text{ miles}}{4 \text{ hours}} = 45$ miles per hour

Answer 45 mile/h

Worked example 3

A racing car covers a 3 mile circuit in $1\frac{1}{2}$ minutes. What is the average speed for the circuit?

Average speed $= \dfrac{\text{distance}}{\text{time}} = \dfrac{3 \text{ miles}}{1\frac{1}{2} \text{ min}} = 2$ miles per minute

2 miles per minute $= 2 \times 60$ miles per hour
$\qquad\qquad\qquad\quad = 120$ mile/h

Answer 120 mile/h

Worked example 4

A cyclist in a road race averages 24.7 mile/h over 5 h. How far does he travel?

Average speed is 24.7 mile/h.
This means 24.7 miles in an hour.
In 5 hours he will travel 5×24.7 miles
$\qquad\qquad\qquad\qquad\quad = 123.5$ miles

Average 123.5 miles

Worked example 5

A car travels 20 miles in 24 minutes. What is its average speed?

We want to find out how far it travels in one hour.
In 24 minutes it travels 20 miles,

in 1 minute it travels $\dfrac{20}{24}$ miles,

in 1 hour it travels $60 \times \dfrac{20}{24} = 50$ miles.

Answer 50 mile/h

Worked example 6

A train travels for 220 miles at an average speed of 55 mile/h. How long does the journey take?

Average speed is 55 mile/h.
This means 55 miles in an hour.
To travel 220 miles will take $\dfrac{220}{55} = 4$ h

Answer 4 h

Worked example 7

How long does it take to travel 112 miles at an average speed of 30 mile/h?

Average speed 30 mile/h means 30 miles in an hour.
To travel 112 miles will take $\dfrac{112}{30}$ h $= 3\dfrac{22}{30}$ h.
$\dfrac{22}{30}$ h $= 44$ min
Answer $3\frac{22}{30}$ h = 3 h 44 min

Where two average speeds are given and two times (or distances) then it is essential to work out the total distance and the total time.

Worked example 8

A man runs for 2 h averaging 8 mile/h and then for 1 h averaging 5 mile/h. What does he average over the whole run?

Averaging 8 miles per hour, in 2 h he covers 2×8 miles $= 16$ miles.
And then in 1 h he covers 5 miles.
Total distance he runs $= 16 + 5 = 21$ miles
Total time taken $= 2$ h $+ 1$ h $= 3$ h
Average over the whole run $= \dfrac{21 \text{ miles}}{3 \text{ h}} = 7$ mile/h

Answer 7 mile/h
Note: Adding 8 mile/h and 5 mile/h and dividing by 2 does not give the right answer.

Worked example 9

A motorist travels for 2 h at an average speed of 40 mile/h; he has a break of 1 h for lunch, and he completes his journey in another 3 h at an average speed of 45 mile/h. What is the average speed for the whole journey?

40 mile/h is 40 miles in an hour.
In 2 h he travels 2×40 miles $= 80$ miles.
In 3 h at 45 miles per hour he travels $3 \times 45 = 135$ miles.
Total distance $= 80$ miles $+ 135$ miles $= 215$ miles.
Total time $= 2$ h $+ 1$ h (lunch) $+ 3$ h $= 6$ h
Average speed $= \dfrac{215 \text{ miles}}{6 \text{ h}} = 35\frac{5}{6}$ mile/h

Answer $35\frac{5}{6}$ mile/h

Worked example 10

A train travels for 90 miles at 45 mile/h and for 120 miles at 40 mile/h. What is the average speed for the journey?

45 mile/h is 45 miles in an hour.
To travel 90 miles would take $\dfrac{90}{45} = 2$ h
To travel 120 miles at 40 mile/h would take $\dfrac{120}{40} = 3$ h
Total distance travelled $= 90$ miles $+ 120$ miles $= 210$ miles
Total time taken $= 2$ h $+ 3$ h $= 5$ h
Average speed $= \dfrac{210 \text{ miles}}{5 \text{ h}} = 42$ mile/h

Answer 42 mile/h

Exercise 1

1   Find the average speed for travelling
    (a) 20 miles in 2 hours   (b) 50 miles in 2 hours
    (c) 60 miles in 2 hours   (d) 45 miles in 3 hours
    (e) 100 miles in 4 hours   (f) 150 miles in 6 hours

2   Find the average speed for travelling
    (a) 40 km in 2 h   (b) 98 km in 2 h
    (c) 140 km in 4 h   (d) 180 km in 5 h
    (e) 630 km in 7 h   (f) 235 km in 5 h

3   Find the average speed for travelling
    (a) 60 miles in $2\frac{1}{2}$ h   (b) 120 km in $1\frac{1}{2}$ h
    (c) 168 miles in $3\frac{1}{2}$ h   (d) 169 km in 3 h 15 min
    (e) 102 miles in 4 h 15 min (f) 168 km in 2 h 20 min

4   What distance is travelled in
    (a) 2 h at 15 mile/h   (b) 3 hr at 32 mile/h
    (c) 6 h at 120 km/h   (d) 9 h at 140 km/h
    (e) 5 h at 350 mile/h   (f) 7 h at 19 km/h

5   What distance is travelled in
    (a) $1\frac{1}{2}$ h at 40 mile/h   (b) $3\frac{1}{2}$ h at 60 mile/h
    (c) 2 h 20 min at 72 km/h (d) 4 h 15 min at 96 km/h
    (e) 40 min at 120 km/h   (f) 2 h 45 min at 48 miles/h

6   How long does it take to travel
    (a) 40 miles at an average speed of 10 mile/h
    (b) 120 miles at an average speed of 40 mile/h
    (c) 168 miles at an average speed of 24 mile/h
    (d) 1035 km at an average speed of 115 km/h
    (e) 840 km at an average speed of 120 km/h
    (f) 361 km at an average speed of 19 km/h

7   How long does it take to travel
    (a) 120 miles at an average speed of 48 mile/h
    (b) 198 miles at an average speed of 36 mile/h
    (c) 99 miles at an average speed of 22 mile/h
    (d) 301 km at an average speed of 86 km/h
    (e) 462 km at an average speed of 84 km/h
    (f) 630 km at an average speed of 140 km/h

8   How long does it take to travel
    (a) 182 miles at an average speed of 56 mile/h
    (b) 152 miles at an average speed of 32 mile/h
    (c) 368 miles at an average speed of 64 mile/h
    (d) 306 km at an average speed of 90 km/h
    (e) 189 km at an average speed of 70 km/h
    (f) 494 km at an average speed of 130 km/h

9   A motorist travels for 3 h at 30 mile/h and then for 2 h at 55 mile/h. What distance has he travelled?

10   A motorist travels 120 miles in 4 h. She rests for an hour. What is her average speed before she commences the next stage of her journey?

11   A motorists travels 100 miles in 2 h, rests for 30 min, and then does 120 miles in $2\frac{1}{2}$ h. What is the average speed for the whole journey?

12   The Eurostar train takes 3 h 30 min to travel from London to Paris, which is 308 miles. What is the average speed of the train?

13   An aeroplane takes 2 h 20 min to fly from Manchester to Malaga, which is 1190 miles. What is the average speed of the plane?

14 The cruise ship *Oriana* has a cruising speed of 24 knots (27.5 mile/h). How long will it take at cruising speed to travel from Southampton to New York? (Answer in days and hours.) Southampton to New York is 2805 miles.

15 A car travels for 2 h at 30 mile/h and then for 3 h at 20 mile/h. What is the average speed for the journey? (Remember to find the total distance travelled and the total time taken.)

16 A motorist left Manchester at 0900 hours and travelled for $2\frac{1}{2}$ h before having a break of 30 min. He arrived in Dover, a distance of 243 miles away, at 1400 hours. What was (a) his average speed for the journey and (b) his average speed on the road?

17 A train travelled 148 miles between 0730 hours and 1112 hours. What was its average speed?

18 A car averaged 30 mile/h for the first hour and then 40 mile/h for the second hour. What was the average speed?

19 A train travelled for 2 h at 80 mile/h and then for 1 h at 50 mile/h. What was the average speed of the train?

20 A car averaged 30 mile/h for the first hour and then 36 mile/h over the next two hours. What was the average speed?

21 A train travelled from one town to another, 80 miles away, at an average speed of 40 mile/h. Stoppages amounted to 24 min. What would have been the average speed of the train without stops?

22 An aeroplane takes 1 h 15 min to fly from Manchester to Paris, a distance of 495 miles. What is the average speed of the plane?

23 A cyclist says he cannot cycle at more than 16 mile/h. What is the minimum time he will take to cycle 68 miles?

24 A motorcyclist travels 84 miles in 2 h and then travels for 3 h at an average speed of 65 mile/h. What is the average speed for the whole journey?

Exercise 2 Multiple choice questions

Work out which is the correct answer in the following questions:

1 A coach travels for 3 h 20 min at an average speed of 60 mile/h. It has travelled a total of
A 180 miles   B 200 miles
C 220 miles   D 240 miles

2 A motorbike travelled 168 miles between 0930 hours and 1300 hours. Its average speed was
A 48 mile/h   B 60 mile/h
C 44 mile/h   D 52 mile/h

3 A car travels 575 km at an average speed of 125 km/h. The journey takes
A 5 h   B 4 h 30 min
C 5 h 6 min   D 4 h 36 min

4 A train travelled 99 miles between 0824 hours and 1012 hours. Its average speed was
A 55 mile/h   B 58 mile/h
C 60 mile/h   D 48 mile/h

5 The TGV travels from Paris to Bordeaux, a distance of 578 km, in 3 h 24 min. Its average speed is
A 184 km/h   B 160 km/h
C 180 km/h   D 170 km/h

6 A car travels for 2 h at 45 mile/h and then for 1 h at 54 mile/h. The average speed for the whole journey is
A 49.5 mile/h   B 50 mile/h
C 48 mile/h   D 52 mile/h

7 A car averaged 30 mile/h for 3 h. It then took 2 h to travel 20 miles. Its average speed overall was
A 25 mile/h   B 22 mile/h
C 24 mile/h   D 30 mile/h

8 A cyclist travelled for 2 h at 11 mile/h and then for 3 h at 14 mile/h. He travelled
A 55 miles   B 70 miles
C 59 miles   D 64 miles

9 140 km at an average speed of 80 km/h takes
A 1 h 45 min   B 1 h 48 min
C 1 h 30 min   D 1 h 40 min

10 Travelling 42 km in 18 min gives an average speed of
A 146 km/h   B 120 km/h
C 140 km/h   D 148 km/h

10 Commercial Arithmetic

1 Introduction

'Money is the root of all evil' goes the chant of an old song; whether it is or not, we cannot manage without it.

This chapter shows how we use addition, subtraction, multiplication and division every day when we deal with money, even though on many occasions we do not realise it.

2 Payslips and Wages

Before any of us can use money we need to earn it; for those who are working or hope to work, a typical payslip, whether paid weekly or monthly, will probably record the details shown in Figure 10.1. Some payslips will record more information and others less: for example, the payslip of a person working part-time in the evenings will probably show only the hours worked each night, the rate of pay per hour, and the amount earned in the week.

Most of the terms explain themselves.

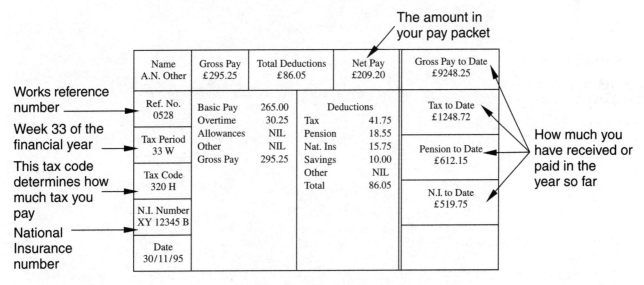

Figure 10.1 Typical payslip

From Figure 10.1 can you work out

(a)   the average gross pay over the weeks to date
(b)   the average tax paid per week
(c)   the total amount of overtime paid over the weeks to date
(d)   the total net pay received over the weeks to date
(e)   the average net pay over this time?

Worked example 1

A woman is paid a basic wage of £3.80 an hour for a 30-hour week. Extra hours (overtime) are paid at time-and-a-quarter. What does she earn if she works 38 hours in one week?

Normal basic wage = 30 × £3.80
            = £114.00

30 hours at £3.80 an hour

Number of hours overtime = 38 − 30 = 8 h

Overtime is paid at time-and-a-quarter, and as the basic rate is £3.80 an hour the overtime rate is £3.80 × $1\frac{1}{4}$:

$$£3.80 \times 1\tfrac{1}{4} = £3.80 \times \frac{5}{4}$$
$$= \frac{£19.00}{4} = £4.75$$

There were 8 hours overtime, therefore she earned 8 × £4.75 = £38 in overtime.

Total pay = basic wage + overtime
        = £114 + £38
        = £152

Answer £152

Note: In the overtime calculation it does not matter whether you increase the payment per hour by a quarter or the hours by a quarter; the result is still the same.

There are 8 hours overtime.

This is paid at time-and-a-quarter.

Overtime is equivalent to $8 \times 1\tfrac{1}{4}\,h = 8 \times \dfrac{5}{4} = 10\,h$

10 h at £3.80 an hour = £38.00

Overtime is £38, the same as before.

Worked example 2

A man works a 44-hour week and his pay is calculated as follows: the first 32 hours at £4.20 an hour, the next 8 hours at time-and-a-quarter, and the rest at time-and-a-half. How much is his total pay for the week?

Number of hours overtime = 44 − 32 = 12 hours

8 hours are at time and a quarter ($1\frac{1}{4}$), leaving 4 hours at time and half ($1\frac{1}{2}$).

Total pay = basic wage + overtime:
32 h at £4.20   = £134.40
8 h at $1\frac{1}{4}$ = 8 h at £5.25 = £42.00
4 h at $1\frac{1}{2}$ = 4 h at £6.30 = £25.20
                              £201.60

Answer £201.60

Worked example 3

A man earns a basic £240 a week, plus £45 in overtime. He pays £36.40 in tax, £22.86 in national insurance, and his pension contribution is £6 for every £100 on his basic pay. What is his net pay for the week?

Gross pay = basic pay + overtime
        = £240 + £45 = £285

Pension contribution on £100 basic pay is £6, on £240 basic pay is

$$\frac{£240}{100} \times 6 = £14.40$$

Deductions total = tax + national insurance + pension
            = £36.40 + £22.86 + £14.40
            = £73.66

Net pay = gross pay − deductions
        = £285 − £73.66 = £211.34

Answer £211.34

Exercise 1

1   A person has a gross pay of £238.43 and deductions total £47.58. What is the net pay?

2   Net pay for a month was £972.46. The gross pay was £1154.30. How much was deducted?

3   A woman works a 32-hour week at £3.60 an hour. How much does she earn in a week?

4   A man's basic pay is £5.60 an hour for a 35-hour week and time-and-a-quarter for overtime. How much does he earn when he works 41 hours?

5   A man's basic pay is £4.80 an hour, but for weekend working he gets double time. In one week he works 42 hours, of which 10 were at the weekend. How much did he earn that week?

6   A woman has gross pay of £760 in a 4-week month. She pays tax of £102.60 and pension costs of £45.60 in the month, her national insurance is £10.50 a week, and she saves £8 a week. What is her monthly net pay?

7   A man works a 44-hour week and his pay is calculated as follows: the first 32 hours at £5.40 an hour, the next 6 hours at time-and-a-quarter, and the remainder at double time. What is his gross pay?

8   A woman earns £4.10 an hour for a 34-hour week. She pays £22.65 in tax and £11.25 in national insurance. Her pension contribution is £5 for every £100 earned on basic pay. What is her net pay for the week?

9   A man earned a total of £238 in one week. He was paid £5.60 an hour for a 32-hour week and time-and-a-half for overtime. How many hours of overtime did he work that week?

10   A woman earns £9500 a year. Her pension contribution is £6 for every £100 earned. She pays £1424 in tax, £707 in national insurance, and she saves £10 per week. How much does she receive in net pay per week? (Answer to nearest £. Assume 52 weeks a year.)

3 Bank Paying-in Slips

When paying money into a bank for yourself or for your company the paying-in slip may require the information shown in Figure 10.2. This has been fully completed for you.

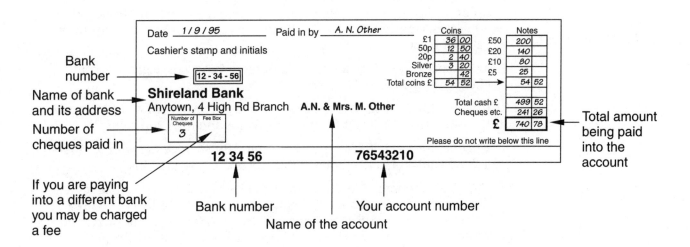

Figure 10.2 Typical bank paying-in slip

Worked example 4   Show how to fill in a bank paying-in slip for the following: three £1 coins, nine 50p coins, five 10p coins, six 5p coins, ten 2p coins, six £20 notes, seven £10 notes, five £5 notes and no cheques.

The answer is shown in Figure 10.3.

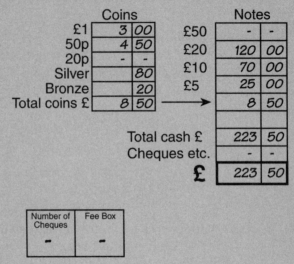

Figure 10.3 Paying-in slip for worked example 4

Exercise 2

Try and complete similar slips (ask for some at a bank or draw some as in the worked example) for the following amounts of cash and/or cheques:

1   Five £1 coins, four 50p coins, eight 20p coins, five 10p coins, six 5p coins, ten 2p coins, three £50 notes, four £20 notes and three £5 notes.

2   Three cheques: one for £46.87, one for £132.94 and one for £58.67.

3   34 £1 coins, 6 £50 notes, 8 £20 notes, 7 £5 notes and cheques for £37.43 and £65.94.

4   Seventeen 50p coins, thirty-two 20p coins, £3.60 in silver, £1.40 in bronze coins, 6 £50 notes, 32 £20 notes and 6 £5 notes.

5   Cheques for £375.21, £604.87, £32.00 and £53.49, together with 9 £50 notes, 75 £20 notes, 87 £10 notes, 43 £5 notes, 76 £1 coins, twenty-three 50p coins, eighteen 20p coins, ninety 10p coins, and bronze coins to the value of £1.30.

6   47 £20 notes, 423 £10 notes, 45 £5 notes, 67 £1 coins, eight 50p coins, and cheques for £86.45, £79.32 and £173.58.

7   Cheques for £378.45, £35.43, £375.65 and £473.98, with 43 £10 notes, 73 £5 notes, 134 £1 coins, fifty-three 50p coins and nine 20p coins.

8   Cheques for £403.68, £43.87, £53.20 and £89.36, together with 9 £50 notes, 143 £20 notes, 436 £10 notes, 73 £5 notes and 254 £1 coins.

9   The total amount paid into a bank was £967.56. There were cheques for £167.45, £210.67 and a third cheque, together with 14 £10 notes, 32 £5 notes, 70 £1 coins, thirteen 50p coins, twenty 20p coins, and silver and bronze amounting to £15.60. For how much was the third cheque?

10 The total amount paid into a bank was £1634.84. There were cheques for £765.43 and £154.76 together with 5 £50 notes, 12 £20 notes, and 15 £10 notes. How much was paid in coins?

4 Postal Charges   All letters and parcels are charged as follows:

- by weight;
- by destination;
- whether first class or second class.

A UK destination is to anywhere in the UK, the Isle of Man, and the Channel Islands.

An overseas destination is to anywhere outside the UK: to Europe (i.e. European Union – EU – or rest of Europe) or outside Europe.

Letters up to 20 g to the European Union (EU) have the same rate as first-class post in the UK. EU Member States at present are Belgium, Denmark, France, Germany, Greece, Ireland, Italy, Luxembourg, Netherlands, Portugal, Spain, and, of course, the UK. First- and second-class post only apply to UK destinations. First-class post aims to have delivery by the following day, whereas second class is likely to be the third day after collection.

The Post Office provides leaflets that include simple tables relating the cost of a letter or parcel to its destination. Some of these tables, or parts of them, are shown as Tables 10.1–10.6. (Postal charges were due to change in July 1996. Ask at a Post Office for details, and see how much the rates have changed.)

Table 10.1 UK letter rates from 1 November 1993

Weight not over	First class	Second class
60 g	25p	19p
100 g	38p	29p
150 g	47p	36p
200 g	57p	43p
250 g	67p	52p
300 g	77p	61p
350 g	88p	70p
400 g	£1.00	79p
450 g	£1.13	89p
500 g	£1.25	98p
600 g	£1.55	£1.20
700 g	£1.90	£1.40
750 g	£2.05	£1.45
800 g	£2.15	Not admissible
900 g	£2.35	over 750 g
1000 g	£2.50	
Each extra 250 g or part thereof	65p	

Table 10.2 UK ParcelForce Standard from 1 November 1993

Weight not over	Price
1 kg	£2.70
2 kg	£3.30
4 kg	£4.70
6 kg	£5.25
8 kg	£6.10
10 kg	£7.10
30 kg	£8.40

Table 10.3 Airmail letters to Europe (including Republic of Ireland), from 1 November 1993

Weight (up to and including)	Price
10 g	–
20 g	EU 25p
	non-EU 30p
40 g	42p
60 g	54p
80 g	66p
100 g	78p
Each additional 20 g Max weight 2 kg	12p extra

Table 10.4 Rest of the world (airmail), from 1 November 1993

Weight (up to and including)	Price	
	Zone 1	Zone 2
10 g	41p	41p
20 g	60p	60p
40 g	92p	£1.02
60 g	£1.24	£1.44
80 g	£1.56	£1.86
100 g	£1.88	£2.28
Each additional 20 g	32p extra	42p extra

Table 10.5 Key to world airmail zones (shown after the name of the country)

Australia 2	Israel 1	Saudi Arabia 1
Brazil 1	Japan 2	South Africa 1
Canada 1	Korea 2	Tonga 2
Egypt 1	Libya 1	USA 1
Falkland Islands 1	Morocco 1	Vietnam 1
Gambia 1	New Zealand 2	Yemen 1
Hong Kong 1	Philippines 2	Zimbabwe 1

A full list of countries and airmail zones can be obtained from any Post Office.

Table 10.6 Worldwide surface mail: letters and small packets, from 1 November 1993

Weight (up to and including)	Letters	Small packets
20 g	30p	48p
60 g	50p	48p
100 g	72p	48p
150 g	£1.01	64p
200 g	£1.30	80p
250 g	£1.59	96p
Each additional 50 g	29p extra	16p extra

How to find the cost of any letter or parcel to any country

The six steps to finding the postage cost of a letter or parcel are

1 What is the weight of the letter or parcel?
2 Where is it going?
3 Is it to be first-class or second-class post?
4 Is it to be airmail or surface mail?
5 Look at the appropriate table.
6 Calculate the cost.

Worked example 5   Find the cost of a first-class letter that weighs 200 g to Manchester, posted in London.

The weight is 200 g.
From Manchester to London is UK letter rate.
It is to be first class. Airmail or surface mail does not apply.
Look at Table 10.1. From this we see that the cost will be 57p.
Answer 57p

Worked example 6   Find the cost of a second-class letter weighing 380 g from Edinburgh to London.

The weight is 380 g. Edinburgh to London is UK postage.
It is to be second class. Look at Table 10.1.
380 g is more than 350 g but less than 400 g.
Table 10.1 says that not more than 400 g will cost 79p by second-class post.
Answer 79p

Worked example 7   Find the cost of sending a letter weighing 120 g from London to Paris.

Weight is 120 g. London to Paris is European rates.
All mail is airmail and first or second class does not apply.
Look at Table 10.3.
120 g is more than 100 g. Each additional 20 g above 100 g is 12p extra.
100 g is 78p, so 120 g will cost 78p + 12p = 90p.
Answer 90p

Worked example 8   Find the cost of an airmail letter weighing 30 g from London to New Zealand.

Weight is 30 g. London to New Zealand is Rest of the World, as New Zealand is not Europe. Look at Table 10.4.
Which zone is New Zealand in? Table 10.5 says it is Zone 2.
Table 10.4 now says that more than 20 g but less than 40 g is £1.02.
Answer £1.02

Worked example 9   Find the cost of sending a Christmas parcel by surface mail from England to Canada if the parcel weighs 1100 g.

Weight is 1100 g. Canada is not Europe and so the parcel is worldwide mail and is to be sent surface mail.
Look at Table 10.6.
Cost for 250 g is 96p and each additional 50 g costs 16p extra.
There are another 17 steps of 50 g to reach 1100 g and 17 steps at 16p each = 17 × 16p = 272p = £2.72.
This is to be added to 96p.

Total cost = 96p + £2.72 = £3.68

Answer £3.78

Exercise 3

Find the cost of sending the following:

1   A first-class letter weighing 100 g from Newcastle to Bristol

2   A first-class letter weighing 400 g from London to Manchester

3   A first-class letter weighing 475 g from Stoke to Glasgow

4   A second-class letter weighing 125 g from Scotland to Wales

5   A second-class letter weighing 285 g from England to Northern Ireland

6   A parcel weighing 4 kg from England to the Isle of Man

7   A letter weighing 423 g from Scotland to the Irish Republic

8   A parcel weighing 2.75 kg from England to the Channel Isles

9   A letter weighing 200 g from England to Germany

10   A letter weighing 328 g from England to France

11   An airmail letter weighing 40 g from England to Australia

12   An airmail letter weighing 25 g from Wales to Egypt

13   An airmail letter weighing 52 g from Scotland to the USA

14   A parcel weighing 1 kg by surface mail from Wales to Korea

15   A small packet weighing 180 g by airmail from England to Hong Kong

16   An airmail letter weighing 65 g from England to the Falkland Islands

17   An airmail letter weighing 17 g from Wales to South Africa

18   A small packet weighing 85 g by airmail from England to Brazil

19   A small packet weighing 106 g by airmail from England to Saudia Arabia

20   A parcel weighing 390 g by surface mail from Wales to Tonga

21   A parcel weighing $4\frac{1}{2}$ kg from Land's End to John o' Groats

22   A letter weighing 60 g from London to Oslo

23   An airmail letter weighing 35 g from Manchester to New York

24   An airmail letter weighing 234 g from London to the Philippines

5 Foreign Currency and Exchange Rates

British currency can be exchanged for foreign currency and vice versa. British currency is the pound (£) sterling, and £1 = 100 pence.

The currencies of some other countries are as follows:

USA	dollars and cents	1 dollar = 100 cents
Germany	marks and pfennigs	1 mark = 100 pfennigs
Switzerland	francs and centimes	1 franc = 100 centimes

For the purpose of this exercise use the following exchange rates, and all calculations will work out exactly (as a matter of interest check any daily paper to see what the exchange rate is now, as it changes every day).

Austria	15.10 schillings
France	7.50 francs
Germany	2.16 marks
Italy	2700 lire
Spain	197.25 pesetas
USA	1.57 dollars

All these figures quote what you will receive for £1 sterling in the currencies of the countries named (when you change money, of course, there will be a charge made by the bank or travel agent with whom you change the money).

When you go abroad one of the major points of interest is money. You will want to know:

(a)   how much foreign currency you will receive for your British money (£ sterling);

(b) when you return how much you can expect to receive in British money (£ sterling) for your foreign currency;

(c) how you can calculate an actual exchange rate.

Finding (a) entails a multiplication sum, while (b) entails a division sum.

When asked to convert one foreign currency to another foreign currency then still use £1 as the standard.

The worked examples show how these questions can be resolved.

The following examples use the exchange rates quoted above.

Worked example 10   How many French francs would you receive for £150?

$$£1 = 7.50 \text{ francs}$$
$$£150 = 150 \times 7.50 \text{ francs}$$
$$= 1125 \text{ francs}$$

$$\begin{array}{r} 750 \\ \times \quad 150 \\ \hline 75\,000 \\ 37\,000 \\ \hline 112\,500 \end{array}$$

Now move the decimal point 2 places:
Answer 1125 francs

Worked example 11   How many US dollars would you receive for £38?

$$£1 = 1.57 \text{ dollars}$$
$$£38 = 38 \times 1.57 \text{ dollars}$$
$$= 59.66 \text{ dollars}$$

$$\begin{array}{r} 157 \\ \times \quad 38 \\ \hline 4710 \\ 1256 \\ \hline 5966 \end{array}$$

Now move the decimal point 2 places:
Answer 59.66 dollars

Worked example 12   How many £s will you get for 302.40 German marks?

$$2.16 \text{ marks} = £1$$
$$302.40 \text{ marks} = £\frac{302.40}{2.16}$$
$$= £140$$

$$\begin{array}{r} 140 \\ 216\overline{)30240} \\ 216 \\ \hline 864 \\ 864 \\ \hline \bullet\bullet\bullet \end{array}$$

Answer £140

Worked example 13   How many £s will you receive for 637.5 French francs?

$$7.5 \text{ francs} = £1$$
$$637.5 \text{ francs} = £\frac{637.5}{7.5}$$
$$= 85 \text{ francs}$$

$$\begin{array}{r} 85 \\ 75\overline{)6375} \\ 600 \\ \hline 375 \\ 375 \\ \hline \bullet\bullet\bullet \end{array}$$

Answer 85 francs

Worked example 14   Convert 129.6 German marks to US dollars.

Use £1 as the standard.

$$2.16 \text{ marks} = £1$$
$$129.6 \text{ marks} = £\frac{129.6}{2.16}$$
$$= £60$$
$$£1 = 1.57 \text{ dollars}$$
$$£60 = 60 \times 1.57 \text{ dollars}$$
$$= 94.20 \text{ dollars}$$

Answer 94.20 dollars

Worked example 15

Convert 243 000 Italian lire to Spanish pesetas.

Use £1 as the standard.

$$2\ 700\ \text{lire} = £1$$

$$243\ 000\ \text{lire} = £\frac{243\ 000}{2700}$$

$$= £90$$

£1 = 197.25 pesetas

£90 = 90 × 197.25 pesetas

= 17 752.50 pesetas

Answer 17 752.50 pesetas

Worked example 16

On returning from holiday I found that the bank gave me £75 in exchange for 727.50 Norwegian kroner. What was the exchange rate?

The exchange rate means: how much is £1 worth?

£75 is worth 727.50 Norwegian kroner

£1 is worth $\dfrac{727.50}{75}$ = 9.70 Norwegian kroner

Answer 9.70 Norwegian kroner

Exercise 4

Using the exchange rates already given, change the following currencies:

1   £100 into (a) Austrian schillings (b) German marks (c) French francs

2   £300 into (a) US dollars (b) Italian lire (c) Spanish pesetas

3   £170 into (a) French francs (b) US dollars (c) Spanish pesetas

4   £2000 into (a) Austrian schillings (b) French francs (c) Italian lire

5   £25 into (a) German marks (b) Spanish pesetas (c) Austrian schillings

6   £60 into (a) Italian lire (b) US dollars (c) French francs

7   £110 into (a) Austrian schillings (b) Spanish pesetas (c) German marks

8   £240 into (a) US dollars (b) French francs (c) Austrian schillings

9   £15 into Italian lire (b) German marks (c) Spanish pesetas

10   £180 into (a) French francs (b) US dollars (c) German marks

Exercise 5

Using the exchange rates given, change the following currencies into £ sterling:

1	151.00 Austrian schillings	2	194.40 German marks
3	197 250 Spanish pesetas	4	75.00 French francs
5	392.50 US dollars	6	67 500 Italian lire
7	172.80 German marks	8	7550 Austrian schillings
9	1350 French francs	10	648 000 Italian lire
11	549.50 US dollars	12	7101 Spanish pesetas
13	280.80 German marks	14	15 100 Austrian schillings
15	412.50 French francs	16	1130.40 US dollars
17	1620 Italian lire	18	5523 Spanish pesetas

19	712.50 French francs	20	97.20 German marks
21	2567 Austrian schillings	22	475.20 German marks
23	23.55 US dollars	24	236 700 Spanish pesetas

Exercise 6

Using the exchange rates given, change the following currencies:

1   2160 German marks into French francs

2   314 US dollars into Italian lire

3   7890 Spanish pesetas into German marks

4   40 500 Italian lire into German marks

5   3750 French francs into US dollars

6   302 Austrian schillings into Spanish pesetas

7   157 US dollars into Italian lire

8   172.80 German marks into US dollars

9   7500 French francs into German marks

10   27 615 Spanish pesetas into US dollars

11   121 500 Italian lire into US dollars

12   251.20 US dollars into French francs

13   164.16 German marks into Austrian schillings

14   3020 Austrian schillings into French francs

15   240 French francs into German marks

16   5917.50 Spanish pesetas into US dollars

17   64 800 Italian lire into Spanish pesetas

18   62.80 US dollars into German marks

19   138.24 German marks into French francs

20   3750 French francs into Austrian schillings

21   1812 Austrian schillings into Spanish pesetas

22   102.05 US dollars into German marks

23   302.40 German marks into Italian lire

24   8284.50 Spanish pesetas into Austrian schillings

Exercise 7

Find the exchange rate to the pound in the following cases:

1   £100 is exchanged for 162 US dollars

2   £1000 is exchanged for 15 300 Austrian schillings

3   £40 is exchanged for 70.40 Swiss francs

4   £60 is exchanged for 145.20 Dutch guilders

5   £90 is exchanged for 20 520 Portuguese escudos

6   £200 is exchanged for 2326 Swedish kroner

7   213.50 Danish kroner is exchanged for £25

8   824.50 Norwegian kroner is exchanged for £85

9   480 French francs is exchanged for £64

10   86.80 Cyprus pounds is exchanged for £124

11   169.60 Australian dollars is exchanged for £80

12   204.70 Israeli shekels is exchanged for £46

13   2992 Belgian francs is exchanged for £68

14   336 New Zealand dollars is exchanged for £140

15   129 120 Italian lire is exchanged for £48

16   243.20 French francs is exchanged for £32

17   £150 is exchanged for 145.50 Irish punts

18   £250 is exchanged for 557.50 German marks

19   £400 is exchanged for 6560 Austrian schillings

20   £1000 is exchanged for 1765 Swiss francs

21   40 326 Spanish pesetas is exchanged for £200

22   148.50 US dollars is exchanged for £90

23   117.60 French francs is exchanged for £15

24   424 000 Italian lire is exchanged for £160

6 Credit Agreements

Some items may be expensive to buy, and usually it is possible to pay for such items by a number of equal payments spread over a number of months. An agreement is signed to do this, and is called a **credit sale** or **credit agreement**.

You can take the goods home after the first payment. Payments are made every month for 6 months or 12 months or 24 months.

The Consumer Credit Act 1985, which has had some additions since, gives a person the following rights:

- the right to cancel a credit agreement signed off the suppliers' premises (you have 5 days in which to change your mind);
- the right to pay off a debt early and usually receive a rebate;
- the right to a signed copy of the agreement, which will show how much you will repay and the amount of interest charged;
- an end to small print.

When using a credit agreement:

- you should expect to pay more than the normal cash price, although sometimes there are special offers with no extra charge;
- you may find it useful to look around to see which firm is charging least.

Buying through a mail order firm using a number of payments is a form of credit agreement.

Worked example 17

A stereo radio-cassette recorder is offered at £57.95 cash or with 6 monthly payments of £10.95 each. How much extra do you pay by buying it over 6 months?

Note that you can take the stereo radio home once you have made the first payment.

Cash price = £57.95

1 monthly payment = £10.95

6 monthly payments = 6 × £10.95

= £65.70

Total amount paid = £65.70

Extra charge = £65.70 − £57.95

= £7.75

Answer £7.75

Worked example 18

A 14-inch colour television is offered at £164.95 or for a deposit of £17 plus 11 monthly payments of £15.65. Find how much extra you pay under this credit agreement.

Cash price = £164.95
Deposit   = £17
 1 monthly payment   = £15.65
11 monthly payments = 11 × £15.65
                    = £172.15
Total amount paid = deposit + monthly payments
                  = £17 + £172.15
                  = £189.15
Extra charge   = £189.15 − £164.95
                  = £24.20
Answer £24.20

Worked example 19

A video recorder is £399.95 cash or it can be bought by 24 monthly payments of £20.99. How much would you save by paying in cash?

Cash price = £399.95
 1 monthly payment = £20.99   2 099
24 monthly payments = 24 × £20.99   24
                    = £503.76   41 980
Saving= £503.76 − £399.95   8 396
     = £103.81   50 376
Answer £103.81
In this case a considerable saving is made by paying cash.

Cars are probably the most expensive thing we buy, apart from a house, and they are often bought by credit agreement.

Worked example 20

A special offer for a car gave the cash price at £5985 or a deposit of $\frac{1}{5}$ the cash price, plus 36 monthly payments of £151.95. What was the total credit price and what was the saving by paying cash?

Cash price = £5985
Deposit   = $\frac{1}{5}$ of the cash price
           = $\frac{1}{5}$ × £5985
           = £1197
 1 monthly payment= £151.95   15 195
36 monthly payments= 36 × £151.95   36
                  = £5470.20   455 850
                                         91 170
                                        547 020
Total credit price = deposit + monthly payments
                   = £1197 + £5470.20
                   = £6667.20
Saving by paying cash = £6667.20 − £5985
                      = £682.20
Answer £682.20

Exercise 8

1. A small radio is £27.95 or it can be bought with 6 monthly payments of £5. Find the extra charge for buying by monthly payments.

2. An item is £148.99 for cash or it can be bought with 6 monthly payments of £27.50. Find the extra charge for paying monthly.

3. An electric cooker is on offer for 9 monthly instalments of £29.49. The cash price is £229.99. How much extra do you pay by accepting the offer?

4. An article is £65.99 cash but under a 6-monthly credit agreement it can be bought for £74.94. How much will be paid monthly under the credit agreement?

5. A hi-fi music centre is on special offer at £399.95 or it can be bought by 12 monthly payments of £36.50. Find the extra charge for paying monthly.

6. A 21 in colour TV is on offer at £229.95 or it can be bought with a deposit of £25 and then 12 monthly payments of £20.49. Find the saving by paying cash.

7. A mini hi-fi is quoted at £252.50. The total credit price for 10 monthly payments is given as £276. How much do you save by paying cash and how much would you pay per month on credit?

8. A fridge-freezer is on offer at £239.99 or it can be bought by 24 monthly payments of £11.99. Find the extra charge for paying monthly.

9. A video recorder is £299 for cash. It can be bought with a deposit of £30 and 12 monthly payments of £28.50. How much can you save by paying cash?

10. A second-hand car is on offer for £2500 or for a deposit of $\frac{1}{5}$ of the cash price plus 24 monthly payments of £110. Find the total credit agreement price.

11. A small new car is on offer at £6995. It can be bought by (a) a deposit of $\frac{1}{5}$ of the cash price plus 24 monthly payments of £266 or (b) 36 monthly payments of £220. Which is the cheaper credit agreement and by how much?

12. The cash price of an article is £89 and the credit price over 12 months is £95.88. How much is paid per month on credit?

13. A three-piece suite is on special offer with 'unbelievable credit terms'. It is £1299 cash or 24 monthly payments of £58.99. How much extra do you pay for 'unbelievable credit terms'?

14. An advertisement says that you can buy a TV for £199.80 with no extra charge if it is paid monthly over 9 months. How much would you pay each month?

15. A second-hand car is 'only' £1899. It is on offer with a deposit of £250 and 12 monthly payments of £150. What does the car cost under the offer?

16. A freezer can be bought by a deposit of $\frac{1}{3}$ of the cash price plus 6 monthly payments of £49.69. The cash price is £395.19. What is the saving by paying cash?

17. A used caravan is £3999. It can be bought (a) with a deposit of £99 and 36 monthly payments of £137 or (b) with a deposit of £599 and 48 monthly payments of £99. Which is cheaper and by how much?

18. The same firm offers a new caravan at £7995 or for a deposit of £2398 and 24 monthly payments of £235. How much extra is paid by using credit?

19. A double-glazing firm offers 3 windows for £1200 or for a deposit of $\frac{1}{4}$ of the cash price and 12 monthly payments of £85. What is the saving by paying cash?

20. A Sony hi-fi system is £655 cash. The shop is offering it with a deposit of $\frac{1}{5}$ of the cash price and 24 monthly payments of £28. What is the saving by paying cash?

7 Bank Loans If you have a bank account then your bank may be prepared to give you a personal loan to buy a cooker, a freezer, a car or any other expensive item.

Payment can be spread over 12 or 24 months just as with a credit agreement. The bank puts the money into your account once you have signed the agreement with them.

Worked example 21 A woman sees a new car priced at £6400. The show room asks for $\frac{1}{5}$ deposit and 24 monthly payments of £246. She goes to the bank, and the bank offers her a loan of £6400 for 24 monthly payments of £290. Which overall payment is cheaper and by how much?

Credit agreement

Deposit $= \frac{1}{5}$ of cash price
$$= \frac{1}{5} \times £6400$$
$$= £1280$$
1 monthly payment = £246
24 monthly payments = £5904
Total amount = deposit + monthly payments
$$= £1280 + £5904$$
$$= £7184$$

Bank

1 monthly payment = £290
24 monthly payments = 24 × £290
$$= £6960$$
Total amount = £6960
Answer Bank payment is cheaper overall.
(Difference = £7184 − £6960 = £224.)

Exercise 9

1 A bank offers a man a personal loan of £500. He has to pay it back in 12 monthly payments of £44.50. How much is paid back to the bank?

2 A mail order company has an outfit on offer for £89, but it can be bought by 12 weekly payments of £8.25. What extra charge is made for paying weekly?

3 A woman wants a bank loan to buy a second-hand car for £5500. The bank wants 24 monthly payments of £260. How much extra will the woman pay to get the £5500 loan?

4 A car firm offers new Fiesta cars with 24 monthly payments of £345. The charge for credit is £285. What is the cash cost of the new car?

5 A bank offers a personal loan of £8000 with 24 monthly payments of £375. A car firm offering a new car at £8000 wants a deposit of $\frac{1}{5}$ of the cash price plus 24 monthly payments of £320. Which overall payment is cheaper and by how much?

6 A customer wants a bank loan of £3600. The bank suggests (a) 12 monthly payments of £340 or (b) 24 monthly payments of £180. Which payment is cheaper for the customer and by how much?

7 A dealer has a motorbike on special offer at £900 cash or with a deposit of $\frac{1}{3}$ of the cash price and 12 monthly payments of £55. A man asks the bank and it offers a personal loan of £900 with 12 monthly payments of £82. Which overall payment is cheaper and by how much?

8   A bank wants to make £360 when it lends money to a customer through a personal loan of £3000 if it is paid over 12 months. How much would the customer pay each month?

9   Items are bought through a mail order company and total £164. Payment can be made with 12 weekly payments of £15.50. What is saved by paying cash?

10 A freezer costs £450 cash. The shop says it can be bought (a) with a deposit of £90 and 12 payments of £34.50 or (b) with 24 monthly payments of £23.20. Which is cheaper and by how much?

8 Insurance

If there is a risk involved then you can insure against it happening, whether it is against fire, theft, damage, or even against being taken ill while on holiday or against it raining on the day of the summer fête.

The greater the risk, the more it costs to insure against it happening. The insurance company weighs up the risk involved: for example, it costs more to insure a house in London than in Taunton, and it will cost more to insure a 17-year-old driver than a 35-year-old driver. Unless specifically stated, insurance is per year (per annum).

Worked example 22

Hi-fi equipment cost £600 and the insurance quote is 60p per £100 insured. What does it cost each year to insure the hi-fi?

The quote is for £100 insurance, so first find how many £100s there are in £600. Answer is 6
£100 insurance costs 60p
£600 insurance costs $6 \times 60\text{p} = £3.60$
Answer £3.60
This is not a lot to give peace of mind.

Worked example 23

A camera and some accessories cost £250. An insurance quote gives £2 per £100 insured. How much does it cost to insure the camera and accessories?

(*Note:* The insurance is likely to be higher for a camera because you carry it around and so it is more easily stolen or just lost.)
£100 insurance cost £2

How many £100 in £250? the answer is $\dfrac{250}{100}$

£250 insurance costs $\dfrac{250}{100} \times £2 = £\dfrac{500}{100} = £5$

Answer £5

Worked example 24

A house is insured for £30 000 and its contents for £10 000. The insurance for buildings is £1.60 per £1000 insured and for contents it is 60p per £100 insured. How much does it cost to insure the house and its contents?

It is usual to calculate the cost of insuring buildings and contents separately.

Buildings

£1000 insurance costs £1.60.
How many £1000 in £30 000? The answer is $\dfrac{30\,000}{100}$.

£30 000 insurance costs $\dfrac{30\,000}{1000} \times £1.60 = 30 \times £1.60$

$$= £48$$

Contents

£100 insurance costs 60p.

How many £100 in £10 000? The answer is $\dfrac{10\,000}{100}$.

£10 000 insurance costs $\dfrac{10\,000}{100} \times 60\text{p}$

$$= 100 \times 60\text{p}$$
$$= £60$$

Total insurance $= £48 + £60$
$$= £108$$

Answer £108

Worked example 25   A house is worth £54 000, the contents £14 000, and special items of jewellery, rings, cameras, etc., are worth £2800. What does it cost to insure everything if insurance for buildings is £1.70 per £1000, contents 50p per £100, and special items £1.20 per £100?

Again, calculate costs for each section separately.

Buildings

£1000 insurance costs £1.70.

£54 000 insurance costs $\dfrac{54\,000}{1000} \times £1.70 = 54 \times £1.70$

$$= £91.80$$

Contents

£100 insurance costs 50p.

£14 000 insurance costs $\dfrac{14\,000}{100} \times 50\text{p} = 140 \times 50\text{p}$

$$= £70$$

Special items

£100 insurance costs £1.20.

£2800 insurance costs $\dfrac{2800}{100} \times £1.20 = 28 \times £1.20$

$$= £33.60$$

Total insurance $= £91.80 + £70 + £33.60$
$$= £195.40$$

Answer £195.40

Car and motorcycle insurance

The amount of insurance payable depends on the risk: the greater the risk the greater the payment. A twenty-year-old who has been involved in three accidents is a greater risk than a thirty-year-old who has never been in an accident.

To compensate for this, car and motorcycle owners who have no accidents are allowed a bonus for not making a claim against the insurance company, called a 'no-claims' bonus, and so they get a reduction in premium. The maximum bonus is usually $\frac{6}{10}$ of the full rate. (As a matter of fact, this bonus is usually expressed as a percentage, and will be fully covered in the next chapter. Nevertheless, the working out of such a bonus is very similar to the example now given.)

Worked example 26 The full insurance on a car is £460 a year. The no-claims bonus is $\frac{1}{10}$ of this full amount each year. (a) What is the annual premium after 1 year? (b) What is the annual premium after 4 years?

No-claims bonus after 1 year = $\frac{1}{10}$ of £460 = £46

Premium after 1 year = £460 − £46
$\qquad\qquad\qquad$ = £414
(a) *Answer = £414*

No-claims bonus after 4 years = $\frac{4}{10}$ of £460 = £184
Premium after 4 years = £460 − £184
$\qquad\qquad\qquad\quad$ = £276
(b) *Answer = £276*

Exercise 10

1 A camera cost £300 and the insurance charged while on holiday is £3.50 per £100 insured. What does the holiday insurance cost?

2 A camcorder costs £700 and special insurance for taking it on holiday is £1.50 per £100 insured. How much is the insurance?

3 A student reckons to have £1880 of hi-fi and audio in her bed-sit in London. The insurance company will insure it for one year at £7.50 per £100 insured. What is the insurance for one year?

4 The contents of a flat are worth £8000 and these are insured at £3.40 per £100, while special items worth £1500 are insured at £2.40 per £100. What is the total insurance?

5 A house is worth £54 000. How much will it cost to insure the full value at £2.40 per £1000?

6 An inner-city house worth £54 000 was costing £5.20 per £1000 to insure. What did this insurance cost?

7 The rates for insuring the contents of a house in Liverpool and Lancaster are quoted as £8.50 and £5.20 per £1000 respectively. How much extra does it cost in Liverpool to insure the contents of a house valued at £16 000?

8 A house is worth £92 000 and its contents are worth £22 000. What does it cost to insure the house and its contents if the insurance for buildings is £1.90 per £1000 and that for contents £6.60 per £1000?

9 Commercial Union quotes £2.20 per £1000 for building insurance, £6.80 per £1000 for contents and £1.40 per £100 for special possessions. What is the total insurance on a house worth £86 000, with contents of £18 000 and special possessions of £3600?

10 AA five-star service for people travelling to Europe in 1995 was

	Vehicle	Personal insurance (children under 4 free)
5 days	£28.50	£5.40 per person per day (first day)
11 days	£37.50	plus 85p per person for
14 days	£42.00	each additional day

(a) How much will it cost using this insurance for a family of 2 adults with 1 child aged 3 going to Europe by car for 5 days?
(b) How much will it cost for a family of 5, 2 adults and 3 children all more than 4 years old, going by car to Europe for 11 days?

(c) How much will it cost for 4 adults travelling by car to France for 14 days?

11 The insurance on a car for the first year is £600. There is a 'no-claims' bonus of $\frac{1}{10}$ for each full year without accident. What will be the insurance for the third year if the full no-claims bonus applies?

12 Car insurance is £500 for the first year. If no claim is made in the first year then the cost for the second year reduces by $\frac{1}{5}$ and if no further claim is made in the second year it reduces by a further $\frac{1}{10}$ of the original cost. What is the insurance charge for the third year assuming no claims are made?

9 Budgeting

How much do you earn? How do you spend it? Keep a check for a week and discover how money seems to disappear.

Such a check, preferably over a period of time but written down each week so as not to be forgotten, is called a **budget**. If you spend more than you earn, you will be dipping into savings or going into debt. Using a check over a period of time may show a pattern of spending, showing particularly the expensive periods.

Discuss whether a table like Table 10.7 below would help to show you where the money goes.

Table 10.7 A typical budget

Week ending	Notes	Food	Entertainment Drink/Eating out	Car/ Bus/Train Transport	Clothing make-up/ toiletries	Newspapers Books Stationery	Rent Mortgage Rates	Gas Water Electricity	Savings	Miscellaneous
1996 4 Jan.	New Year's Eve Jan. sales	32.40	18.50	9.50	32.65	1.65	22.00		3.00	2.85
11 Jan.	Gas budget a/c	25.30	3.40	11.20		1.65	22.00	12.00	3.00	1.62
18 Jan.	Electr. budget a/c	23.80		11.20	4.60	1.65 2.20	22.00	8.50	3.00	
25 Jan.		29.20	8.90	10.00		1.65	22.00		3.00	6.80 credit agreement
Total	361.22	110.70	30.80	41.90	37.25	8.80	88.00	20.50	12.00	11.27
1 Feb.		38.50	13.25	8.65		1.65	22.00		3.00	3.46
8 Feb.	Shoes	26.30	2.60	10.40	27.50	1.65	22.00	12.00	3.00	2.25
15 Feb.	TV repairs	28.00	5.20	10.90		1.65 0.50	22.00	8.50	3.00	43.65
22 Feb.		31.20	3.40	11.40	3.80	1.65	22.00		3.00	6.80 credit agreement
Total	404.86	124.00	24.45	41.35	31.30	7.10	88.00	20.50	12.00	56.16

Exercise 11 Multiple choice questions

Work out which is the correct answer in the following questions:

1 A woman earns £4.20 an hour for a 32-hour week and overtime is calculated at time-and-a-quarter. For a 40-hour week she earns
  A £176.40   B £168
  C £170   D £170.60

2 A man earns £4.20 an hour for a 30-hour week. Overtime is calculated at time-and-a-half. In one week he earns £170.10. How many hours overtime does he work?
  A 10.5 h   B 6 h   C 7 h   D 9 h

3 A man has take-home pay of £186.40 a week after paying £36.10 in tax, £18.75 in national insurance, £12.50 in pension contribution and savings of £10. He earns in one year
  A £14 200   B £13 715
  C £12 500   D £14 150

4 A shopkeeper takes to the bank cheques for £125.58, £86.40 and £25. In addition there are 18 £20 notes, 14 £10 notes, 7 £5 notes, 32 £1 coins, thirty 50p coins, twenty-nine 20p coins and other coins amounting to 74p. The total paid in is
  A £852.54   B £806.88
  C £825.52   D £848.84

5 A man exchanges £160 into French francs, and the exchange rate is £1 = 7.82 francs. He receives
A 167.82 francs   B 1251.20 francs
C 20.46 francs   D 1310 francs

6 A woman exchanged 313.20 German marks into £ sterling when the exchange rate was £1 = 2.16 marks. She received
A 676 marks   B 145 marks
C 315.36 marks   D 152 marks

7 An electric cooker costing £600 is bought on credit over 24 months, each payment being £27.75. The extra charge for credit is
A £44   B £24   C £66   D £82

8 A TV costs £320 and there is a charge of £76 if it is paid over 12 months. The monthly payment would be
A £33   B £6.33   C £26.66   D £30

9 A freezer costs £350 and is paid for by monthly instalments of £39.20, which makes the cooker cost an extra £42. The number of payments is
A 12   B 14   C 10   D 24

10 A bank loan of £800 is paid off in 12 monthly payments of £82. The bank makes a charge of
A £184   B £82   C £66.66   D £150

11 House insurance costs £2.40 per £1000 insured. A house is worth £62 000. The house insurance for it is
A £138.60   B £124
C £148.80   D £162.40

12 House contents are worth £22 000. The contents insurance costs £127.60. The rate of contents insurance per £1000 is
A £6.20   B £7.00   C £5.20   D £5.80

11 Percentages

1 Introduction

Per cent means 'per hundred'. The symbol % is completely interchangeable with the words 'per cent'. A percentage is simply a fraction with 100 as denominator.

20% means $\dfrac{20}{100}$ or $\dfrac{1}{5}$.

35% means $\dfrac{35}{100}$ or $\dfrac{7}{20}$.

$8\% = \dfrac{8}{100} = \dfrac{2}{25}$.

$9\% = \dfrac{9}{100}$.

2 Percentage as a Fraction

To express a percentage as a fraction we write down the percentage as a fraction with denominator 100 and then reduce it to its lowest terms.

Worked example 1

What is 25% as a fraction?

25% is $\dfrac{25}{100}$

Now reduce to lowest terms (look again at section 2 in Chapter 2):

$\dfrac{25}{100} = \dfrac{5}{20} = \dfrac{1}{4}$

Answer $\dfrac{1}{4}$

Worked example 2

Change 18% to a fraction.

18% is $\dfrac{18}{100} = \dfrac{9}{50}$

Answer $\dfrac{9}{50}$

Worked example 3

What is $17\frac{1}{2}\%$ as a fraction?

$17\frac{1}{2}\% = \dfrac{17\frac{1}{2}}{100}$

Eliminate fractions in the numerator by multiplying by the denominator of the fraction, in this case 2.

Then $17\frac{1}{2}\% = \dfrac{17\frac{1}{2}}{100} = \dfrac{35}{200}$

$\quad\quad\quad = \dfrac{7}{40}$

Multiply denominator and numerator by 2.

Cancel by 5.

Answer $\dfrac{7}{40}$

Worked example 4   What is $23\frac{1}{3}\%$ as a fraction?

$$23\frac{1}{3}\% = \frac{23\frac{1}{3}}{100} = \frac{\overset{7}{\cancel{70}}}{\underset{30}{\cancel{300}}} = \frac{7}{30}$$

Multiply numerator and denominator of $\frac{23\frac{1}{3}}{100}$ by 3.

Answer $\frac{7}{30}$

Worked example 5   What is 140% as a fraction?

$$140\% = \frac{\overset{7}{\cancel{140}}}{\underset{5}{\cancel{100}}} = \frac{7}{5} = 1\frac{2}{5}$$

Cancel by 10 and 2.

Answer $1\frac{2}{5}$

Exercise 1

Change the following percentages to fractions, cancelling where possible.

1	50%	2	75%	3	40%	4	70%
5	20%	6	15%	7	55%	8	85%
9	24%	10	32%	11	72%	12	96%
13	9%	14	$33\frac{1}{3}\%$	15	$12\frac{1}{2}\%$	16	$62\frac{1}{2}\%$
17	$22\frac{1}{2}\%$	18	$42\frac{1}{2}\%$	19	18%	20	21%
21	120%	22	150%	23	140%	24	230%
25	$2\frac{1}{4}\%$	26	46%	27	82%	28	$66\frac{2}{3}\%$
29	$43\frac{1}{3}\%$	30	52%	31	61%	32	250%
33	$72\frac{1}{2}\%$	34	$23\frac{1}{3}\%$	35	92%	36	11%
37	28%	38	$63\frac{1}{3}\%$	39	125%	40	17%

3 Percentage as a Decimal

To change a percentage to a decimal just divide by 100, which means moving the decimal point 2 places.

Worked example 6   Change 15% to a decimal.

$$15\% = \frac{15}{100} = 0.15$$

Move decimal point 2 places to the left.

Notice how the percentage is put over 100 to emphasise what is meant by percentage.
Answer 0.15

Worked example 7   Change 64% to a decimal.

$$64\% = \frac{64}{100} = 0.64$$

Answer 0.64

Worked example 8   Change $32\frac{1}{2}\%$ to a decimal.

$$32\frac{1}{2}\% = \frac{32\frac{1}{2}}{100} = \frac{32.5}{100} = 0.325$$

Answer 0.325

Worked example 9   Change 75.8% to a decimal.

$$75.8\% = \frac{75.8}{100} = 0.758$$

Answer 0.758

Worked example 10 | Change 145% to a decimal.

$$145\% = \frac{145}{100} = 1.45$$

Answer 1.45

Worked example 11 | Change 0.35% to a decimal.

$$0.35\% = \frac{0.35}{100} = 0.0035$$

Answer 0.0035

Exercise 2

Change the following percentages to decimals.

1	50%	2	40%	3	70%	4	85%
5	15%	6	95%	7	120%	8	25%
9	33%	10	48%	11	82%	12	7%
13	11%	14	5.8%	15	9.9%	16	0.5%
17	0.12%	18	$3\frac{1}{2}$%	19	$72\frac{1}{2}$%	20	0.47%
21	3%	22	123%	23	24.8%	24	86.5%
25	$19\frac{1}{2}$%	26	0.07%	27	94.6%	28	71%
29	$15\frac{1}{4}$%	30	$28\frac{1}{4}$%	31	$\frac{1}{4}$%	32	$\frac{1}{2}$%
33	$10\frac{1}{2}$%	34	90%	35	101%	36	305%
37	80.25%	38	57%	39	19.5%	40	$1\frac{1}{4}$%

4 Changing Any Fraction or Decimal to a Percentage

To change any fraction or decimal to a percentage simply multiply by 100%.

Worked example 12 | Change $\frac{1}{4}$ to a percentage.

Multiply the fraction by 100%.

$$\tfrac{1}{4} = \frac{1}{4} \times 100\% = \frac{100}{4}\% = 25\%$$

Answer 25%

Worked example 13 | Change $\frac{2}{5}$ to a percentage.

Multiply the fraction by 100%:

$$\tfrac{2}{5} = \frac{2}{5} \times 100\% = \frac{200}{5}\% = 40\%$$

Answer 40%

Worked example 14 | Change $3\frac{1}{2}$ to a percentage.

$$3\tfrac{1}{2} = 3\tfrac{1}{2} \times 100\% = \frac{7}{2} \times 100\% = \frac{700}{2}\% = 350\%$$

Answer 350%

Worked example 15 | Change $\frac{7}{8}$ to a percentage.

$$\frac{7}{8} = \frac{7}{8} \times 100\% = \frac{\overset{175}{\overset{350}{\cancel{700}}}}{\underset{2}{\cancel{8}}} = 87\frac{1}{2}\%$$

Answer $87\frac{1}{2}\%$

Worked example 16 | Change 0.7 to a percentage.

Multiply the decimal by 100%:

$0.7 = 0.7 \times 100\% = 70\%$

Answer 70%

| Move decimal point 2 places. |

Worked example 17 | Change 0.28 to a percentage.

$0.28 = 0.28 \times 100\% = 28\%$

Answer 28%

Worked example 18 | Change 6.47 to a percentage.

$6.47 = 6.47 \times 100\% = 647\%$

Answer 647%

Exercise 3

Change the following fractions to percentages.

1 $\frac{1}{2}$	2 $\frac{1}{5}$	3 $\frac{3}{4}$	4 $\frac{4}{5}$	5 $\frac{9}{10}$
6 $\frac{1}{4}$	7 $\frac{3}{5}$	8 $\frac{7}{10}$	9 $\frac{1}{10}$	10 $\frac{3}{2}$
11 $\frac{1}{8}$	12 $1\frac{1}{2}$	13 $1\frac{3}{4}$	14 $\frac{5}{8}$	15 $\frac{7}{8}$
16 $\frac{9}{25}$	17 $2\frac{1}{4}$	18 $\frac{3}{8}$	19 $\frac{3}{10}$	20 $\frac{12}{25}$
21 $3\frac{1}{2}$	22 $\frac{7}{40}$	23 $\frac{18}{25}$	24 $\frac{11}{40}$	25 $\frac{9}{20}$
26 $\frac{5}{4}$	27 $\frac{17}{25}$	28 $\frac{13}{20}$	29 $1\frac{1}{5}$	30 $\frac{7}{4}$
31 $\frac{3}{20}$	32 $\frac{2}{5}$	33 $\frac{21}{25}$	34 $\frac{13}{10}$	35 $\frac{7}{20}$
36 $\frac{17}{40}$	37 $\frac{27}{20}$	38 $\frac{24}{25}$	39 $\frac{9}{8}$	40 $4\frac{1}{2}$

Exercise 4

Change the following decimals to percentages.

1 0.5	2 0.7	3 0.3	4 0.75
5 0.6	6 0.25	7 0.42	8 0.86
9 0.95	10 0.09	11 0.16	12 0.57
13 0.95	14 2.10	15 5.25	16 0.94
17 1.07	18 1.19	19 0.72	20 0.08
21 0.516	22 0.748	23 0.904	24 0.084
25 3.051	26 1.008	27 0.106	28 2.075
29 0.003	30 0.568	31 1.504	32 0.0725
33 0.5825	34 3.0006	35 1.2005	36 0.1
37 0.36	38 2.1	39 0.806	40 0.17

5 One Number as a Percentage of Another

In comparing two numbers, a fraction is probably the natural answer but a percentage answer often makes comparisons easier. First, find as a fraction and then change to a percentage.

Worked example 19   I get 32 marks in an examination where the total marks are 80. What percentage mark is this?

32 marks out of 80 can be written as $\dfrac{32}{80}$

$\dfrac{32}{80}$ as a percentage $= \dfrac{32}{80} \times 100\% = 40\%$

My percentage mark is 40%

Worked example 20   An evening class has 24 adult students, of whom 15 are women. What percentage of the class is men?

24 adult students are in the class
If 15 are women, then 9 are men

9 men out of 24 can be written as $\dfrac{9}{24}$ are men

$\dfrac{9}{24}$ as a percentage $= \dfrac{9^{3}}{24_{8_{2}}} \times 100^{25}\% = \dfrac{75}{2}\% = 37\tfrac{1}{2}\%$

Answer $37\tfrac{1}{2}\%$ of the class is men

Exercise 5

1   What is 60 as a percentage of 100?

2   What is 45 as a percentage of 100?

3   What is 32 as a percentage of 50?

4   What is 45 as a percentage of 90?

5   What is 5 as a percentage of 25?

6   What is $6\tfrac{1}{4}$ as a percentage of 25?

7   What is $42\tfrac{1}{2}$ as a percentage of 100?

8   There are 7 men in an adult class of 20. What percentage are men?

9   A student gains 32 marks out of 40 in a test. What percentage is this?

10   There are 56 women in a staff total of 80. What percentage are women?

11   A garden hedge has 24 privet trees and 8 beech trees. What percentage of the hedge is privet?

12   A small estate has 16 houses and 4 bungalows. What percentage of the estate is bungalows?

13   A bed of wallflowers has 24 red and 16 yellow flowers. What percentage of the bed is yellow flowers?

14   A large bag of toffees had 9 treacle and 15 Devon milk. What percentages of sweets was treacle?

15   A line is 20 cm long but in measuring quickly a student put it down as 20.5 cm. What percentage error is this of the original line?

16   In a car park there were 24 Ford cars, 18 Vauxhalls, 10 Rovers and 8 others. What percentage of Ford cars was in the car park?

17   A shop sold 31 paperback books to every 9 hardbacks. What percentage of books sold was paperbacks?

18   A wallet contains 5 £20 notes, 8 £10 notes and 7 £5 notes. What percentage of notes are £5 notes?

19   A student gains 42 marks out of 50 in maths and 48 out of 60 in English. In which subject does she have the best percentage and by how much?

20   A car journey is 125 miles, and 85 were covered in the first two hours. What percentage of the journey is still to be done?

21   Vanilla and chocolate ice cream are preferred in the ratio 3 : 5. What percentage prefer chocolate ice cream?

22   36 tabloid newspaper are sold to every 12 broadsheets. What percentage of tabloid newspapers are sold?

23   In a survey, 26 people lived in two-bedroom houses, 42 in three-bedroom houses and 12 in four-bedroom houses. In this survey, what percentage of people lived in 4-bedroom houses?

24   In a fashion show there were 16 red dresses, 12 blue dresses and 4 yellow dresses. What percentage in the show were red dresses?

6 Percentages in Money

Percentages that refer to money will probably occur more often in our lives than any other type of percentage.

To do the following type of question, first change the percentage to a decimal or a fraction. Either method will do, but as most questions deal with money and decimal currency it may be easier to concentrate on decimals. (Both methods will be shown initially.)

Worked example 21

Find 35% of £4.

Decimal method

$$35\% = \frac{35}{100} = 0.35$$

$$35\% \text{ of } £4 = 0.35 \times £4$$
$$= £1.40$$
Answer £1.40

Fraction method

$$35\% = \frac{35}{100}$$

$$35\% \text{ of } £4 = \frac{35}{100} \times £4$$

$$= £\frac{140}{100}$$

$$= £1.40$$
Answer £1.40

Worked example 22

What is 30% of £60?

$$30\% = \frac{30}{100} = 0.30$$

$$30\% \text{ of } £60 = 0.30 \times £60$$
$$= £18.00$$
Answer £18.00

Or $$30\% = \frac{30}{100}$$

$$30\% \text{ of } £60 = \frac{30}{100} \times £60$$

$$= 3 \times £6$$
$$= £18$$
Answer £18

Worked example 23

A sale offers 15% off normal prices. What will be the sale price of a suit if the normal price is £80?

The sale offers a reduction of 15%.
First, find 15% of the normal price.

$$15\% = \frac{15}{100} = 0.15$$

15% of £80 = 0.15 × £80 = £12.00
Sale price = £80 − £12 = £68

$$Or \ 15\% = \frac{15}{100}$$

$$15\% \text{ of } £80 = \frac{\overset{3}{\cancel{15}}}{\underset{2 \ \ 1}{\cancel{100}}} \times £\overset{4}{\cancel{80}} = £12$$

Sale price = £80 − £12 = £68
Answer £68

Worked example 24

A woman earns £90 a week, but after wage talks she is given an increase of 7%. What is her new wage?

Increase is 7%.

$$7\% = \frac{7}{100} = 0.07$$

7% of £90 = 0.07 × £90 = £6.30
New wage = £90 + £6.30 = £96.30
Answer £96.30

Exercise 6

Calculate the following:

1 50% of £20	**2** 25% of £12	**3** 60% of £40
4 15% of £8	**5** 35% of £40	**6** 75% of £18
7 55% of £12	**8** 140% of £40	**9** 130% of £25
10 20% of £8.60	**11** 24% of £3.50	**12** 60% of £25.40
13 $37\frac{1}{2}$% of £4.80	**14** 70% of £45.90	**15** $22\frac{1}{2}$% of £80.40

16 Increase £38 by 25%	**17** Increase £60 by 15%
18 Increase £28 by 130%	**19** Decrease £50 by 12%
20 Decrease £24 by 45%	**21** Decrease £32 by 35%
22 Decrease £180 by $37\frac{1}{2}$%	**23** Decrease £55 by 26%

24 A man earns £320 a week but then he has a rise of 4%. What is his new wage?

25 All items in a sale are reduced by 30%. What is the sale price of a pullover if the normal price is £60?

26 The price of a house decreased last year by 3%. At the beginning of the year it was £64 000. What was it worth at the end of the year?

27 Items in a closing-down sale are reduced by 40%. Before the sale, a video recorder was £540. What is the sale price?

28 A sales assistant is paid £180 per week plus 8% commission on all she sells. Last week she sold items totalling £720. How much did she earn last week?

29 The chief executive of a large company earned £650 000 last year. He expects a rise of 6.5%. How much will he earn this year?

30 A new car can be bought at a discount of 14%. The new car price is £11 500. What is the discounted price?

7 Percentages of Other Quantities

Percentages can apply to any quantity, whatever the units, and not just money. The method used is the same as that for money.

Worked example 25

Find 15% of 6 km.

$$15\% = \frac{15}{100} = 0.15$$

15% of 6 km = 0.15 × 6 km
= 0.90 km
Answer 0.90 km

Worked example 26

Find 8% of 12 ft.

$$8\% = \frac{8}{100} = 0.08$$

8% of 12 ft = 0.08 × 12 ft
= 0.96 ft
Answer 0.96 ft
If the answer is required in inches then multiply this answer by 12.

Worked example 27

A firm tells the union negotiator that the workforce has to be cut by 12%. The firm employs 1400 men. How many men are likely to lose their jobs?

$$12\% = \frac{12}{100} = 0.12$$

12% of 1400 men = 0.12 × 1400 men
= 168 men
Answer 168 men

Worked example 28

A factory produces 3800 cars a week. Productivity has to increase by 3% next week. How many cars are being asked for next week?

$$3\% = \frac{3}{100} = 0.03$$

3% of 3800 cars = 0.03 × 3800 cars
= 114 cars
Number asked for = 3800 + 114 = 3914 cars
Answer 3914 cars

Exercise 7

Find the following:

1 30% of 10 miles	2 25% of 12 cm	3 35% of 20 km
4 70% of 8 litres	5 18% of 30 kg	6 24% of 25 cl
7 15% of 20 ft	8 4% of 5 kg	9 34% of 50 cm
10 26% of 35 km		

11 A hospital has 1400 staff. On any one day there are 8% absent. How many staff are absent on that day?

12 A firm says it has to shed 4% of its workforce. 1800 are working now. How many jobs will be lost?

13 A factory makes 4500 cars a week. Productivity goes up by 2.2%. How many cars are now made in a week?

14 There are 2800 full-time students at a college, and it reckons that 9% will be without a job at the end of the year. How many students will be unemployed at the end of the year?

15 A bridge is 800 m long. On a hot day it expands by 0.002%. How many cm does it expand on that day?

16 A large shop 'loses' 3.5% of items each week. It stocks 7200 items. How many items are 'lost' in a week?

17 A firm guarantees 95% germination in a packet of seeds. There are 3800 poppy seeds in a packet. What is the minimum number of poppies you can expect to germinate?

18 Sales of the *Mirror* are 4 200 000 a day. It has a scoop for tomorrow and expects a rise in sales of 7.2%. How many extra papers does it expect to sell tomorrow?

19 Football attendances are expected to increase next year by 4%. A football club had average attendances of 28 600 this year. What can it expect next year?

20 There were $5\frac{1}{2}$ million tourists in Spain last year. This is expected to drop by 1.5% this year. How many fewer tourists will there be?

21 P & O says that in five years' time the number of people going on a cruise, now 300 000 a year, will have increased by 220%. How many are they expecting in five years' time?

22 The cruise ship *Oriana* holds 2000 people including crew. On any one day 2.3% visit the doctor. How many visit the doctor in a day?

23 Dannimac rejects 0.6% of items, and they are sold as seconds. It makes 18 500 items in one factory. How many are sold as seconds?

24 The total number of cars sold in the UK last year was 1.24 million. This year a rise of 2.5% is expected. How many cars are expected to be sold this year?

8 Percentage Increase or Decrease

A percentage increase or decrease is calculated on the original quantity, as shown in the following examples.

Worked example 29

A man has his working hours cut from 40 to 37 a week. What percentage decrease is this?

Original number of hours = 40 h
Decrease in hours = 3 h

Fractional decrease $= \dfrac{3\,h}{40\,h}$

The decrease is always compared with original amount.

Percentage decrease $= \dfrac{3\,h}{\overset{2}{40}\,h} \times \overset{5}{100}\%$

$= \dfrac{15}{2} = 7\frac{1}{2}\%$

Answer $7\frac{1}{2}\%$

Worked example 30

A newsagent increased turnover from £50 000 a year to £65 000 the next year. What was the percentage increase in turnover?

Original turnover = £50 000
Increase = £15 000

$$\text{Fractional increase} = \frac{£15\,000}{£50\,000}$$

The increase is compared with the original amount.

$$\text{Percentage increase} = \frac{£15\,000}{£50\,000} \times 100\%$$

$$= 30\%$$

Answer 30%

Worked example 31 The council tax bill for a house last year was £800, and this year it is £836. What has been the percentage increase in council tax?

Original council tax charge = £800
Increase = £36

$$\text{Percentage increase} = \frac{£36^9}{£800_2} \times 100\%$$

$$= \frac{9}{2}\%$$

$$= 4\tfrac{1}{2}\%$$

Answer $4\tfrac{1}{2}\%$

9 Value Added Tax

A tax is levied on all goods and services, called **value added tax** (VAT); at present goods and services are either zero rated (no tax at all), or are charged at a rate of $17\tfrac{1}{2}\%$, though gas and electricity bills are charged at 8%. The tax goes to the government.

Assume in all examples that VAT is $17\tfrac{1}{2}\%$.

Worked example 32 A photocopy of a drawing is 40p + VAT. Find the total cost of the copy.

First, VAT = $17\tfrac{1}{2}\%$ = 17.5%. Find 17.5% of 40p to see how much VAT is charged. Then add the amount of VAT to 40p.

$$17.5\% = \frac{17.5}{100} = 0.175$$

17.5% of 40p = 0.175 × 40 = 7p
VAT = 7p
Total cost = 40p + 7p = 47p
Answer 47p

Worked example 33 Sunday lunch in a restaurant is advertised as £10 + VAT. How much is the total?

VAT = $17\tfrac{1}{2}\%$ = 17.5%

$$17.5\% = \frac{17.5}{100} = 0.175$$

0.175 of £10 = 0.175 × £10 = £1.75
Total charge = £10 + £1.75 = £11.75
Answer £11.75

Worked example 34 A sunroof for a car is advertised at £160 + VAT. Find the total cost.

VAT = $17\tfrac{1}{2}\%$ = 17.5%

$$17.5\% = \frac{17.5}{100} = 0.175$$

17.5% of £160 = 0.175 × £160 = £28

Total cost = £160 + £28
            = £188
Answer £188

Worked example 35   A quarterly telephone bill may look like this:

	£61.51	Call charges
plus	£24.49	Advance charges 1 Jun 95 to 31 Aug 95
	£86.00	Subtotal excluding VAT
plus	£15.05	VAT at 17.5%
	£101.05	Total amount now due

Exercise 8

(Assume in all cases that VAT is 17.5%.)

Find the total cost of the following:

1 £20 + VAT   2 £30 + VAT   3 £140 + VAT
4 £24 + VAT   5 £52 + VAT   6 £18 + VAT
7 £120 + VAT

8 A garage advertises the cost of a car service as £60 plus parts plus VAT. If no parts are required, what is the cost of the car service?

9 A new car tyre costs £42 + VAT. What is the total cost?

10 A quarterly telephone bill shows a fixed charge of £24 plus 1200 units at 5p a unit. What is the total amount payable if VAT is charged on all items?

11 Office World advertises the cost of all items plus VAT. A box of typing paper (5 reams) is £14.80 + VAT. What is the total cost?

12 A wholesale warehouse has an item for £26.40 + VAT. What is the total cost of the item?

13 A solicitor's bill for selling a house came to £462 + VAT. What was the total amount of the bill?

14 A conference hotel gives a quote to a firm for its Christmas party as £22 per person excluding VAT. What will it cost the firm, including VAT, if 72 people attend?

10 Gas and Electricity Bills

Both types of bill are calculated each quarter (3 months) as a charge for each unit plus a fixed quarterly charge plus VAT. VAT at present is 8% on gas and electricity bills.

Note: The units for gas and electricity are kilowatt-hours. The gas bill shows in great detail how to convert the hundreds of cubic feet used into kilowatt-hours, as the actual heating value of each cubic foot of gas varies from one gas board to another.

Gas

A typical gas bill is shown in Figure 11.1 on the next page.

Worked example 36   A gas bill shows the equivalent of 10 200 kilowatt-hours used in a quarter at a cost of 1.470p per kWh. If the standing charge per quarter is £10.06 how much is the gas bill with VAT at 8%?

- Find the cost of the gas used.
- Add on the standing charge.
- Find the VAT at 8%.
- Find the total amount.

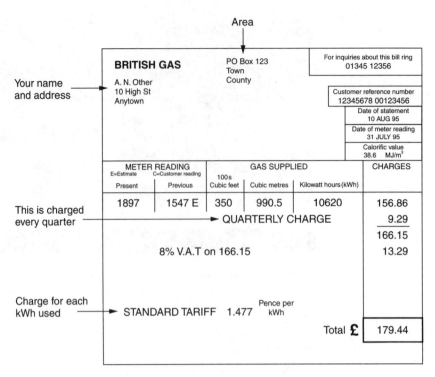

Figure 11.1 Typical gas bill

Gas costs 1.470p per kWh
10 200 kWh cost 10 200 × 1.470p = £149.94
Standing charge   =   10.06
                                          £160.00
8% VAT on £160.00   =   12.80
Total amount   = £172.80
Answer £172.80

Electricity

A typical electricity bill is shown in Figure 11.2 on the next page. Note the VAT is not payable on the cooker, as this would have been included in the original charge for the cooker.

Worked example 37

An electricity bill shows a previous meter reading of 46 192 and the present reading as 47 492. The price per unit is 6.470p. The quarterly standing charge is £10.39. How much is the total bill?

Find how many units are used.
Meter reading is 47 492 and previously was 46 192
Number of units used = 47 492 − 46 192
                     = 1300 units
Cost per unit = 6.470p
Cost of 1300 units = 1300 × 6.470p
                   = 8411p
                   = £84.11
Standing charge   =   10.39
                        £94.50
8% VAT on £94.50 =   7.56
Total amount   = £102.06
Answer £102.06

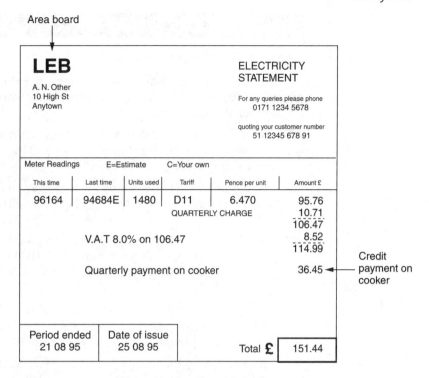

Area board

LEB

A. N. Other
10 High St
Anytown

ELECTRICITY
STATEMENT

For any queries please phone
0171 1234 5678

quoting your customer number
51 12345 678 91

Meter Readings	E=Estimate	C=Your own			
This time	Last time	Units used	Tariff	Pence per unit	Amount £
96164	94684E	1480	D11	6.470	95.76

QUARTERLY CHARGE   10.71
106.47

V.A.T 8.0% on 106.47   8.52
114.99

Quarterly payment on cooker   36.45 ◄── Credit payment on cooker

Period ended 21 08 95	Date of issue 25 08 95	Total £	151.44

Figure 11.2 Typical electricity bill

Budget accounts

It is possible to pay gas and electricity bills by paying a fixed amount each month into a special account called a **budget account**. The gas and electricity boards estimate how much gas or electricity you will use over a year, and this is then spread out over 12 months.

Worked example 38

An electricity budget account is estimated at £42 a month. In the first quarter 1400 units are used at 6.470p a unit. The quarterly standing charge is £12.42. Is the budget account in credit or not at the end of the first quarter, and by how much?

Cost per unit   = 6.470p
Cost for 1400 units = 1400 × 6.470p
                     = 9058p
                     = £90.58
Standing charge   =   12.42
                        £103.00
8% VAT on £103.00 =   8.24
Total amount   = £111.24

Budget account:

£42 a month is paid
In 3 months, 3 × £42 is paid = £126
Electricity bill is £111.24
Therefore, the account is in credit by £126 − £111.24
                                      = £14.76

Answer £14.76 credit

Exercise 9

Assume VAT in all cases to be 8%.

1   A gas bill showed that 5000 kWh were used in the summer quarter at a price of 1.470p per kWh. If the standing charge was £14.00, how much was the bill for this quarter?

2   The winter quarter showed that 11 600 kWh were used with the price still 1.470p a kWh, but the standing charge had gone up to £15.98. How much was the bill for the winter quarter?

3   The gas bill for a large house showed that 19 800 kWh were used at a price of 1.540p a kWh. The standing charge was £13.08. What was the total gas bill?

4   A householder bought a gas cooker on credit sale at £35 a quarter, and this was put on the gas bill. In the quarter, 10 700 kWh were used at 1.520p a kWh, and the standing charge was £15.36. What was the total of the quarterly bill?

5   A couple arranged for a budget account of £45 a month. For the first quarter 7200 kWh were used at 1.480p a kWh. The standing charge was £12.44. Were the couple in credit or not after the first quarter, and by how much?

6   An electricity bill shows a previous meter reading of 47 209 and the present reading as 48 349. If the price per unit is 6.20p a unit and the standing charge is £12.82, how much is the bill?

7   An electricity meter reading showed 38 754 at the beginning of a quarter and 40 174 at the end. With a standing charge of £12.36 and electricity at 6.70p a unit how much should the electricity bill be at the end of the quarter?

8   An electricity budget account is £45 a month. In the winter quarter 1930 units were used at 6.40p a unit. The standing charge was £12.48. By how much was the budget account in debit at the end of this quarter?

9   An electricity bill was £115.02. The standing charge was £12.90 and the VAT £8.52. Electricity was 6.50p a unit and the meter reading at the beginning of the quarter was 57 248. What was the meter reading at the end of the quarter?

10 A couple buy a cooker on credit sale at £34.40 a quarter and a freezer at £28.40 a quarter, both of which are to go on the electricity bill. In one quarter the meter reading goes from 38 716 to 40 396. If electricity is 6.50p a unit and the standing charge is £11.30, what is the total bill at the end of the quarter?

11 Profit and Loss

It is important to know when we sell anything whether we have made a profit (a gain) or a loss. We have a **buying price** (what it cost us to buy the object) and a **selling price** (what we sell the object for).

Worked example 39

A radio is bought for £58 and sold for £46. What is the profit or loss?

If it is sold for less than what was paid for it then we have made a *loss*.

Loss = £58 − £46 = £12

Usually the profit or loss is asked for as a **percentage**.

Worked example 40

A shop buys radios at £16 and sells them for £20. What is the percentage profit?

The method of working is as follows:

1   Find the actual cash profit or loss.
2   Express this as a fraction of the buying price.

3 Work out this fraction as a percentage.

Selling price = £20
Buying price = £16
Profit   = £4
This is a profit of £4 on the buying price of £16.

$$\frac{\text{Profit}}{\text{Buying price}} = \frac{£4}{£16}$$

$$\text{Percentage profit} = \frac{£4^1}{£16_4} \times 100^{25}\% $$

$$= 25\%$$

Answer 25%

Unless instructed to the contrary always give the percentage profit or loss as a percentage of the buying price.

Worked example 41 **An item is bought for £40 and sold for £43. Find the percentage profit.**

Selling price = £43
Buying price = £40
Profit   = £3

$$\frac{\text{Profit}}{\text{Buying price}} = \frac{£3}{£40}$$

Both parts of the fraction *must* be in the same units, but as the top and bottom of the fraction are in the same units these can be cancelled:

$$\text{Percentage profit} = \frac{3}{40_2} \times 100^5\% = \frac{15\%}{2}$$

$$= 7\frac{1}{2}\%$$

Answer 7½%

Worked example 42 **Biro pens are bought in a box of 100 costing £5. They are sold at 7p each. What is the percentage profit?**

How much do you get when you sell all the pens?
1 pen is sold for 7p
100 pens are sold for $100 \times 7p = £7$
Selling price = £7
Buying price = £5
Profit   = £2

$$\frac{\text{Profit}}{\text{Buying price}} = \frac{£2}{£5}$$

$$\text{Percentage profit} = \frac{2}{5_1} \times 100^{20}\%$$

$$= 40\%$$

Answer 40%

Worked example 43 **A dress is bought for £36 and sold one month later for £22.50. What is the percentage loss?**

Buying price = £36.00
Selling price = £22.50
Loss   = £13.50

$$\frac{\text{Loss}}{\text{Buying price}} = \frac{£13.50}{£36} = \frac{£13\frac{1}{2}}{£36} = \frac{27}{72}$$

$$\text{Percentage loss} = \frac{27}{72} \times 100\% = \frac{75}{2}\%$$

$$= 37\frac{1}{2}\%$$

Answer $37\frac{1}{2}\%$

Worked example 44

A 25 lb box of apples is bought for £4 and sold for 28p a lb. At the bottom of the box it was found that 2 lb of apples were bruised and could not be sold. What is the percentage profit?

Only 23 lb of apples can be sold.
23 lb at 28p a lb = $23 \times 28p$
$= £6.44$
Selling price $= £6.44$
Buying price $= £4.00$
Profit $= £2.44$

$$\frac{\text{Profit}}{\text{Buying price}} = \frac{£2.44}{£4} = \frac{244}{400}$$

$$\text{Percentage profit} = \frac{244}{400} \times 100\%$$

$$= 61\%$$

Answer 61%

Worked example 45

An old car was bought for £350 and after a respray was sold at a profit of 20%. How much was it sold for?

Buying price = £350
Profit is calculated on the buying price.

$$20\% = \frac{20}{100} = 0.2$$

Profit = 20% of £350 = $0.2 \times £350$
$= £70$
Selling price = £350 + £70
$= £420$
Answer £420

How do you find the cost price if the selling price and profit (loss) are given?

Worked example 46

An article is sold for £60, giving a profit of 50%. What was the buying price?

The percentage profit is always worked out on the buying price.
The buying price = 100% (the original whole one).
Profit = 50%
Then selling price = 150%
Now relate these percentages to the question:
Selling price 150% = £60

$$\text{which means } 1\% = \frac{£60}{150}$$

Buying price = 100%

$$100\% = 100 \times \frac{£60}{150}$$

$$= £40$$

Buying price = £40
Answer £40

Worked example 47   An article is sold for £60, giving a loss of 20%. What was the buying price?

Buying price = 100%
Loss   = 20%
Selling price = 80%
Selling price 80% = £60

$$1\% = \frac{£60}{80}$$

Buying price = 100% = $100 \times \dfrac{£\overset{3}{\cancel{60}}}{\underset{4}{\cancel{80}}}$

= £75

Answer £75

Exercise 10

Find the selling price:

1	Buying price = £40	Profit = 50%
2	Buying price = 80p	Profit = 25%
3	Buying price = £25	Profit = 20%
4	Buying price = 30p	Profit = 10%
5	Buying price = £26	Profit = 10%
6	Buying price = £140	Profit = 30%
7	Buying price = £240	Loss = 25%
8	Buying price = £120	Loss = 22%
9	Buying price = £50	Loss = 15%
10	Buying price = £70	Loss = 33%
11	Buying price = £55	Loss = 40%
12	Buying price = 90p	Loss = 20%

Exercise 11

Find the percentage profit or loss:

1	Buying price = £10	Selling price = £12
2	Buying price = £16	Selling price = £12
3	Buying price = 32p	Selling price = 40p
4	Buying price = £25	Selling price = £16
5	Buying price = £7.50	Selling price = £10
6	Buying price = £3.20	Selling price = £2.40
7	Buying price = 40p	Selling price = 35p
8	Buying price = £180	Selling price = £198
9	Buying price = £54	Selling price = £37.80
10	Buying price = £1200	Selling price = £1308
11	Buying price = £6.40	Selling price = £8.32
12	Buying price = £15.20	Selling price = £9.12

Exercise 12

Find the cost price:

1 Selling price = £15   Profit = 25%

2 Selling price = £44   Profit = 10%

3 Selling price = £69   Profit = 15%

4 Selling price = £312   Profit = 30%

5 Selling price = 35p   Profit = 25%

6 Selling price = £9.12   Profit = 14%

7 Selling price = £18   Loss   = 25%

8 Selling price = £36   Loss   = 10%

9 Selling price = £15.30   Loss   = 15%

10 Selling price = 42p   Loss   = 30%

11 Selling price = £21.12   Loss   = 12%

12 Selling price = £54   Loss   = 40%

Exercise 13

1 Apples are bought in 20 lb boxes for £8 and sold at 60p a lb. What is the percentage profit when all are sold?

2 Biro pens are bought at £5 per 100. They are sold at 8p each. What is the percentage profit on the sale of a pen?

3 Toffees are bought in a 4 lb jar for £16. They are sold at £1.20 a quarter lb. What is the percentage profit?

4 A box of 32 Mars bars can be bought for £6. They are sold at 30p each. What is the percentage profit when all are sold?

5 A dealer can buy a new car for £7500, and he can sell it for £9000. What is his percentage profit?

6 A second-hand car is bought for £8000. It is sold two years later for £4200. What percentage loss is made on selling the car?

7 A market trader buys a job lot of 80 shirts for £200. She sells half at £6 and half at £5. (a) What profit does she make and (b) what is the percentage profit?

8 A specialist music shop buys CDs at £6 and sells them for £9. What percentage profit is made?

9 A box of 100 pears is bought for £20. Some 8% are found to be soft and cannot be sold. The rest are sold at 32p each. What is the percentage profit when all the rest are sold?

10 A shopkeeper aims to make a profit of 30%. He buys some items at £12. At what price does he sell them?

11 By selling an article for £40 a dealer made a profit of 25%. At what price should it be sold to make 30%?

12 All items in a sale are offered at 30% off normal price. The normal price of a dress is £60. (a) What is the sale price? (b) Even then the shop makes a profit of 40%. What price did the shopkeeper pay for the dress originally?

12 Interest   Interest is money paid for use of money lent or money borrowed. The rate at which you are paid or have to pay the interest is given as a percentage.

An interest rate is quoted per annum (p.a.): that is per year.

You will be paid interest for saving with a building society or in a Post Office savings account or bank deposit account or savings certificates.

Worked example 48   I save £200 with a building society for 1 year with interest at 7% p.a. How much interest is paid to me at the end of the year?

$$7\% = \frac{7}{100} = 0.07$$

$$7\% \text{ of } £200 = 0.07 \times £200$$
$$= £14$$

Interest is £14

Answer £14

Note that the interest after 6 months would have been $\dfrac{£14}{2} = £7$

For 3 months it would have been $\dfrac{£14}{4} = £3.50$

Worked example 49   What is the interest after a year on £540 at an interest rate of 8% p.a.?

$$8\% = \frac{8}{100} = 0.08$$

$$8\% \text{ of } £540 = 0.08 \times £540$$
$$= £43.20$$

Answer £43.20

13 Simple Interest   This is interest reckoned on the original capital only. It is most likely to be used when money is borrowed.

Expect to pay a higher interest charge to borrow money than when lending it.

For example, if you save (lend) money in a building society (see section 16 below) you may get 4% interest on your money, but if you borrow money from the same society you could be charged 9%.

Worked example 50   A bank quotes an interest rate of 15% to borrow money. I need £5000 to buy a car. How much does it cost to borrow money over 2 years?

First, find the interest for one year.

$$15\% = \frac{15}{100} = 0.15$$

$$\text{Interest} = 15\% \text{ of } £5000 = 0.15 \times £5000$$
$$= £750$$

Interest for one year = £750
Interest for two years = $2 \times £750$
$$= £1500$$

Answer £1500

This is called **simple interest**; the interest remains the same in every year.

Worked example 51   Find the simple interest on £400 for 3 years at 6% p.a.

$$6\% = \frac{6}{100} = 0.06$$

Interest for one year = 6% of £400 = 0.06 × £400
$$= £24$$
Simple interest for 3 years = 3 × £24
$$= £72$$
Answer £72

Worked example 52   Find the simple interest on £600 for $2\frac{1}{2}$ years at $8\frac{1}{2}$% p.a.

$$8\frac{1}{2}\% = \frac{8.5}{100} = 0.085$$

Interest for one year = $8\frac{1}{2}$% of £600 = 0.085 × £600
$$= £51$$
Simple interest for $2\frac{1}{2}$ years = $2\frac{1}{2}$ × £51
$$= £127.50$$
Answer £127.50

14 Compound Interest

Savings are often for more than a year, and the calculation of interest is likely to be compound interest; the interest at the end of the year is added on to the savings and this itself earns interest.

This is the method adopted in savings schemes.

Worked example 53   Find the compound interest on £2000 saved for 2 years at 5% p.a.

First, find the interest after one year.

$$5\% = \frac{5}{100} = 0.05$$

5% of £2000 = 0.05 × 2000
$$= £100$$
After one year we have original capital of £2000 plus £100 interest = £2100
Now find the interest for the second year.
5% of £2100 = 0.05 × £2100
$$= £105$$
After two years we have £2100 + £105 = £2205
Compound interest = £2205 − £2000
$$= £205$$
Answer £205

Worked example 54   Find the compound interest on £500 for 2 years at 8% p.a.

The setting-out can be made more compact than in the example above.

$$8\% = \frac{8}{100} = 0.08$$

1st Year:	Original capital	£500	
	Interest	40	(0.08 × £500)
2nd Year:	New capital	540	
	Interest	43.20	(0.08 × £540)
	New capital	£583.20	

Interest = £583.20 − £500
$$= £83.20$$
Answer £83.20

Worked example 55   £5000 is placed with a building society for 3 years. To how much does it grow if the interest rate is 10% p.a.?

$$10\% = \frac{10}{100} = 0.10$$

1st Year:	Original capital	£5000	
	Interest	500	(0.10 × £5000)
2nd Year:	New capital	5500	
	Interest	550	(0.10 × £5500)
3rd Year:	New capital	6050	
	Interest	605	(0.10 × £6050)
	After three years	£6655	

Answer £6655

All savings schemes work on the compound interest principle.

Exercise 14

1 How much interest is earned on £400 in one year at 6% p.a.?

2 What is the interest earned in one year on £600 at 5% p.a.?

3 What is the interest earned in one year on £250 at 6% p.a.?

4 How much interest is earned in one year on £800 at $5\frac{1}{2}$% p.a.?

5 How much interest is earned in one year on £1250 at $4\frac{1}{2}$% p.a.?

6 How much interest is earned in one year on £750 at 3% p.a.?

7 How much interest is earned in 6 months on £4000 at $4\frac{1}{2}$% p.a.?

8 How much interest is earned in 3 months on £150 at 6% p.a.?

9 How much interest do I pay on a bank loan of £2500 that is paid back in one year at 8% p.a.?

10 £4000 is borrowed from a bank to buy a second-hand car. Interest is charged at $9\frac{1}{2}$% p.a. How much is paid to the bank every month in order to pay off the loan and the interest in one year?

11 A house is sold for £66 000 and, before another is bought, the money is invested in a building society at 6% p.a. The money is withdrawn after 1 month. How much interest has been earned?

12 A shop charges customers an interest rate of $18\frac{1}{2}$% p.a. for goods bought on credit sale. A dishwasher is bought for £600. How much is paid to the shop each month in order to pay off the cost of the dishwasher and the interest in one year?

Exercise 15

Find the simple interest on the following:

1 £400 for 2 years at $4\frac{1}{2}$% p.a.

2 £500 for 2 years at 6% p.a.

3 £200 for 3 years at 5% p.a.

4 £150 for 2 years at $4\frac{1}{2}$% p.a.

5 £1200 for 2 years at $6\frac{1}{2}$% p.a.

6 £360 for 3 years at 5% p.a.

7 £720 for 4 years at 6% p.a.

8 £450 for 2 years at $5\frac{1}{2}$% p.a.

9 £1060 for 3 years at 6% p.a.

10 £600 for 2 years at 8% p.a.

11 A bank charges simple interest on its loans. What will be the interest charged on a loan of £8000 for 2 years at 9% p.a.?

12 What will it cost per month to pay back the loan and the interest to a bank that charges 8% simple interest on a loan of £600 taken over 2 years?

13 (a) What is the total amount of interest on an interest-only loan of £30 000 for 20 years at 8% p.a.?
    (b) How much is this per month?

14 (a) What is the total amount of interest on an interest-only loan of £50 000 for 25 years at 6%?
    (b) How much is this per month?

Exercise 16

Find the value of the following, using compound interest:

1 £1000 invested for 2 years at 6% p.a.

2 £600 for 2 years at 5% p.a.

3 £300 for 2 years at 4% p.a.

4 £1200 for 2 years at 7% p.a.

5 £10 000 for 2 years at 6% p.a.

6 £8000 for 3 years at 5% p.a.

7 £20 000 for 3 years at 6% p.a.

8 £2000 for 2 years at $6\frac{1}{2}$% p.a.

9 £4000 for 6 months at 8% p.a.

10 £4000 for 18 months at $5\frac{1}{2}$% p.a.

11 £50 000 is invested in a building society for 2 years at $5\frac{1}{2}$% p.a. How much money is in the account after 2 years?

12 One building society advertises a rate of $4\frac{1}{2}$% with interest calculated yearly; another advertises a rate of 4% with interest calculated six monthly. For an investment of £5000, what is the difference in interest after 1 year?

15 Income Tax

Income tax is a tax on a person's earnings after certain allowances have been made; as a rule, the greater the earnings the greater the tax. After allowances have been deducted from earnings all the income left is taxed. The tax goes to the government.

The tax year runs from 6 April in one year to 5 April in the following year. For 1995/96 the income tax rates were as follows:

Rate of tax	Income after allowances have been deducted
20%	Up to £3200
25%	£3201–£24 300
40%	over £24 300

The 25% rate is called the **basic rate**.

Each adult has an allowance of £3525, which means that tax is payable only on an income above £3525. There are allowances for married couples, for children, for certain senior citizens etc. Pick up a leaflet from any tax office and see what allowances are given and how they change from year to year.

Worked example 56 | A woman has taxable income, after allowances have been deducted, of £8200. How much does she pay per year in income tax?

Look at the tax bands to see what rates of tax are likely to be used.
£8200 is below £24 300 and so does not invoke a tax of 40%.
The first £3200 is taxable at 20%.

$$20\% = \frac{20}{100} = 0.20$$

Tax on £3200 = £3200 × 0.20
= £640
Rest of taxable income = £8200 − £3200
= £5000

This is taxable at 25%.

$$25\% = \frac{25}{100} = 0.25$$

Tax on £5000 = £5000 × 0.25
= £1250
Total tax paid = £640 + £1250
= £1890   (this is about £35 a week)
Answer £1890

Worked example 57 | A man earns £14 000 a year and has allowances of £3525. How much income tax does he pay in one year?

First, find the taxable income by deducting all the allowances from the earned income:

Taxable income = earned income − allowances
= £14 000 − £3525
= £10 475

Look at the tax bands to see what rates of tax are likely to be used.
The first £3200 is taxable at 20%.

$$20\% = \frac{20}{100} = 0.20$$

Tax on £3200 = £3200 × 0.20
= £640
Rest of taxable income = £10 475 − £3200
= £7275

This is taxable at 25%.

$$25\% = \frac{25}{100} = 0.25$$

Tax on £7275 = £7275 × 0.25
= £1818.75
Total tax = £640 + £1818.75
= £2458.75
Answer £2458.75

Worked example 58 | A woman earns £380 a week. How much, to the nearest £, does she pay in income tax each week, if her allowances are £3525 a year?

Find how much she earns in a year.

She earns £380 a week

Earnings per year $= 52 \times £380$
$= £19\ 760$
Allowances $= £3525$
Taxable income $= £19\ 760 - £3525$
$= £16\ 235$

The first £3200 of this is taxable at 20%.

$20\% = 0.20$
Tax on £3200 $= £3200 \times 0.20$
$= £640$
Rest of taxable income $= £16\ 235 - £3200$
$= £13\ 035$

This is taxable at 25%.

$25\% = 0.25$
Tax on £13 035 $= £13\ 035 \times 0.25$
$= £3258.75$
Total tax per year $= £640 + £3258.75$
$= £3898.75$
Tax per week $= £3898.75 \div 52$
$= £74.98$
$= £75$ (to nearest £)

Answer £75

Worked example 59 A woman has an income of £36 000 a year and total allowances of £5800. How much does she pay in income tax for that year?

Taxable income $= £36\ 000 - £5800$
$= £30\ 200$

This taxable income is above £24 000 and so some tax will be payable at 40%. Work out how much taxable income there is in each tax band.

Up to £3200 is taxed at 20%.
All between £3200 and £24 300 is taxed at 25%: that is,
£24 300 − £3200 = £21 100 is taxed at 25%
All from £24 300 to £30 200 is taxed at 40%: that is,
£30 200 − £24 300 = £5900 is taxed at 40%
Total tax payable $= £3200$ at 20% + £21 100 at 25% + £5900 at 40%
$= £3200 \times 0.20 + £21\ 100 \times 0.25 + £5900 \times 0.40$
$= £640 + £5275 + £2360$
$= £8275$

Answer £8275

Exercise 17

Use the rates given in section 15 for any question on income tax.

1   Find the income tax payable on a taxable income of £8000.

2   Find the income tax payable on a taxable income of £15 000.

3   Find the income tax payable on a taxable income of £30 000.

4   A woman earns £19 000 a year and has personal allowances of £3525. How much income tax does she pay in one year?

5   A married man earns £360 a week and has allowances of £5245. How much, to the nearest £, does he pay in income tax each week?

6   A barrister is said to earn £120 000 a year. If his allowances amount to £28 000, how much does he pay in income tax that year?

7   The chairman of one of the large companies has a taxable income, after allowances, of £850 000 a year. How much income tax does he pay in a year?

8   A man earns £13 200 and his wife £12 500. The allowances for such a couple are £7050 plus £1720. The joint income is used for calculating the income tax payable. What is the total income tax paid by the couple in one year?

16 Building Societies

These are large financial institutions that began by persuading people to save money with them, paying the savers interest for doing so, and then lending this money to other people who wanted to buy property, charging them a higher rate of interest for borrowing money than that paid to savers. The Building Societies' Acts, under a government official known as the Registrar, make stringent conditions on societies as to what savers' money can be used for.

Many societies, by agreement with the Registrar, have now become much more wide-ranging in their financial dealing. Lending money for properties is obviously long term, and may be over 5, 10, 20, 25 or even 30 years. The money lent to buy a property is called a **mortgage**.

The majority of mortgages now are by way of interest only: that is, the interest only is paid on the loan and the loan itself is paid off at the end of 25 years, say by an insurance policy, by a charge on pension entitlement, or by so much extra being paid each year to pay off the loan. The figures are large. For example, one building society is offering an interest-only mortgage of 8.5% with payments over 25 years.

What would it cost for a £40 000 loan?

For a £40 000 loan at 8.5% over 25 years:

£40 000 at 8.5% for 1 year $= £40\,000 \times 0.085$
$$= £3400$$
For 25 years $= 25 \times £3400$
$$= £85\,000$$

This is for **interest only**. Now add on the £40 000 loan and

Total amount paid over 25 years $= £85\,000 + £40\,000$
$$= £125\,000$$

All building societies have to tell you what the total cost of the mortgage will be – it is usually in small print. Pick up leaflets from different societies and compare the total costs.

At present, there is a small amount that can be reclaimed each year from income tax, as an allowance for the interest paid on a mortgage.

17 Percentages with the Calculator

The percentage key must be used at the end of the calculation. Do not put it at the beginning.

Worked example 60 $60 \times 8\%$.

60 ⊠ 8 ％ $\to 4.8$ | There is no need to press the = key.
Answer 4.8

Worked example 61 $32.5 \times 62.5\%$.

32 · 5 ⊠ 62 · 5 ％ $\to 20.3125$
Answer 20.3125

Worked example 62 | Find 12% of 150.

Remember 'of' means multiply.
$12\% \times 150$:
Put percentage at the end so it becomes $150 \times 12\%$.
150 ☒ 12 ☒ → 18
Answer 18

Worked example 63 | What is 15% of £32.40?

This is the same as £32.40 $\times$ 15%.
32 · 40 ☒ 15 ☒ → 4.86
Answer £4.86

Worked example 64 | What is 250 as a percentage of 400?

In arithmetic this would be changed first to a fraction.

i.e. $\dfrac{250}{400}$ (or $250 \div 400$)

Do this on the calculator and press ☒.
250 ☒ 400 ☒ → 62.5
Answer 62.5%

Worked example 65 | What is 32.5 as a percentage of 120?

32 · 5 ☒ 120 ☒ → 27.08
Answer 27.08%

Where you increase (or decrease) an amount by a percentage, apply $+$ or $-$ after the normal percentage calculation.

Worked example 66 | Increase 120 by 30%.

120 ☒ 30 ☒ ☒ ☒ 156
Answer 156

Worked example 67 | Decrease 280 m by 18%.

280 ☒ 18 ☒ ☒ ☒ 229.6
Answer 229.6 m

Worked example 68 | How much do you pay for a suit costing £80 if there is a discount of 15%?

Discount is a decrease in price, so the question now becomes 'decrease £80 by 15%'.
80 ☒ 15 ☒ ☒ ☒ 68
Answer £68

Exercise 18

1   Find
  (a)   42% of 250
  (b)   85% of 40
  (c) $19\frac{1}{2}$% of 3200
  (d)   7.5% of £160
  (e)   15% of £120
  (f) $12\frac{1}{2}$% of 4 m
  (g)   2.7% of £120 000
  (h) $22\frac{1}{2}$% of 1500 m

2   Find the price I have to pay if there is a discount of
  (a)   15% on £60
  (b)   10% on £24.50
  (c) $12\frac{1}{2}$% on £120
  (d) $7\frac{1}{2}$% on £44
  (e)   20% on £248
  (f)   30% on £580
  (g) $12\frac{1}{2}$% on £7500
  (h)   25% on £72.60

3   Find the new cost if there is an increase of
  (a)   10% on £62
  (b)   5% on £110
  (c) $12\frac{1}{2}$% on £124.80
  (d) $2\frac{1}{2}$% on £84
  (e)   7% on £515
  (f)   3.2% on £180
  (g)   9.4% on £420
  (h)   6.25% on £8800

4   Find the following fractions as percentages
  (a) $\dfrac{5}{8}$
  (b) $\dfrac{7}{25}$
  (c) $\dfrac{17}{40}$
  (d) $\dfrac{7}{8}$
  (e) $\dfrac{4}{7}$
  (f) $\dfrac{4}{11}$
  (g) $\dfrac{5.6}{8.4}$
  (h) $\dfrac{6}{9}$

5   Council tax for Band C is to be increased by 3.7% in the coming year. Find the new council tax where the amount paid last year in different parts of the country was
  (a)   £520
  (b)   £470
  (c)   £684
  (d)   £806
  (e)   £324
  (f)   £475.50
  (g)   £622.50
  (h)   £784.80

6   A shop has a sale in which a discount of 15% is given on the shop price of any article. Find what you will pay if the shop price is
  (a)   £15
  (b)   £25.60
  (c)   £92.40
  (d)   £326.20
  (e)   £938.80
  (f)   £7.40
  (g)   £72
  (h)   £38.20

Exercise 19 Multiple choice questions

Work out which is the correct answer in the following questions:

1   32% as a fraction is
  A   3.2
  B $\frac{8}{25}$
  C $3\frac{1}{5}$
  D $\frac{1}{4}$

2   10.25% as a decimal is
  A   0.010 25
  B   10.25
  C   1025
  D   0.1025

3   $\frac{4}{5}$ as a percentage is
  A   80%
  B   400%
  C   40%
  D   20%

4   35% of 6200 is
  A   620
  B   2500
  C   2710
  D   2170

5   To get 30 marks out of a possible 60 marks is
  A   30%
  B   50%
  C   40%
  D   20%

6   A dealer wants a 15% deposit on a car costing £5400. The deposit is
  A   £540
  B   £150
  C   £810
  D   £1080

7   A dress is reduced from £60 to £45. The reduction is
  A   25%
  B   15%
  C $33\frac{1}{3}$%
  D   20%

8   A suit is sold for £190 at a profit of 52%. The suit cost
  A   £138
  B   £140
  C   £125
  D   £130

9   A car service costs £84 + VAT (17.5%). The cost is
  A   £101.50
  B   £98.70
  C   £95
  D   £66.50

10   A second-hand car bought for £3200 is sold for £1600. The loss is
  A   100%
  B   200%
  C   160%
  D   50%

11   An electricity bill drops from 1500 units to 1200 units. The decrease is
  A   300%
  B   20%
  C   25%
  D   30%

12   An item is sold for £75.20 including VAT (17.5%). The VAT is
  A   £17.50
  B   £11.20
  C   £14.00
  D   £13.60

13   The simple interest on £400 for 3 years at $5\frac{1}{2}$% p.a. is
  A   £120
  B   £22
  C   £66
  D   £84

14 The compound interest on £800 for 2 years at 5% p.a. is
A £82   B £80   C £40   D £100

15 The total interest on an interest-only loan of £40 000 for 30 years at 8% p.a. is
A £120 000   B £32 000
C £96 000   D £104 000

16 On taxable income of £15 000 the income tax payable is
A £3590   B £3000   C £3750   D £6000

17 The price of a book goes up from £7.95 to £9.95. The percentage increase is approximately
A 20%   B 28%   C 25%   D 32%

18 A tie is sold at £12 and the profit is 20%. To make a profit of 50% the tie has to be sold for
A £24   B £15   C £14   D £20

19 An insurance company raises its charges on house insurance by $7\frac{1}{2}$%. A householder previously paid £620. The insurance is now
A £666.50   B £695.00
C £573.50   D £650.00

20 A salesman gets 8% commission on all sales. He receives £3200 in commission. The sales are
A £4000   B £32 000
C £40 000   D £24 000

12 Graphs, Substitution, Coordinates and Surveys

1 Graphs

A graph is a good way of communicating information. Graphs provide a picture of information; someone once said 'a picture can take the place of 1000 words'.

A graph is a diagram showing the relationship between two quantities. To draw or plot a graph two reference lines, called **axes**, are drawn at right angles to each other. The point where they cross is called the **origin**. The horizontal axis is usually called the x-axis and the vertical axis is called the y-axis.

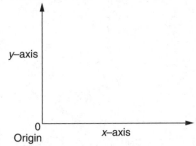

A scale is then marked along each axis to cover the variation in each of the two quantities. The scales chosen do not have to be the same on each axis, but they should be as simple as possible and should normally be as large as the paper permits. You must name the graph: in other words, state what the graph is representing. The illustrations that follow try to emphasise these points.

2 Line Graphs

Sets of figures or data are often represented by a graph because it is easy to understand and comparisons may be made. A type of graph with which we may be familiar is a monthly rainfall graph. Note the two quantities involved: month (period of time) and rainfall (amount of rain falling).

Note: Any reference to a suitable scale in this chapter assumes the graph paper to be 230 mm × 180 mm.

Worked example 1

Draw a line graph to represent the monthly rainfall in Preston from July 1994 to June 1995 (taken at the Jeremiah Horrocks Observatory).

	1994							1995				
	Jul	Aug	Sep	Oct	Nov	Dec	Jan	Feb	Mar	Apr	May	Jun
mm of rain	55	107	117	142	104	162	167	112	71	17	45	29

It is usual, when a graph is drawn, for the axes and the graph to be in pencil, and for figures and writing to be in ink.

1 Draw two axes at right angles to each other about 1 or 2 cm from the bottom and left-hand side of the paper; this leaves room for you to write the names of the quantities represented.

2 Look at the range of values for each quantity and then choose a suitable scale. The scale does not have to be the same on each axis, but the scales should normally be as large as the paper will allow, unless a scale has been given already. Scales must be evenly spaced.

In this example we have to represent up to 12 months and rainfall up to 167 mm. A suitable scale would be 1 cm = 1 month, horizontally, taking up 12 cm; and 1 cm = 10 mm of rain, vertically, taking up 17 cm. Any scale chosen must continue along the same axis at the same rate.

3 Plot the graph. Beginning at July 1994 put in a rainfall of 55 mm (indicated by a small pencilled dot or cross), for August a rainfall of 107 mm, for September a rainfall of 117 mm, and so on. Join successive dots by a straight pencil line.

4 Name the graph at the top or bottom of the graph paper to state what the graph is representing. The completed graph is shown in Figure 12.1.

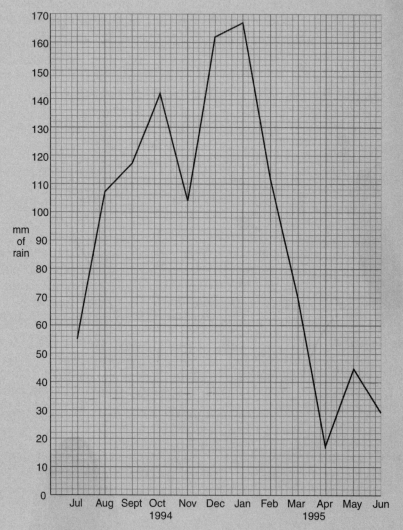

Figure 12.1 Monthly rainfall for Preston, July 1994–June 1995

A scale does not have to begin at 0 (nought), as this may give a graph appearing at the top or bottom of a page.

Worked example 2 | Draw a line graph to represent the number of pedestrians killed in the UK in road accidents over the ten years given:

	1984	1985	1986	1987	1988	1989	1990	1991	1992	1993
Number of pedestrians killed	1868	1789	1841	1703	1753	1706	1694	1496	1347	1241

There are 10 years, and 1 cm = 1 year would be suitable for the horizontal scale.

The range of pedestrians killed goes from 1241 to 1868, so if the graph ranges from 1200 to 1900 it will cover all possible values.

Suggested scale: horizontally 1 cm = 1 year
    vertically   1 cm = 50 pedestrians killed

The completed graph is shown in Figure 12.2 below. With the scale starting at 0, the same graph would have looked like Figure 12.3 on page 142. These two graphs are representing the same figures, and show why great care must be taken when interpreting a graph.

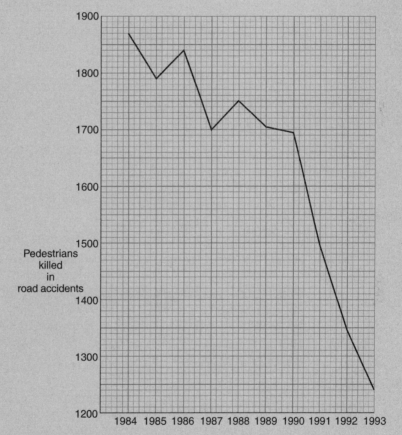

Figure 12.2 Graph of number of pedestrians killed in road accidents in the UK (worked example 2)

Worked example 3 | The numbers of people found guilty of fraud/forgery offences from 1985 to 1993 were as follows:

	1985	1986	1987	1988	1989	1990	1991	1992	1993
Number found guilty of fraud/forgery (thousands)	25.5	22.8	22.5	22.7	22.3	21.9	21.2	20.0	17.5

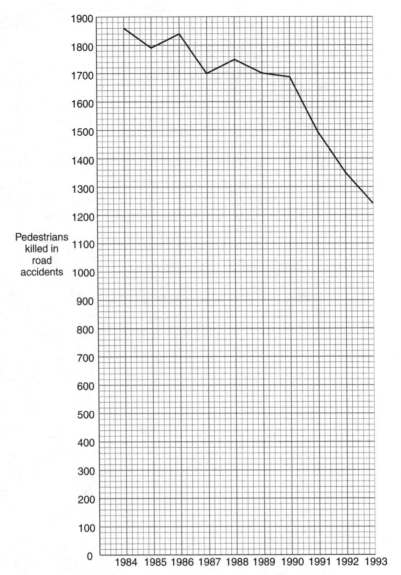

Figure 12.3 Alternative graph of number of pedestrians killed in road accidents in the UK (for worked example 2)

The information in the chart at the foot of page 141 has been put on two graphs (Figure 12.4 and Figure 12.5 opposite), one to show that there was apparently little decrease between 1985 and 1993, and the other to show that there was a dramatic decrease. From identical data you can produce a representation to suit your needs.

Sometimes it is a help to put two graphs on the same piece of paper for the purpose of comparison. Make sure you can distinguish between them, by for example drawing one with broken lines.

Worked example 4 Monthly sales for 1994 and 1995 of a clothing firm were as follows:

	Jan	Feb	Mar	Apr	May	June
1994 (£000)	50.0	40.6	45.4	51.8	63.2	54.0
1995 (£000)	58.7	46.4	42.3	49.0	66.4	58.2

Suggested scales: 2 cm = 1 month horizontally;
                  1 cm = £2000 sales vertically. Begin at £40 000.

The completed graph is shown in Figure 12.6 on page 144.

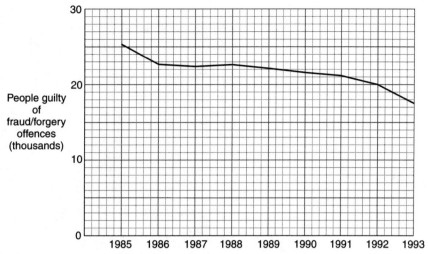

Figure 12.4 Graph of people found guilty of fraud/forgery offences (for worked example 3)

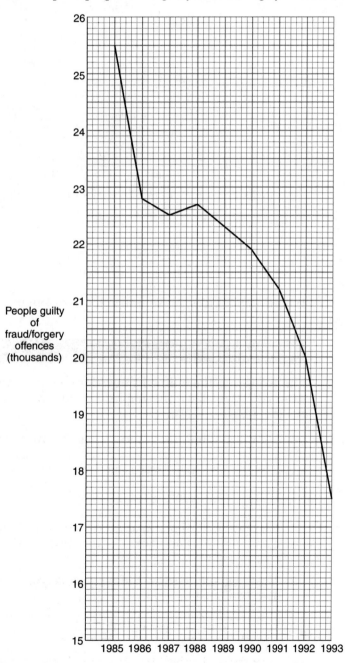

Figure 12.5 Alternative graph of people found guilty of fraud/forgery offences
(for worked example 3)

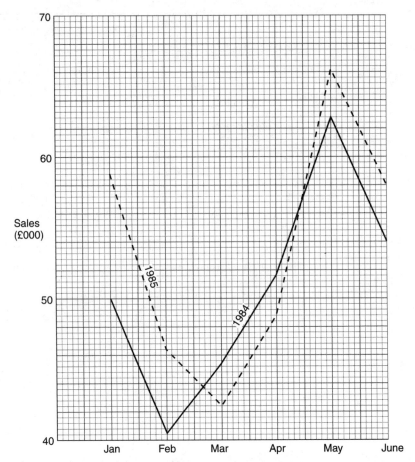

Figure 12.6 Graph of monthly sales for 1994 and 1995 (for worked example 4)

Where graphs cross, make sure you can distinguish one graph from another.

Exercise 1

The answers to the following questions are meant to be drawn as line graphs. After you have drawn the graphs try and form your own conclusions as to what the graphs are suggesting.

1   Draw a graph to show the average monthly rainfall for Jerusalem in 1994.

	Jan	Feb	Mar	Apr	May	Jun	Jul	Aug	Sep	Oct	Nov	Dec
mm of rain	136	120	64	28	4	2	2	4	6	18	72	84

Suggested scales: horizontally, 1 cm represents 1 month
                         vertically,   1 cm represents 10 mm of rain

2   Draw a graph to show the average daily maximum temperature in °C for the Dead Sea area in 1994.

	Jan	Feb	Mar	Apr	May	Jun	Jul	Aug	Sep	Oct	Nov	Dec
°C	21	22	26	32	33	37	39	38	36	32	27	22

Suggested scales: horizontally, 1 cm represents 1 month
                         vertically,   1 cm represents 2 °C

3   Plot a graph to show the number of road casualties suffered by young people under 16, for each quarter from January 1993 to March 1995.

	1993				1994				1995
Quarter	1st	2nd	3rd	4th	1st	2nd	3rd	4th	1st
Road casualties under 16	8421	12 078	12 480	9611	9627	12 421	12 608	10 495	8993

Suggested scales: horizontally, 1 cm represents one quarter (3 months)
                  vertically,   1 cm represents 1000 road casualties

4   Draw two graphs on one pair of axes to show the number of people in employment making cars and parts and those in hotels and catering for the years given. The numbers are in thousands.

	1988	1989	1990	1991	1992	1993	1994
Cars and parts	271	264	249	225	229	205	200
Hotels and catering	1123	1217	1278	1255	1233	1217	1228

5   Plot a graph to show how the first child allowance has changed over the years given.

	1984	1985	1986	1987	1988	1989	1990	1991	1992	1993	1994
First child allowance (£)	6.85	7.00	7.10	7.25	7.25	7.25	7.25	8.25	9.65	10.00	10.20

6   Draw two graphs on one pair of axes to show the average daily hours of sunshine of two places for the months given.

	Oct	Nov	Dec	Jan	Feb	Mar	Apr
Majorca	7.8	6.0	5.4	5.3	6.2	7.2	9.0
London	3.5	2.0	1.6	1.8	2.0	4.0	5.6

7   Draw a graph to show the number of steers and heifers slaughtered in the months of 1994; the numbers are in thousands.

	Jan	Feb	Mar	Apr	May	Jun	Jul	Aug	Sep	Oct	Nov	Dec
Steers and heifers	223	183	186	223	181	175	195	180	197	251	209	185

8   Draw two graphs on the same axes to show the number of dwellings completed in UK by local authorities and private developers for the years given.

	1985	1986	1987	1988	1989	1990	1991	1992	1993
Local authorities	30 303	25 070	21 095	21 129	18 627	17 653	11 132	5 453	3 206
Private authorities	163 395	178 017	191 212	207 387	187 504	166 655	159 290	147 094	144 604

9   Plot two graphs on one pair of axes to show the number of males and females leaving school/college with 2 or more A-levels for the years given.

	1982	1983	1984	1985	1986	1987	1988	1989	1990	1991
Males (thousands)	68	70	67	66	66	67	69	72	72	75
Females (thousands)	63	65	60	61	62	64	69	74	76	82

10   Plot two graphs on the same axes to show the number of offenders found guilty of robbery and drugs offences for the years given; the numbers are in thousands

	1984	1985	1986	1987	1988	1989	1990	1991	1992	1993
Robbery	4.3	4.4	4.2	4.4	4.3	4.6	4.8	4.8	5.1	5.3
Drugs	18.7	19.5	16.9	16.9	18.8	22.6	24.6	23.5	22.7	21.9

3 Bar Graphs (Bar Charts)

A bar graph (or bar chart) is often used when the horizontal scale is simply a list of categories, for example countries, holidays, transport, etc., whereas a line graph is often used when the horizontal axis has some kind of timescale (hours, days, months, etc.). It is possible, of course, to draw a bar graph or a line graph for each of these lists of data.

The quantities are represented by the heights of the bars. The bars are of equal width.

Worked example 5   Draw a bar graph to represent the average recordings of atmospheric pollution of sulphur dioxide for the towns given in 1993–94.

	Sulphur dioxide (micrograms per cubic metre)
Barnsley	189
Norwich	32
Belfast	160
Plymouth	30
Mansfield	120
Cardiff	43
Stoke	108
Glasgow	43

Make sure the horizontal scale points are sufficiently far apart to allow for the drawing of a bar, with the vertical scale evenly spaced.
Suggested scales: horizontally, 2 cm represents 1 town
            vertically,   1 cm represents 10 micrograms
The completed bar graph is shown in two forms in Figure 12.7 opposite, with the bars apart and with them touching. It is a matter of taste as to which is the preferable method.

Bar graphs are a useful presentation when percentages are given.

Worked example 6   Draw a bar graph to represent the countries stayed in by UK residents on holidays abroad in 1994.

	France	Spain/Majorca	Greece	USA	Portugal	Other countries
Percentage of total	24.7	22.0	7.8	7.2	4.8	33.5

Suggested scales: horizontally, 2 cm represents each country
            vertically,   2 cm represents 10% of total
The completed graph is shown in Figure 12.8 on page 148.

Perhaps the most useful value of bar graphs is in comparison of two or three quantities.

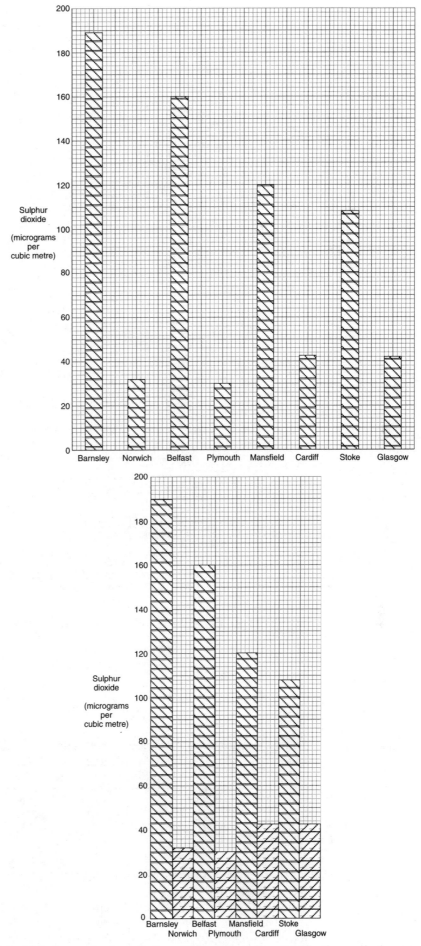

Figure 12.7 Atmospheric pollution, 1993–94: sulphur dioxide (for worked example 5)

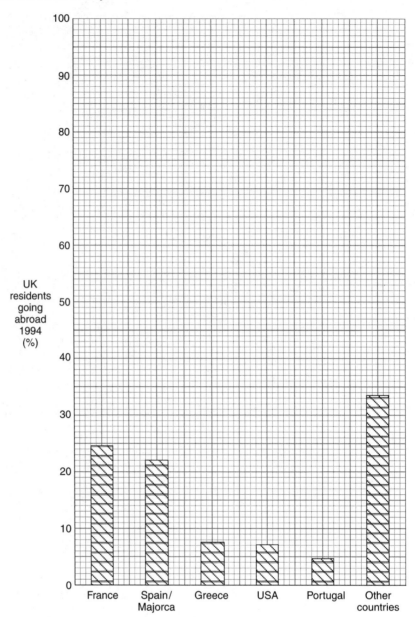

Figure 12.8 UK residents going abroad, 1994 (for worked example 6)

Worked example 7

Draw a bar graph to show the percentages of males/females in various age groups of the UK population at the end of 1993.

Age (years)	Under 16	16–39	40–64	65–79	80+
Males (%)	21.6	36.2	29.2	10.6	2.4
Females (%)	19.6	33.5	28.4	13.1	5.4

As there are two different bars for each group, turn the paper so that the long side is horizontal.
Suggested scales: horizontally, 3 cm for each age group
    vertically,   2 cm represents 5% of total
The completed graph is shown in Figure 12.9 opposite.

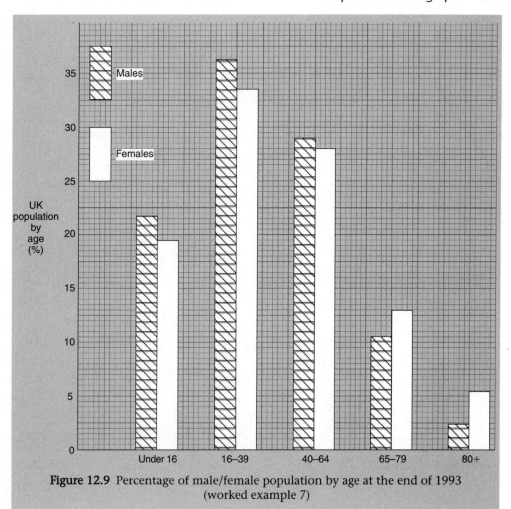

Figure 12.9 Percentage of male/female population by age at the end of 1993
(worked example 7)

4 Proportionate Bar Graphs

This type of graph tries to give a picture of all quantities on one bar. (It can be drawn vertically or horizontally with the bar the same width throughout.) However, it is not always easy to do accurately, and the two examples given provide one easy proportionate bar chart and one more difficult.

Worked example 8

The average daily hours of sunshine in March for London are 4.0 hours and for the Algarve are 6.8 hours. Show this information as a vertical proportionate bar chart.

Suppose the total height of the proportionate bar chart is to be 8 cm.

Total hours to be represented = 4.0 + 6.8 = 10.8 h

Proportion for London hours $= \dfrac{4.0}{10.8}$

Proportion for Algarve hours $= \dfrac{6.8}{10.8}$

Proportion of 8 cm bar for London hours $= \dfrac{4.0}{10.8} \times 8\,\text{cm} = 2.96\,\text{cm}$

Proportion of 8 cm bar for Algarve hours $= \dfrac{6.8}{10.8} \times 8\,\text{cm} = 5.04\,\text{cm}$

The proportionate bar chart is shown in Figure 12.10.

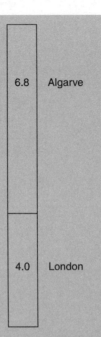

Figure 12.10 Average daily hours of sunshine in March

Worked example 9 The Coats Viyella group reported turnover for 1994 as in the table.

Geographic location	Turnover
UK	£816m
Rest of Europe	£459m
North America	£441m
South America	£136m
Rest of world	£332m
Total	£2184m

Represent this information as a horizontal proportionate bar chart.

Suppose the proportionate bar chart is to be 12 cm long.

$$\text{Proportion of total turnover for UK} = \frac{£816m}{£2184m}$$

$$\text{Proportion of 12 cm bar for UK turnover} = \frac{816}{2184} \times 12\,\text{cm} = 4.48\,\text{cm}$$

$$\text{Proportion of 12 cm bar for Rest of Europe} = \frac{459}{2184} \times 12\,\text{cm} = 2.52\,\text{cm}$$

$$\text{Proportion of 12 cm bar for North America} = \frac{441}{2184} \times 12\,\text{cm} = 2.42\,\text{cm}$$

$$\text{Proportion of 12 cm bar for South America} = \frac{136}{2184} \times 12\,\text{cm} = 0.75\,\text{cm}$$

$$\text{Proportion of 12 cm bar for Rest of world} = \frac{332}{2184} \times 12\,\text{cm} = 1.82\,\text{cm}$$

(Can you say why this totals 11.99 cm and not 12 cm?)
The proportionate bar chart is shown in Figure 12.11.

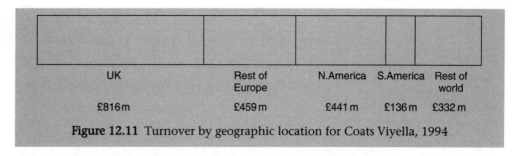

Figure 12.11 Turnover by geographic location for Coats Viyella, 1994

Exercise 2

(All the questions that were asked in exercise 1 can also be used for practice in drawing bar graphs.)

1   Draw a bar graph to show the average daily maximum temperature °C for Jerusalem.

	Jan	Feb	Mar	Apr	May	Jun	Jul	Aug	Sep	Oct	Nov	Dec
°C	12	14	16	21	26	27	30	30	27	26	19	13

2   Draw a bar graph to show the production of cars under 1000cc for 1994.

	Jan	Feb	Mar	Apr	May	Jun	Jul	Aug	Sep	Oct	Nov	Dec
Production of cars under 1000cc	4089	5000	8999	6229	9113	10 583	10 639	3370	10 157	10 828	10 988	8184

Why is production smallest in August?

3   Draw a bar graph to show the production of cars over 1000cc and under 1600cc for 1994.

	Jan	Feb	Mar	Apr	May	Jun	Jul	Aug	Sep	Oct	Nov	Dec
Production of cars over 1000cc and under 1600cc	48 250	56 545	76 288	61 532	64 731	74 776	61 608	38 010	63 218	62 312	75 789	46 339

Why do you think so many cars are produced in November?

4   Draw a bar graph to show the manufacture of men's pullovers in the quarter years given; the numbers are in millions.

	1991				1992			
	1st Qtr	2nd Qtr	3rd Qtr	4th Qtr	1st Qtr	2nd Qtr	3rd Qtr	4th Qtr
Men's pullovers	42.7	46.3	82.7	86.1	42.8	39.8	75.1	68.5

What conclusions can you draw between the first and second half of the years, and also between 1991 and 1992?

5   Draw a proportionate bar chart 10 cm long to show the following information: a small orchard has 9 apple trees, 5 pear trees, 4 cherry trees and 2 plum trees.

6   Draw a proportionate bar chart to show the following information: the number of thousands unemployed in July 1994 by region was South East 825, Greater London 432, Yorkshire & Humberside 225, North West 290, Scotland 237, and Wales 121.

7   Draw two bar graphs on the same axes (see example 7) to show net receipts by HM Customs & Excise for petrol and tobacco for the years given.

	1990	1991	1992	1993	1994
Petrol (£million)	9467	10 558	11 283	12 500	13 987
Tobacco (£million)	5512	5963	6418	7397	7297

Is it too early to draw any conclusions about tobacco?

8 Draw two bar graphs on the same axes to show the number of TV licences for the years given; the numbers are in thousands.

	1987	1988	1989	1990	1991	1992	1993	1994
Colour TV	16 902	17 310	17 847	18 086	18 149	18 708	19 250	19 667
Monochrome	2283	2012	1762	1518	1259	1068	927	803

In what year do you think monochrome TV will disappear?

9 Draw two bar graphs on the same axes to show the number of air passengers to Spain and Greece in 1993 and 1994; numbers are in thousands.

	1993				1994			
	1st Qtr	2nd Qtr	3rd Qtr	4th Qtr	1st Qtr	2nd Qtr	3rd Qtr	4th Qtr
Spain	1066	2857	4219	1932	1193	3543	5159	2263
Greece	120	1404	2407	617	176	1536	2556	694

What can you say about the number of passengers going to Spain and Greece over the two years? Is Spain doing better than Greece in comparison?

10 Draw two bar graphs on the same axes to show how the general index of retail prices has changed over the years. (January 1987 = 100)

	1989	1990	1991	1992	1993	1994
Retail prices (all items)	115.2	126.1	133.5	138.5	140.7	144.1
Tobacco and alcohol	110.8	120.6	136.2	148.8	155.1	161.4

11 Draw a bar graph to show the purchasing power of the £ since 1980.

	1980	1981	1982	1983	1984	1985	1986	1987	1988	1989	1990	1991	1992	1993	1994
Purchasing power	100	89	82	79	75	71	68	66	63	58	53	50	48	48	46

12 Draw two bar graphs on the same axes to show the number of divorced males and females in a particular age group over the years given.

	Males			Females		
	1971	1981	1991	1971	1981	1991
Age group 35–44 (thousands)	52	191	423	72	240	487

Can anything be deduced from these graphs about the rates of divorce for males and females?
Why are the figures for males and females not the same?

(The graphs in this exercise can also be used for practice in drawing line graphs.)

5 Pie Charts   A pie chart is a diagram in which a circle is divided into sectors. The size of each sector represents the proportion of the whole.

Worked example 10

Draw a pie chart to show a liquid containing 25% carbon, 40% hydrogen and 35% oxygen.

Carbon = 25%, hydrogen = 40%, oxygen = 35%. Total = 100%.

First, draw a circle of any radius between, say, 3 and 4 cm.
25% of this circle is to represent carbon.

In a circle there are 360°

$$1\% \text{ of the circle} = \frac{360°}{100}$$

$$25\% \text{ of the circle} = \frac{360}{100} \times 25 = 90°$$

$$40\% \text{ of the circle (hydrogen)} = \frac{360}{100} \times 40 = 144°$$

$$35\% \text{ of the circle (oxygen)} = \frac{360}{100} \times 35 = 126°$$

As a check, add up these figures to make sure the total comes to 360°. Draw a reference line from the centre of the circle to the circumference OX as in Figure 12.10. With OX as base line draw an angle of 90°, XOY. With OY as base line now draw an angle of 144°, YOZ. Check that the remaining angle, XOZ, is 126°. Label the chart. The completed pie chart is drawn as Figure 12.12.

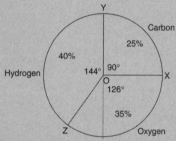

Figure 12.12 Elements contained in a liquid

Worked example 11

A small orchard has 10 apple trees, 8 pear trees, 4 cherry trees and 2 plum trees. Illustrate this on a pie chart.

Whole orchard = 24 trees (10 + 8 + 4 + 2)
The 24 trees have to be represented by a circle, 360°
24 trees = 360°

$$1 \text{ tree} = \frac{360°}{24} = 15°$$

10 trees = 150°
8 trees = 8 × 15° = 120°, 4 trees = 60°, 2 trees = 30°

Draw the pie chart divided into angles of 150°, 120°, 60°, 30°. The chart is shown as Figure 12.13.

Alternatively, the angles could have been calculated by a proportion sum.

Whole orchard = 24 trees

$$\text{Proportion of apple trees} = \frac{10}{24}$$

$$\text{Proportion of circle} = \frac{10}{24} \times 360° = 150°$$

The angles to represent the other trees could have been calculated in a similar way.

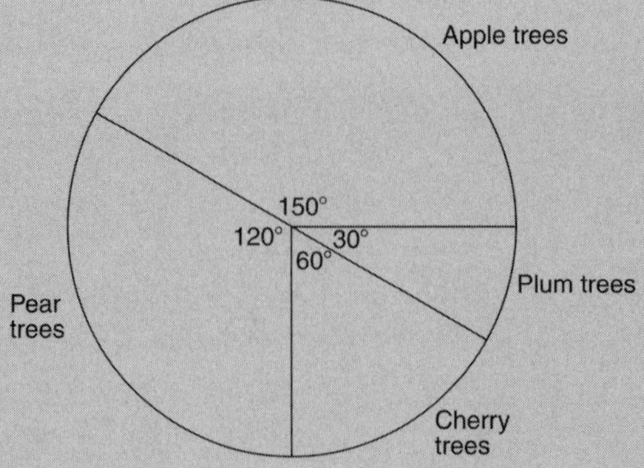

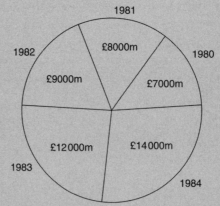

Figure 12.13 Trees in an orchard

Where figures are given, add them up to find the whole, and then find individual proportions.

Worked example 12

The amount of money out on hire purchase (credit agreements) and other credit for 1980 was £7000m, 1981 £8000m, 1982 £9000m, 1983 £12 000m and 1984 £14 000m.

Show this on a pie chart.

Total amount = £50 000m

$$\text{Proportion for 1980} = \frac{£7000m}{£50\,000m} = \frac{7}{50}$$

$$\text{Proportion of the circle} = \frac{7}{50} \times 360° = 50.4°$$

$$\text{Proportion for 1981} = \frac{£8000m}{£50\,000m} = \frac{8}{50}$$

$$\text{Angle} = \frac{8}{50} \times 360° = 57.6°$$

$$\text{Angle for 1982} = \frac{9}{50} \times 360° = 64.8°$$

Angle for 1983 = 86.4°. Angle for 1984 = 100.8°

Check that all these angles add up to 360°.
The pie chart is drawn as Figure 12.14.

Figure 12.14 Amount of money out on hire purchase and other credit

Exercise 3

1 Draw a pie chart to represent an adult language class of 8 males and 12 females.

2 Draw a pie chart to represent a farm having 40% arable land, 35% pasture land, and 25% woods and scrubland.

3 Draw a pie chart to represent a drink having 2 parts gin and 3 parts tonic.

4 Draw a pie chart to represent an alloy having 3 parts copper, 4 parts brass, and 3 parts zinc.

5 Draw a pie chart to represent turnover of a company to be 35% in the UK, 30% in America, 25% in Asia, and 10% in the rest of the world.

6 Draw a pie chart to represent the sales of a high street shop as 32% newspapers and magazines, 18% stationery and office supplies, 28% books, and 22% other items.

7 Draw 2 pie charts to represent the goals scored for and goals scored against for the top and bottom clubs of the Premier Football Division in 1994/95.

Blackburn Rovers	Goals for 80	Goals against 39
Ipswich	Goals for 36	Goals against 93

8 Notifiable offences in England and Wales for 1994 were, in thousands: violence against the person 58, sexual 9, burglary 310, robbery 14, and theft 652. Represent these offences on a pie chart. (Hints: Find out what each offence is as a percentage of the whole and draw the pie chart, or find what each offence is as a fraction of the whole and see what this fraction is of 360°.)

9 Draw a pie chart to show how the turnover of BAA was due to 35% traffic, 16% property, 3% cargo and freight, 43% retail, and other items 3%. If the total turnover for BAA in 1994 was £1.1 bn, how much was earned in the retail areas?

10 Draw a pie chart to represent the nuclear electricity industry's estimate of market share in 1996/97 as privatised nuclear company 22%, Magnox Company 8%, Electricité de France 5%, National Power 23%, Powergen 16%, independent power plants 21%, Scottish power/hydroelectrics 5%.

6 Pictograms

A pictogram is similar to a bar graph except that the bar is replaced by a simple drawing of the quantities being represented, and each drawing represents a stated amount.

Worked example 13

The figures below show the registration of new private cars (thousands) for 1994:

Month	Jan	Feb	Mar	Apr	May	Jun	Jul	Aug	Sept	Oct	Nov	Dec
New cars registered (thousands)	190.0	137.0	172.9	134.0	141.0	124.2	31.9	434.1	135.8	116.4	121.2	70.4

A pictogram of this data could be shown as in Figure 12.5 on the next page, with each drawing of a car representing 60 000 cars.

Pictograms such as this are often seen in daily newspapers; note that the 'pictures' usually go horizontally. It is not easy to draw small fractions of the picture, whether it is cigarettes, cars, ships, trees or whatever, and the actual values can be written alongside the pictures. Comparisons can be seen as easily as a bar graph.

7 Straight-line Graphs

A straight-line graph results when there is a definite fixed relationship between two quantities.

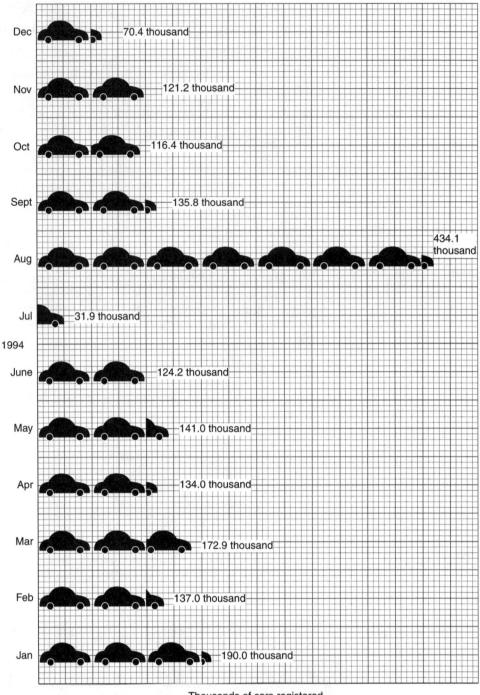

Thousands of cars registered

= 60 000 cars

Figure 12.15 Registration of new private cars for 1994 (for worked example 13)

Worked example 14   Draw a graph to show the relationship between pounds and dollars if £100 = $156.

Suitable scale: 1 cm = £10 horizontally
                1 cm = $10 vertically
An important fact for this type of graph is that you will receive no dollars for no pounds.
Start the scales at 0.
Put in the point for £100 = $156.
Join this point by a straight line to 0, 0. The point 0, 0 is called the **origin**.

This type of graph may be called a **conversion graph**, because it can be used for converting pounds to dollars and vice versa. The completed graph is shown as Figure 12.16.

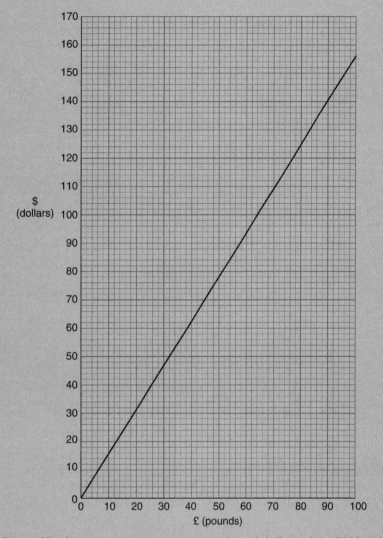

Figure 12.16 Relationship between pounds and dollars when £100 = $156

From the graph you can read off how many dollars for £30. How many for £70? How many for £45?
How many £s for 120 dollars? 90 dollars? 25 dollars?

A similar type of graph could be drawn for such things as 500 ballpoint pens cost £30 (remember 0 ballpoints = 0 charge), or 1 metre = 39.3 in (0 metres = 0 in).

Not all straight-line graphs go through the point 0, 0 (origin).

Worked example 15

A supplier offers to make metal brackets at a cost of 1000 for £250, on a pro rata basis, plus a fixed charge of £50. Draw a graph to show the costs of up to 1000 brackets.

Cost of 1000 brackets = £250 + £50 fixed charge = £300.
Cost of no brackets = £50 fixed charge.
These are the two points needed in order to draw the graph.
Scale: 1 cm = 100 brackets horizontally;
        1 cm = £25 vertically.
The completed graph is shown as Figure 12.17 on the next page.

Notice from the graph that 500 brackets cost more than half the cost of 1000 brackets.

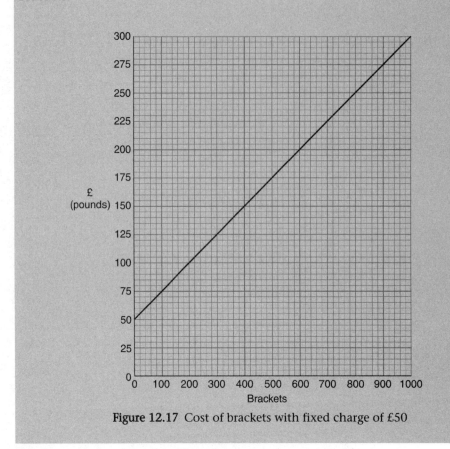

Figure 12.17 Cost of brackets with fixed charge of £50

8 Curved Graphs

When the points of a graph have been plotted, as in worked example 1, it may be that joining by straight lines is not the best solution – some graphs suggest that a smooth curve can be drawn through the points.

Worked example 16

A *Leylandii* tree was 2 ft high when planted, and its height was measured every 5 years. Draw a smooth curved graph to show the relationship between its height and age.

Years after planting	0	5	10	15	20	25	30
Height in ft	2	21	39	53	64	71	76

Scale: 2 cm = 5 yr horizontally;
        2 cm = 10 ft vertically.

The completed graph is shown in Figure 12.18 opposite. From this graph you can estimate what the height was after 8 yr, 17 yr, 22 yr, etc., or how long it took to reach 30 ft, 50 ft, 70 ft, and so on.

Worked example 17

When a number is multiplied by itself the results are as follows:

Number	0	1	2	3	4	5	6	7	8	9	10
Number multiplied by itself	0	1	4	9	16	25	36	49	64	81	100

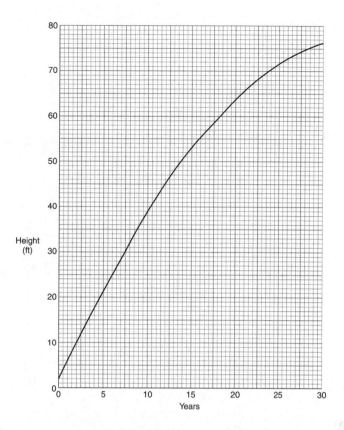

Figure 12.18 Growth of a tree (for worked example 16)

Plot a smooth curved graph to show the relationship between a number and the result of multiplying the number by itself.

The completed graph is shown in Figure 12.19 on the next page.

Exercise 4

1 Draw a straight-line graph to show the relationship between miles and kilometres if 50 miles = 81 km. From the graph find (a) how many km in 35 miles and (b) how many miles in 25 km.

2 Draw a graph using the fact that 640 acres (1 square mile) = 259 hectares. From the graph find (a) how many hectares in 200 acres and (b) how many acres in 200 hectares.

3 Draw a graph using the fact that 1 gallon (8 pints) = 4.55 litres so that the graph can be used to show up to 12 gallons. From the graph find (a) how many litres in 8.5 gallons and (b) how many gallons in 40 litres.

4 Draw a graph using the fact that 2240 lb (1 ton) = 1016 kg. From the graph find (a) how many kg in 1000 lb and (b) how many lb in 90 kg.

5 In June 1995 £500 = 3800 French francs. Draw a graph to show this relationship. From the graph find (a) how many £ you would receive for 200 francs and (b) how many francs for £180.

6 In June 1995 £400 was worth 620 American dollars. Draw a graph to illustrate this fact. From the graph find (a) how many £ you would receive for 400 dollars and (b) how many dollars for £320.

7 0 °C = 32 °F and 100 °C = 212 °F. Draw a straight-line graph connecting

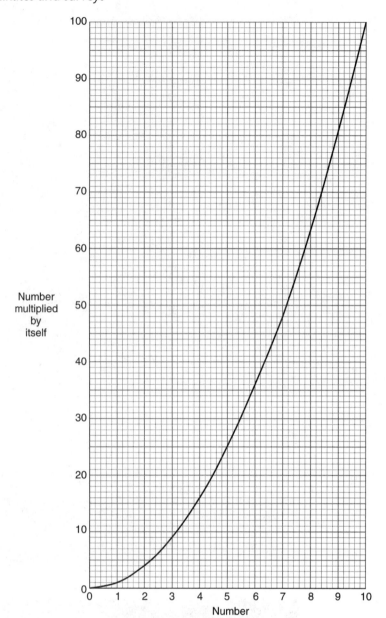

Figure 12.19 Graph to show the relationship between a number and the number multiplied by itself (for worked example 17)

these two facts. From the graph find (a) what 37 °C is in °F and (b) what 70 °F is in °C. Can you also say what 0 °F is in °C?

8   A supplier offers to make hinges at a cost of 1000 for £150, on a pro rata basis, plus a fixed charge of £40. Draw a graph to show the costs of up to 1000 hinges. From the graph find (a) how much 400 hinges cost and (b) how much 100 cost.

9   When a number is multiplied by itself 3 times (this is known as the cube of the number) the results are as follows:

Number	0	1	2	3	4	5	6	7	8	9	10
Number multiplied by itself 3 times	0	1	8	27	64	125	216	343	512	729	1000

Draw a smooth graph to illustrate these facts. From the graph find how much is (a) 3.5 multiplied by itself 3 times (b) 7.5 multiplied by itself 3 times and (c) what number multiplied by itself 3 times gives 600.

10 A tree was measured in height every 2 years with the following results:

Age of tree (years)	2	4	6	8	10	12	14	16
Height (metres)	0.8	1.9	2.7	3.2	3.7	4.1	4.4	4.6

Draw a smooth curved graph to show the results.

9 Substitution

Later in this chapter we shall be looking at simple algebraic graphs. First, we shall consider some simple algebra.

Symbols or letters can be used sometimes in place of numbers. Even when you have letters, they still follow the pattern of arithmetic.

$a + b$ means a plus b; $\dfrac{a}{b}$ means $a \div b$

$a - b$ means a minus b

$a \times b$ means a multiplied by b, and this is usually written ab

$4b$ means $4 \times b$

Using these facts it is possible to substitute given numbers in place of symbols.

Worked example 18

Find the value of $a + b$ if $a = 7$ and $b = 6$.

To find the value we substitute the value 7 wherever we see a and substitute 6 wherever we see b.

$a + b = 7 + 6 = 13$
Answer 13

Worked example 19

If $a = 7$ and $b = 6$ find the value of $2a + 3b$.

In $2a + 3b$ write down what each term means:

$2a$ means $2 \times a$, $\qquad 3b$ means $3 \times b$

Now substitute the values $a = 7$ and $b = 6$:
$$\begin{aligned} 2a + 3b &= 2 \times a + 3 \times b \\ &= 2 \times 7 + 3 \times 6 \\ &= 14 + 18 \\ &= 32 \end{aligned}$$
Answer 32

Worked example 20

Find the value of the following expressions if $r = 2$, $s = 3$, $t = 4$:

(a) $3r + 5s - 2t$ $\qquad$ (b) $\dfrac{3r + 5t}{2}$

(a) $\quad 3r + 5s - 2t = 3 \times r + 5 \times s - 2 \times t$
Now substitute the values given:
$$\begin{aligned} &= 3 \times 2 + 5 \times 3 - 2 \times 4 \\ &= 6 + 15 - 8 \\ &= 13 \end{aligned}$$
Answer 13

(b) $\quad \dfrac{3r + 5t}{2} = \dfrac{3 \times r + 5 \times t}{2}$

Substitute the values given:
$$= \dfrac{3 \times 2 + 5 \times 4}{2}$$
$$= \dfrac{6 + 20}{2}$$
Answer 13

Exercise 5

If $a = 3$, $b = 4$, $c = 2$, $d = 7$, find the value of

1 $4a$	**2** $5c$	**3** $2a + 3d$
4 $4b + 2c$	**5** $3a + 2b + d$	**6** $3c + 4b + 2a$
7 $5b - 2d$	**8** $2a + b - 3c$	**9** $5d - 2b + a$

10 $3b - c - 2a$ **11** $\dfrac{2a + b}{2}$ **12** $\dfrac{3b + 2d}{2}$

13 $\dfrac{2b + d}{a}$ **14** $\dfrac{3d + a}{2b}$ **15** $\dfrac{5b - c}{2\,a}$

16 $\dfrac{4a + 3b + 2c}{2d}$

10 Further Substitution

$a \times b$ can be written as ab

$a \times b \times c$ can be written as abc

Where the letter (symbol) is multiplied by itself, such as $a \times a$, it can be written a^2 (a squared).

Similarly, $b \times b = b^2$ (b squared).

The substitution of values is made easy if you remember what is meant by each expression. For example, $2x^2$ means $2 \times x^2$.

Worked example 21

Find the value of the following expressions if $x = 3$, $y = 2$:
(a) $4y$ (b) x^2 (c) $2x + y^2$ (d) $2x^2$ (e) $3x^2 - 2y^2$

In each case write down what each term means:
(a) $4y = 4 \times y$
Substitute the value $y = 2$; then
$4y = 4 \times y = 4 \times 2 = 8$
Answer 8
(b) $x^2 = x \times x$ Now substitute $x = 3$
       $= 3 \times 3 = 9$
Answer 9
(c) $2x + y^2 = 2 \times x + y \times y$ Substitute $x = 3$, $y = 2$
       $= 2 \times 3 + 2 \times 2$
       $= 6 + 4 = 10$
Answer 10

(d) $2x^2 = 2 \times x^2 = 2 \times x \times x$
              $= 2 \times 3 \times 3$ since $x = 3$.
              $= 18$
Answer 18

(e) $3x^2 - 2y^2 = 3 \times x \times x - 2 \times y \times y$
            $= 3 \times 3 \times 3 - 2 \times 2 \times 2$ $x = 3$, $y = 2$
            $= 27 - 8$
            $= 19$
Answer 19

Worked example 22

Find the value of the following expressions if $r = 4$, $s = 3$, $t = 2$.

(a) $3r + 5s - 2t$ (b) $\dfrac{3r + 2s}{3}$ (c) $\dfrac{3r^2}{2t}$ (d) rs^2 (e) $\dfrac{2r^2 + 8s}{t + 2}$

(a) $3r + 5s - 2t = 3 \times r + 5 \times s - 2 \times t$
                 $= 3 \times 4 + 5 \times 3 - 2 \times 2$
                 $= 12 + 15 - 4$
                 $= 23$

Answer 23

(b) $\dfrac{3r+2s}{3} = \dfrac{3 \times r + 2 \times s}{3} = \dfrac{3 \times 4 + 2 \times 3}{3}$

$$= \dfrac{12+6}{3} = \dfrac{18}{3} = 6$$

Answer 6

(c) $\dfrac{3r^2}{2t} = \dfrac{3 \times r \times r}{2 \times t} = \dfrac{3 \times 4 \times 4}{2 \times 2} = \dfrac{48}{4} = 12$

Answer 12

(d) $rs^2 = r \times s \times s$
    $= 4 \times 3 \times 3 = 36$

Answer 36

(e) $\dfrac{2r^2 + 8s}{t+2} = \dfrac{2 \times r \times r + 8 \times s}{t+2}$

$$= \dfrac{2 \times 4 \times 4 + 8 \times 3}{2+2}$$

$$= \dfrac{32+24}{4} = 14$$

Answer 14

Exercise 6

1 If $a = 3$, $b = 2$, $c = 5$, find the value of
   (a) $3b + 2c$ (b) $5b - c$ (c) $4a + 2c - 3b$
   (d) $5c - 3a - 4b$ (e) $2c - 2a - 2b$

2 If $r = 4$, $s = 1$, $t = 3$, find the value of
   (a) t^2 (b) $2r^2$ (c) $4s + 2t^2$
   (d) $5t - 4s + 2r^2$ (e) rst

3 If $x = 4$, $y = 2$, $z = 5$, find the value of
   (a) $4x + \dfrac{2z}{y}$ (b) $\dfrac{3x + 4z}{2y}$ (c) $2xy + 3yz$
   (d) $\dfrac{4z^2}{2x + y}$ (e) $2xy + 4xz + 2z - 2xzy$

4 If $a = 3$, $b = 1$, $c = 4$, $d = 6$, find the value of
   (a) $2a^2 + cd$ (b) $ab + 2bc + d$ (c) $acd + 2c^2 - d^2$
   (d) $bcd - 2bd + a^2$ (e) $c^2b + 3ac - cd + 4b$

11 Formulae and Equations

ab is an expression but if we put $R = ab$ (R equals ab) then we have an **equation**. This could be called a **formula**.

Worked example 23

A gas bill used to show the following information:

Cost of gas = standing charge plus   (the price of a therm times the number of therms used)
= standing charge + price of a therm × number of therms

If c = cost of gas, s = standing charge (£), t = price of a therm (£) and n = number of therms used, then $c = s + tn$, and this formula was used for working out all gas bills.

Similarly, the cost of electricity was expressed as $E = s + np$, where E = cost of electricity, s = standing charge (£), p = cost per unit (£) and n = number of units used.

(Now look at an up-to-date gas/electricity bill to see the considerable changes, including the addition of VAT, as described in Chapter 11.)

Worked example 24 Find a formula for the salary of a salesman, which consists of a basic salary plus 20% commission on all sales.

Salary = basic salary + 20% commission on all sales
$S = B + 20\% \ C$ where S = salary (£)
$S = B + 0.2 \ C$ B = basic salary (£)
                           C = all sales (£)

Answer $S = B + 0.2C$

Worked example 25 Find a formula for temperature in Fahrenheit, if Fahrenheit temperature is $\frac{9}{5}$ of Celsius temperature plus 32.

Fahrenheit temperature = $\frac{9}{5}$ of Celsius temperature + 32
               $F = \frac{9}{5}$ of C + 32   where F = Fahrenheit temperature
                                          C = Celsius temperature

Answer $F = \frac{9}{5}C + 32$

Given a formula it is easy to substitute values into that formula.

Worked example 26 If $F = \frac{9}{5}C + 32$ find F when $C = 20$.

$$F = \frac{9 \times 20}{5} + 32$$

$$= 36 + 32$$
$$= 68$$
Answer $F = 68$ when $C = 20$

Worked example 27 If $S = \left(\dfrac{U + V}{2}\right) \times t$ find S when $U = 8$, $V = 12$, $t = 6$.

As for arithmetic, first work out the brackets when the values have been substituted.

$$S = \left(\frac{8 + 12}{2}\right) \times 6$$

$$= \left(\frac{20}{2}\right) \times 6$$

$$= 10 \times 6$$
$$= 60$$
Answer $S = 60$

Exercise 7

1 Find a formula for the salary of a salesperson at Marks & Spencer who gets a basic salary plus 10% commission on all sales.

2 Find a formula for the final cost if it is equal to cost of production plus cost of distribution plus profit.

3 Find the formula for the perimeter of a rectangle if it is equal to twice the length of the long side plus twice the length of the short side.

4 Find a formula for the voltage of a circuit if it equals current times resistance.

5   Find a formula for the speed of a vehicle if it equals distance travelled divided by the time taken.

6   If $F = \frac{9}{5}C + 32$ find F when $C = 30$.

7   If $v = u + ft$ find v when $u = 5$, $f = 3$, $t = 6$.

8   If $C = S + BT$ find C when $S = 10$, $B = 0.15$, $T = 300$.

9   If $I = \dfrac{PRT}{100}$ find I when $P = 500$, $R = 2$, $T = 3$.

10 If $s = \dfrac{(u + v)}{2} \times t$ find s when $u = 4$, $v = 16$, $t = 5$.

12 Coordinates, Maps and Grid references

Coordinates

Chapter 1 made reference to the number line, and it was drawn horizontally. Similarly, we can have a vertical number line, and combining the two, together with the x-axis and y-axis as in section 1, we have the following:

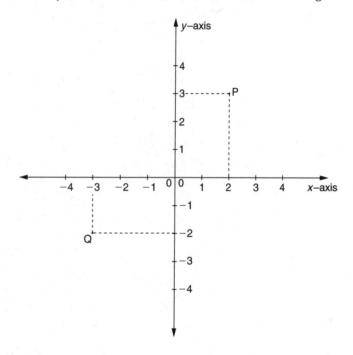

Starting at the origin, any point on this graph can be found if we know how far to go horizontally and then how far to go vertically. By doing this we use what are known as **coordinates**. For instance, where is a point whose coordinates are (2, 3)? The first number (2) gives the horizontal distance from the origin, and the second number (3) gives the vertical distance from the origin. It is marked on the drawing as P.

The point Q is (−3, −2)

Note: The origin on this drawing is now 0, 0.

Exercise 8

From the graph in Figure 12.20 on the next page give the coordinates of the points denoted by capital letters.

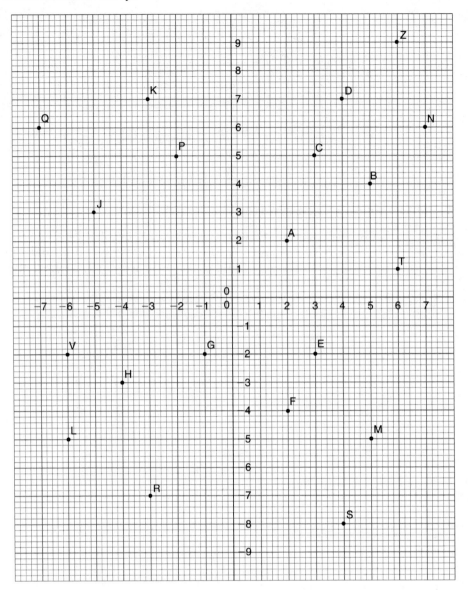

Figure 12.20 Graph for exercise 8

Maps and grid references

In Chapter 7, section 3, we saw how the scale of a map is referred to as
1 : 25 000, 1 : 50 000 or 1 : 100 000 etc. Look at any map and notice the
numbered horizontal lines and vertical lines. This means that coordinates can be
given, as with graphs, and the position of any place can be given accurately. The
horizontal coordinate is given first followed by the vertical coordinate. Anything
between the main coordinates has to be estimated, in tenths, in order to
pinpoint a particular place.

The drawing in Figure 12.21 opposite gives the main coordinates of the
Ordnance Survey 1 : 25 000 Burton in Kendal & Caton map. Note there is no 0, 0
on this particular grid. The grids recur every 100 km.

When going horizontally you have to estimate, in tenths, how far a point is
between 55 and 56. If you think it is about 6 tenths along then the coordinate is
556.

Going vertically you estimate, again in tenths, how far a point is between 69 and
70. If you think it is about 2 tenths then the coordinate is 692. The **grid
reference** is now given as 556692. This is a place called Netherby.

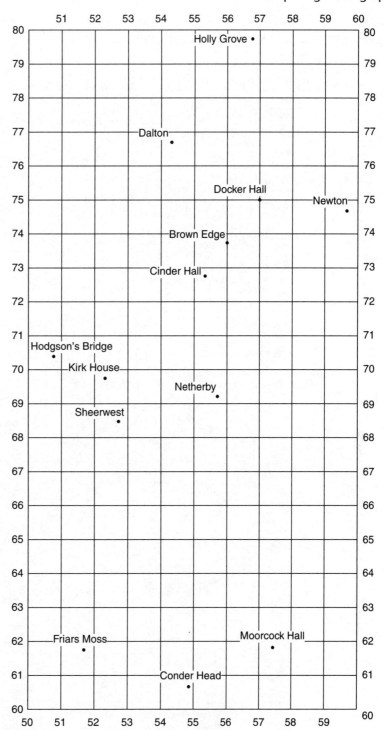

Figure 12.21 Main coordinates of the Ordnance Survey 1: 25 000 Burton in Kendal & Caton map

Can you give the grid references for

1	Conder Head	2	Friars Moss	3	Moorcock Hall
4	Holly Grove	5	Sheerwest	6	Dalton
7	Docker Hall	8	Newton	9	Brown Edge
10	Cinder Hall	11	Hodgson's Bridge	12	Kirk House

Road atlas

This may still be in a scale of miles to the inch; nevertheless, each numbered page has a particular grid, and so places can be given an accurate reference.

13 Simple Algebraic Graphs   These graphs stem from an expression using symbols where certain values have to be substituted into the expression.

Worked example 28

Using values of x from 1 to 10, plot a graph of $y = 2x$.

$y = 2x$ is called an **equation** (y equals $2x$), and will always be true.
First, if $x = 1$ what does y equal?

$y = 2x$ so when $x = 1$, $y = 2 \times x = 2 \times 1 = 2$

When $x = 2$, $y = 2x = 2 \times x = 2 \times 2 = 4$
$\quad\quad x = 3$, $y = 2 \times 3 = 6$ and so on
Notice that if $x = 0$, then $y = 2 \times 0 = 0$.

You may find it easier to put the results in the form of a table as follows:

Value of x	0	1	2	3	4	5	6	7	8	9	10
$y = 2x$	0	2	4	6	8	10	12	14	16	18	20

The graph is drawn by always putting values of x horizontally, and values of y vertically.
Scale: 1 cm = 1 unit for x, horizontally
$\quad\quad$ 1 cm = 1 unit for y, vertically.
The completed graph is shown in Figure 12.22.

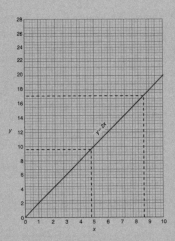

Figure 12.22 Graph of $y = 2x$

When the points are plotted it is easy to see that they are all in a straight line. Compare it with Figure 12.2. Notice that, having drawn the graph, you can use it to read off the value of y for any value of x, and vice versa.

For example, what is y when $x = 8.6$?
Answer $y = 17.2$ when $x = 8.6$ (the dotted lines show the 'reading off')
What is the value of x when $y = 9.6$?
Answer $x = 4.8$ when $y = 9.6$

Worked example 29

A relationship will often involve a number as well as x and y. Using values of x from 1 to 10, draw the graph of $y = 2x + 7$. Give values to x of 1, 2, 3, 4, etc.

For $x = 1$, $y = 2x + 7 = 2 \times 1 + 7 = 2 + 7 = 9$
$\quad\quad x = 2$, $y = 2x + 7 = 2 \times 2 + 7 = 4 + 7 = 11$
$\quad\quad x = 3$, $y = 2x + 7 = 2 \times 3 + 7 = 6 + 7 = 13$
Note, when $x = 0$ then $y = 7$.

Continuing the values of x produces the following table:

Value of x	0	1	2	3	4	5	6	7	8	9	10
$y = 2x$	0	2	4	6	8	10	12	14	16	18	20
+7	+7	+7	+7	+7	+7	+7	+7	+7	+7	+7	+7
$y = 2x + 7$	7	9	11	13	15	17	19	21	23	25	27

Try and keep the number separate in the table because it does not alter no matter what the value of x is.

Scale: 1 cm = 1 unit for x horizontally;
    1 cm = 2 units for y vertically.

The completed graph is shown as Figure 12.23. Notice the close resemblance of this graph to Figure 12.22.

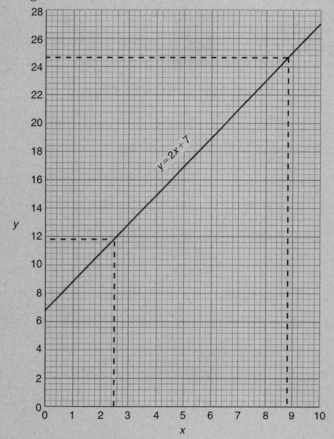

Figure 12.23 Graph of $y = 2x + 7$

What is the value of y when $x = 2.4$?
Answer: y = 11.8 when x = 2.4.
What is the value of x when $y = 24.6$?
Answer: x = 8.8 when y = 24.6.

Worked example 30   **There are negative numbers as well as positive numbers.**
Draw the graph of $y = 2x - 10$ from $x = 0$ to $x = 10$.

Values of x from $x = 0$ to $x = 10$ produce the following table for $y = 2x - 10$:

Value of x	0	1	2	3	4	5	6	7	8	9	10
$y = 2x$	0	2	4	6	8	10	12	14	16	18	20
−10	−10	−10	−10	−10	−10	−10	−10	−10	−10	−10	−10
$y = 2x - 10$	−10	−8	−6	−4	−2	0	+2	+4	+6	+8	+10

Scale: 1 cm = 1 unit for x horizontally;
 1 cm = 1 unit for y vertically.

The completed graph is shown as Figure 12.24 on the next page.

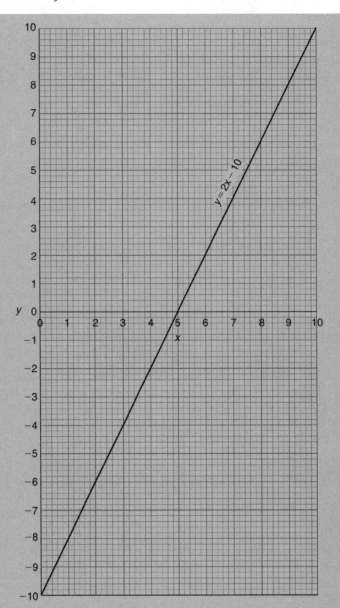

Figure 12.24 Graph of $y = 2x - 10$

To accommodate the value of y going from -10 to $+10$ the x-axis is drawn in the middle of the paper.

Worked example 31   Draw the graph of $y = 15 - 3x$ from $x = 0$ to $x = 10$.

Using the values of x given produces the following table of results for $y = 15 - 3x$:

Value of x	0	1	2	3	4	5	6	7	8	9	10
$y = 15$	15	15	15	15	15	15	15	15	15	15	15
$-3x$	0	-3	-6	-9	-12	-15	-18	-21	-24	-27	-30
$y = 15 - 3x$	15	12	9	6	3	0	-3	-6	-9	-12	-15

The completed graph is shown as Figure 12.25 on the next page. Note how the graph 'slopes' the other way.

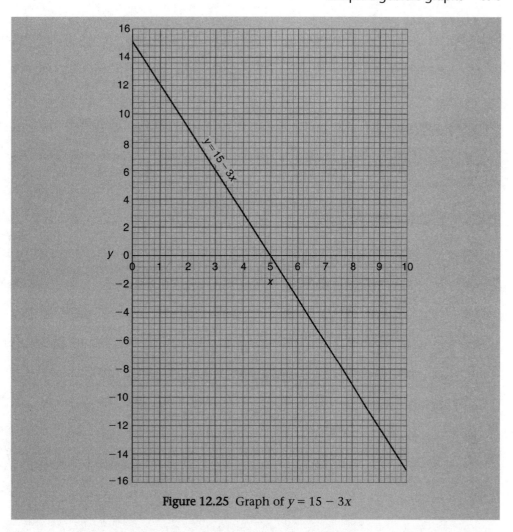

Figure 12.25 Graph of $y = 15 - 3x$

Exercise 9

1 Draw a graph of $y = x$ for values of $x = 0$ to $x = 12$. From the graph find the values of y when $x = 2.5$, 7.5, 3.6 and 8.4.

2 Draw the graph of $y = 4x$ for values of $x = 0$ to $x = 10$. From the graph find the values of y when $x = 0.8$, 3.9 and 6.6.

3 Draw the graph of $y = x + 9$ for values of $x = 0$ to $x = 10$. From the graph find the values of y when $x = 2.5$, 4.7 and 7.5.

4 Draw the graph of $y = 3x + 2$ for values of $x = 0$ to $x = 10$. From the graph find the values of y when $x = 3.5$, 5.8, and 8.2.

5 Draw the graph of $y = 2x - 8$ for values of $x = 0$ to $x = 12$. From the graph find the values of y when $x = 0.6$, 4.2 and 10.4.

6 Draw the graph of $y = 4x - 9$ for values of $x = 0$ to $x = 12$. From the graph find the values of y when $x = 1.4$, 4.7 and 9.3.

7 Draw the graph of $y = 25 - 4x$ for values of $x = 0$ to $x = 12$. From the graph find the values of y when $x = 2.3$, 6.25 and 8.2.

8 Draw the graph of $a = 2b + 6$ for values of $b = 0$ to $b = 20$. From the graph find the values of a when $b = 4.7$, 12.5 and 16.2.

9 Draw the graph of $y = 15 - 2x$ for values of $x = 0$ to $x = 12$. From the graph find the values of y when $x = 1.8$, 5.2 and 9.8.

10 Draw the graph of $y = 5x - 8$ for values of $x = 0$ to $x = 12$. From the graph find the values of y when $x = 0.8$, 3.6 and 10.2.

14 Data and Graphs

A dictionary says that data is a series of observations, measurements, or facts, information. Data can be used graphically, which may make it easier to understand.

Worked example 32

A primary school year of 56 pupils had a simple test a few days before a national 7+ test. These were the scores of the 56 pupils, who were listed in alphabetical order:
7, 10, 4, 6, 8, 0, 6, 9, 2, 5, 5, 7, 8, 3, 1, 4, 5, 7, 5, 7, 9, 4, 6, 7, 5, 4, 8, 2, 8, 2, 4, 1, 5, 5, 7, 9, 6, 6, 4, 5, 2, 5, 8, 6, 7, 3, 5, 3, 5, 2, 7, 7, 4, 6, 3, 6
What do you make of these?

First, set about putting them into some sort of order. What is the range of scores? They range from 0 to 10. Count the number of each score. A common way to do this is to use a **tally chart**. A tally mark is 1; 111 is a count of 3, ~~1111~~ is a count of 5, one tally mark being used to collect them altogether. A tally chart for these scores would be as shown below.

Score	Tally	How often same score occurs
0	1	1
1	11	2
2	~~1111~~	5
3	1111	4
4	~~1111~~ 11	7
5	~~1111~~ ~~1111~~ 1	11
6	~~1111~~ 111	8
7	~~1111~~ 1111	9
8	~~1111~~	5
9	111	3
10	1	1

Notice how the tally ~~1111~~ makes it easy to count in 5s. How often the same score occurs is called the **frequency**: that is, a score of 5 occurs 11 times. The majority of scores are distributed round the half-way mark, and it is this frequency distribution that is so important.

The frequencies can now be used to produce a bar chart: a common method for all forms of statistics.

The bar chart is shown in Figure 12.26 opposite.

If you are taking an examination this year it is likely that your examination mark will be used in a similar way, but the examination board will be using a computer and not a tally chart! It will tend to show that the majority of entrants have about half-marks.

Worked example 33

Look at the paragraph at the beginning of this section, where it says 'A dictionary says that data is a series of observations, measurements or facts, information. Data can be used graphically, which may make it easier to understand'.

What is the frequency of the letters in this paragraph?

The tally chart would be as shown in Figure 12.27 opposite.

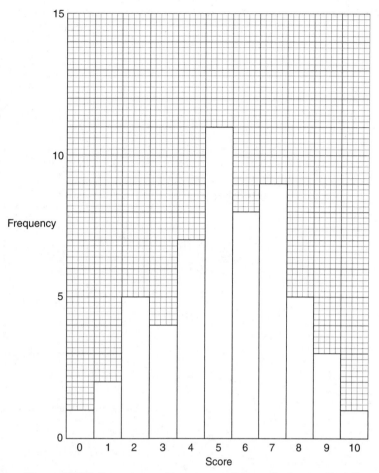

Figure 12.26 Frequency of test scores (for worked example 32)

Letter	Tally	Frequency	Letter	Tally	Frequency
a	~~1111~~ ~~1111~~ ~~1111~~ ~~1111~~	20	n	~~1111~~ 111	8
b	11	2	o	~~1111~~ 111	8
c	~~1111~~	5	p	1	1
d	~~1111~~ 1	6	q	0	0
e	~~1111~~ ~~1111~~ 11	12	r	~~1111~~ 1111	9
f	111	3	s	~~1111~~ ~~1111~~ 111	13
g	1	1	t	~~1111~~ ~~1111~~ 11	12
h	1111	4	u	111	3
i	~~1111~~ ~~1111~~ 1	11	v	1	1
j	0	0	w	1	1
k	1	1	x	0	0
l	11	2	y	1111	4
m	~~1111~~	5	z	0	0

Figure 12.27 Tally chart (for worked example 33)

Now pick out the letters in order of frequency:

a	20 times	d	6 times
s	13 times	c, m	5 times
e, t	12 times	h, y	4 times
i	11 times	f, u	3 times
r	9 times	b, l	2 times
n, o	8 times	g, k, p, v, w	1 times
		j, x, z, q	0 times

For the resulting bar chart pick out the letters that occur most frequently and arrange for these to form the middle bars of the chart. Arrange the other frequencies, in order, from the middle bars on either side.

The resulting bar chart is shown in Figure 12.28 on the next page.

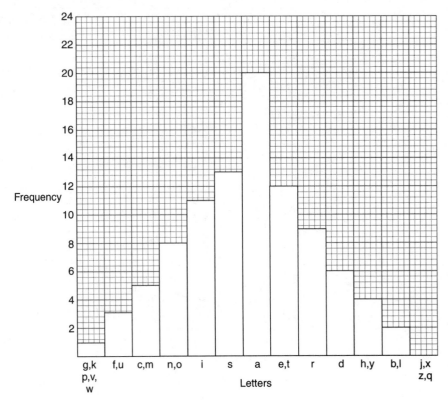

Figure 12.28 Frequency of alphabetical letters in a paragraph

Important check

In worked examples 32 and 33 data is translated into a tally chart. In worked example 32 there were 56 scores; notice how the total of all the frequencies was also 56, i.e. *none was missed out*. In worked example 33 the number of letters in the paragraph was 132, and, again, notice how the total of all the frequencies of letters was also 132.

Whenever you are analysing data and you have a resulting tally chart, or table, or graph, or diagram, make sure that you have not missed out anything.

Exercise 10

1 These are the marks, maximum 25, from a class of 42 students:
   13, 18, 14, 13, 13, 11, 16, 9, 13, 12, 14, 10, 13, 14, 15, 12, 12, 11, 15, 10, 13,
   12, 13, 15, 12, 13, 11, 13, 16, 14, 13, 12, 16, 13, 15, 11, 14, 13, 13, 12, 14,
   12.
   Make a tally chart and then a frequency distribution. Represent the frequency distribution on a bar chart.

2 Tests on cars travelling at 60 mile/h gave these stopping distances when full brakes were applied (distances to nearest 10 ft):
   240, 230, 260, 240, 270, 240, 260, 250, 250, 240, 230, 270, 240, 250, 230,
   270, 240, 250, 260, 240, 240, 260, 250, 250, 240.
   Draw a tally chart and frequency distribution for this set of tests. Draw a bar chart to show the frequency distribution.

3 A similar test was carried out for cars travelling at 30 mile/h, and the stopping distances in ft were:
   40, 45, 42, 37, 38, 43, 47, 40, 32, 43, 53, 39, 45, 51, 35, 40, 50, 41, 46, 40,
   42, 45, 41, 47, 41
   Using these distances complete the following table:

Distances (ft)	Tally	Frequency
31–34		
35–38		
39–42		
43–46		
47–50		
51–54		

The groupings 31–34, 35–38, etc., are called **classes**. Draw a bar chart to show the frequency distribution.

4 In 1993, the age distribution for the UK, in thousands, was given as:

	Age groups							
	15–19	20–29	30–44	45–49	60–64	65–74	75–84	85+
Number in age groups (thousands)	3430	9061	12 313	10 670	2839	5169	3020	982

Draw a bar chart to show the frequency distribution of age groups.

5 The census of 1991 gave the following facts for the number of marriages, in thousands, in different age groups:

	Age groups				
	15–19	20–24	25–34	35–44	45–54
Number of marriages (thousands)					
Males	7	284	2346	3011	2641
Females	37	576	2815	3124	2632

Draw a bar chart to show the frequency distribution by age group of marriages for males and females; use the same axes.

6 Using the first paragraph of section 3 (p 146) from 'A bar graph ...' to '... lists of data', draw a bar chart to show the frequency distribution of letters in the paragraph.

15 Questionnaires, Surveys and Results

Hardly a day goes by without the results of a questionnaire or survey being published.

Some surveys can be carried out by simple observation. For example, how much traffic passes along the main road nearest to you? Easy. Just stand there and count.

But now this can become as complicated as you like, depending on how general or specific you want to be. Over which half-hour is the road busiest? Over which half-hour is it quietest? How many cars pass? Are they English cars or foreign cars? How many lorries pass? How many buses?

Once there is more than one question the results need to be tabulated as shown in the following worked examples (have the table prepared before going out).

Worked example 34

Find out how many cars (saloons, estates, English, foreign), how many lorries (up to 6 wheels, over 6 wheels), how many buses pass on a Tuesday morning along the A6 at the junction of the B5269. Traffic going in a northerly direction.

Two students: one to record, one to call out what is passing.

The resulting tally chart is shown in Figure 12.29, and the results of the traffic survey at the junction of the A6 and B5259 are given in Figure 12.30.

Date: 13 June 1995			Time	
	9am — 9.30am	9.30 — 10.00	10.00 — 10.30	10.30 — 11.00
English cars: Saloons	~~1111~~ ~~1111~~ ~~1111~~ ~~1111~~ ~~1111~~ ~~1111~~ ~~1111~~ ~~1111~~ ~~1111~~ ~~1111~~ ~~1111~~ ~~1111~~ ~~1111~~ ~~1111~~ ~~1111~~ ~~1111~~ ~~1111~~ ~~1111~~ 111	~~1111~~ ~~1111~~ ~~1111~~ ~~1111~~ ~~1111~~ ~~1111~~ ~~1111~~ ~~1111~~ ~~1111~~ ~~1111~~ ~~1111~~ ~~1111~~ ~~1111~~ 11	~~1111~~ ~~1111~~ ~~1111~~ ~~1111~~ ~~1111~~ ~~1111~~ ~~1111~~ ~~1111~~ ~~1111~~ 111	~~1111~~ ~~1111~~ ~~1111~~ ~~1111~~ ~~1111~~ ~~1111~~ ~~1111~~ ~~1111~~ ~~1111~~ ~~1111~~ 111
Estates	~~1111~~ ~~1111~~ ~~1111~~ ~~1111~~ ~~1111~~ ~~1111~~ ~~1111~~ 1111	~~1111~~ ~~1111~~ ~~1111~~ 111	~~1111~~ ~~1111~~ 1	111
Foreign cars: Saloons	~~1111~~ ~~1111~~ ~~1111~~ ~~1111~~ ~~1111~~ ~~1111~~	~~1111~~ ~~1111~~ ~~1111~~ 111	~~1111~~ ~~1111~~ 1	~~1111~~ 11
Estates	~~1111~~ ~~1111~~ 11	~~1111~~ 111	1111	1111
Lorries Up to 6 wheels	~~1111~~ 111	~~1111~~ ~~1111~~ 11	~~1111~~ 11	111
Lorries Over 6 wheels	~~1111~~	111	111	11
Buses	1111	11	11	11

Figure 12.29 Worked example 34: tally chart for traffic survey

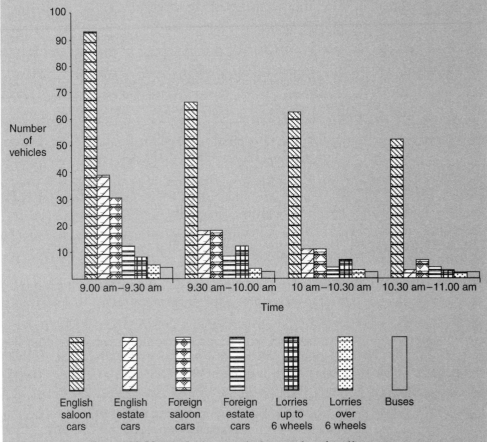

Figure 12.30 Worked example 34: results of traffic survey

(a)   Roughly, what is the proportion of foreign cars to English cars between 9 a.m. and 9.30 a.m.?

(b)   Roughly, what is the proportion of all estate cars to all saloon cars between 9 a.m. and 9.30 a.m.?

(c)   Roughly, what is the proportion of lorries in total traffic between 9 a.m. and 11 a.m.?

(d)   Roughly, what is the proportion of cars in total traffic between 9 a.m. and 10 a.m.?

(a) Number of foreign cars 9 a.m.–9.30 a.m. = 42
Number of English cars 9 a.m.–9.30 a.m. = 132
Proportion of foreign cars to English cars = 42 : 132
Roughly, 1 : 3
(b) Number of all estate cars 9 a.m.–9.30 a.m. = 51
Number of all saloon cars 9 a.m.–9.30 a.m. = 123
Proportion of estate cars to saloon cars = 51 : 123
Roughly, 2 : 5
(c) Number of lorries 9 a.m.–11 a.m. = 43
Number of total traffic 9 a.m. 11 a.m. = 493
Proportion of lorries to total traffic = 43 : 493
Roughly, 1 : 12
(d) Number of cars 9 a.m.–10 a.m. = 285
Total traffic 9 a.m.~10 a.m. = 319
Proportion of cars to total traffic = 285 : 319
Roughly, 9 : 10

The business section of a newspaper once suggested that, if you are thinking of buying a shop, one thing you should do over different periods of time, over different days, is simply stand outside the shop and count the number of customers that go into the shop!

The following exercise gives some suggestions for observational surveys. (Have your tabulations all prepared before going out.) Two students to each survey.

Exercise 11

1 How many people go into the local post office on a Monday morning? (Make sure all entrances are covered, and do not bother about people coming out.) How many are male? How many are female? How many, in your opinion, are over 60 and how many below 60? Draw a bar chart of the results, with number of people on the vertical scale.

2 Over a period of 2 hours, say, what is the most popular colour of car passing on the main road near you? Choose main colours such as red, blue, white, etc., so that red would cover maroon, cherry, cerise etc. Draw a bar chart of the results using number of cars for the vertical scale. Find the percentage of main colour to total cars.

3 Find a small residential estate. Count the number of dwellings by finding out how many are detached bungalows, semi-detached bungalows, detached houses, semi-detached houses, and terraced houses. Draw a bar chart using number of dwellings for the vertical scale. Find the percentage of bungalows on the estate.

4 On a summer morning for those going through the main entrance of a college find out the main colours being worn for shirt, T-shirt, blouse, sweatshirt etc., for males and females. Draw a bar chart of the results. What is the most popular colour, as a percentage, worn by males and by females?

5 Survey the local primary school at close of afternoon school. How many children leave? How many boys? How many girls? How many boys, girls leave in the care of an adult? How many leave on their own? Can you say from your results whether a girl or a boy is more likely to be met?

6 Ask, politely, whether you may see the subject registers. From the ones for mathematics, English, French, physics, biology, business studies, geography, and history, find out the number of males and females in each subject. Draw a bar chart for each subject, if possible all on the same axes, and find out the percentage of male and female students for each subject.

7 Find out how many use the local fish and chip shop on a Friday between 12 noon and 2 p.m. How many are male? How many are female? How many are of school age (up to 18), how many are over 50, in your opinion? How many eat them immediately and how many take them away? How many come out with a drink as well? Draw a bar chart.

8 Between 9 a.m. and 10 a.m. on the nearest main road to you, how many people are there in each car that passes? Is it 1, 2, 3, 4, or more than 4? Draw a bar chart for the results, and then find out the percentage of cars that have passed with only the driver on board.

16 Surveys by Questioning or Questionnaire

For a survey by questioning, plan beforehand what you are trying to find out. Have simple questions so that, if possible, the answer is 'yes' or 'no', or so that the question has a definite answer.

Arrange your questionnaire so that the questions and answers do not take longer than 2 minutes (if you are organised it is surprising what information can be gained in 2 minutes).

By far the most important thing for a question survey is to be polite. For example, you are more likely to have someone spend two minutes of their time answering questions if the approach is 'Excuse me, I am Joe Bloggs, from Anytown College, and we are conducting a survey on how people travel to work. Could you please give two minutes of your time to answer 10 questions?' rather than 'Hi there. I am from Anytown College and we've been told to ask you some questions; can you answer them?'

Worked example 35

Suppose five students are outside the Town Hall at 8.45 a.m. asking people entering about how they travel to work.

Questions

This morning, did you travel to work by car, train, bus, cycle, walk, other means?
Did you travel up to 2 miles? 2–5 miles? 5–10 miles? over 10 miles?

The result for each student could be tabulated as follows:

Survey on travelling to work on 20 June 1995
Place: Outside Town Hall, Anytown.

Total interviewed	Would not reply	Transport						Distance in miles			
		Car	Train	Bus	Cycle	Walk	Other	0–2	2–5	5–10	10+
1		1						1			
1		1							1		
1				1				1			
1	1										
1			1								1
1		1									1
1						1		1			
1				1						1	
1		1						1			
1					1			1			
1				1				1			

The results from all sheets must be brought together to obtain a final result. Having a column for 'Total interviewed' saves time.

Such a simple survey can provide a wealth of information: for example, what percentage travel by car, bus etc.? What percentage travel 2–5 miles, etc.?

Written questionnaires

These are compiled by professionals, usually with the intention of finding out how many people support particular ideas or views, or for market research to find out trends with regard to goods and services. (Write to a market research firm to see if they are prepared to let you have a copy of survey questions asked many years ago.) Two recent surveys (1995) have been on arming the police, and on the issue of Clause 4 in the Labour Party's constitution.

Arming the police
Out of 126 000 officers up to the rank of chief inspector, nearly 74 000 replied. There was a parallel survey of 1000 members of the public.

The responses from different parts of the country showed some variation but the overall results were as shown in Figure 12.31.

Police (%)	Overall survey results
All officers armed at all times	☐ 5.6
All officers armed while on duty	☐ 15.6
All officers armed when necessary	☐ 18.6
Not all but more than now	☐ 42.8
Present number armed	☐ 17.0
General public (%)	
All officers armed at all times	☐ 10.3
All officers armed while on duty	☐ 15.6
All officers armed when necessary	☐ 37.3
Only specialist officers	☐ 34.8
No view	☐ 2.0

Figure 12.31 Arming the police
Source: The Electoral Reform Society

Clause 4
Result of polls of Labour councillors in Castle Point, Essex, and Trafford, Greater Manchester, on 11 and 12 May 1995.
Response rate: Trafford 56%, Castle Point 61%.
The poll carried out by *The Independent* newspaper.
Some of the findings:
Did you vote in favour of revising Clause 4?

	Castle Point	Trafford
Yes	76	81
No	19	12
No comment	5	7

Other recent questionnaires are given below.

Did you vote for Tony Blair in the leadership election?

Yes	66	68
No	14	24
No comment	20	8

Were you happy with Tony Blair's decision to send his son to an opted-out school?

Yes	66	18
No	19	62
No comment	15	20

Do you think that income tax should be raised for those earning over £35 000?

Yes	33	50
No	52	25
No comment	13	25

Source: The Independent newspaper

17 Flowcharts

A simple flowchart is a series of small diagrams showing the order of operations and decisions to be made for a process to be completed.

The shape of each diagram has a particular meaning. A minimum of words is used. The main diagram shapes are as follows:

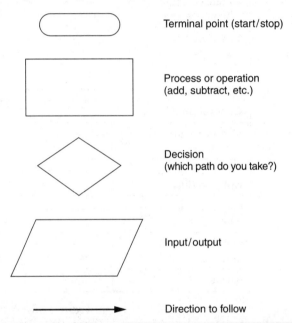

Terminal point (start/stop)

Process or operation (add, subtract, etc.)

Decision (which path do you take?)

Input/output

Direction to follow

Worked example 36 **What methods can I use to deal with savings of a large amount of money?**

The beginning of a flowchart to set me thinking might be as follows:

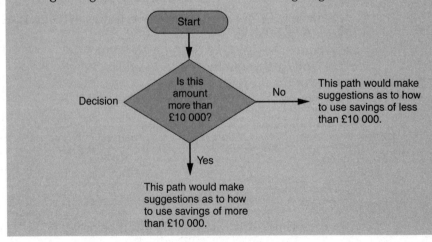

Worked example 37   To have a drink of water might be shown as follows:

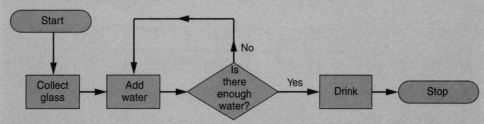

Worked example 38   The flowchart gives the answer to a calculation carried out on a series of numbers.

Number   0 1 2 3 4 5 6
Answer

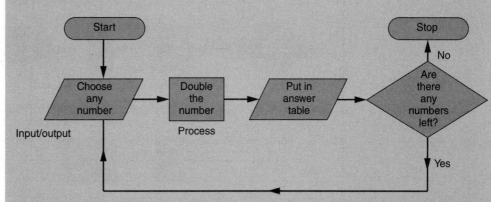

Follow the arrows and instructions as given on the flowchart.

• Start.
• Choose any number, say 3.
• Double the number, making 6.
• Write 6 in the answer table.
• Are there any numbers left? Yes.
• Choose any number, say 4.

Repeat the process until all numbers have been used.

Exercise 12

1   The flowchart shows how to calculate an answer from a given number.
    What is the answer, (a) given a number 3; (b) given a number 5?

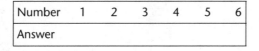

Number	1	2	3	4	5	6
Answer						

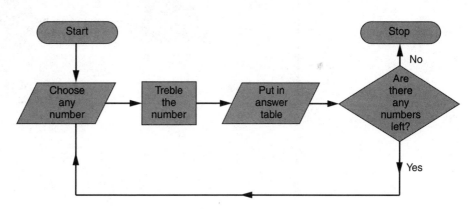

2 The flowchart shows how to calculate an answer from a given number. Complete the answers for the numbers given.

Number	1	2	3	4	5	6
Answer						

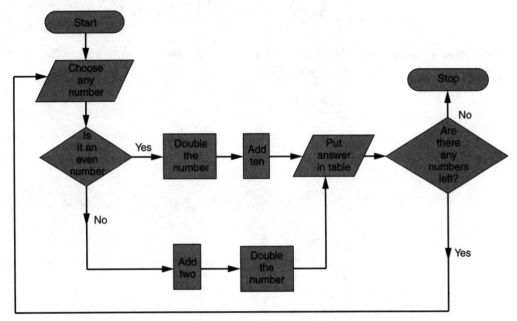

3 The flowchart shows how to sort a letter.

Into which coloured bag does a letter weighing 30 g go?

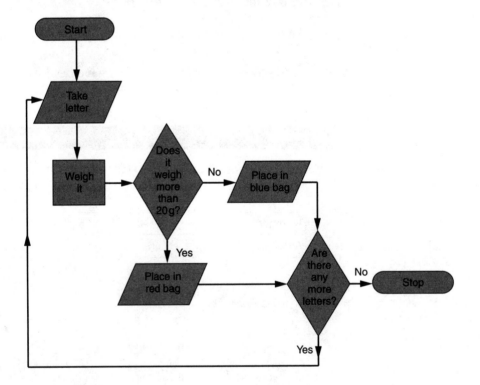

4   The stages of preparing an orange drink, not in order, are drink, add orange, collect glass, taste, add water.

Write in the various instructions on the flowchart.

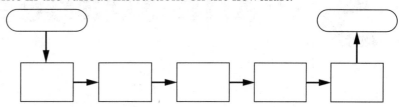

5   Where in the flowchart of question 4 would you place the following decision?

6   Try to draw a simple flowchart for a vending machine selling coffee only, with or without milk and with or without sugar.

7   Try to draw a simple flowchart for a vending machine selling coffee, tea, and fruit drink with no other choices.

8   The flowchart is for sorting parcels. Into which bag will a parcel go weighing
(a) 45 kg   (b) 8.5 kg   (c) 17 kg   (d) 15 kg   (e) 23.5 kg?

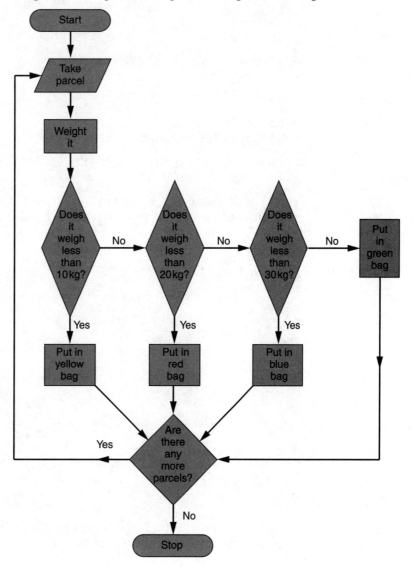

13 Plane Shapes

1 Common Shapes The most common shapes are lines, angles, triangles, rectangles, squares, and circles. We shall consider some of the main facts associated with these shapes.

2 Straight Lines and Angles An angle is the rotation of a straight line fixed at one end to a point. A complete rotation (a circle) represents 360 degrees, written 360°.

A unit of angular measure is a **degree**.

A simple instrument for measuring angles is a **protractor**.

Worked example 1 Measuring an angle:

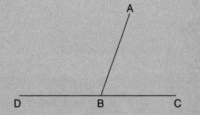

Angle ABC is the angle between line AB and line BC; imagine that BC has rotated anticlockwise until it has reached BA.

Similarly, angle ABD is the angle between line DB and BA; imagine DB rotating clockwise until it reaches BA.

Place the base line of a protractor (0–180) so that it coincides with line DC and the centre of the protractor coincides with point B, as shown in Figure 13.1.

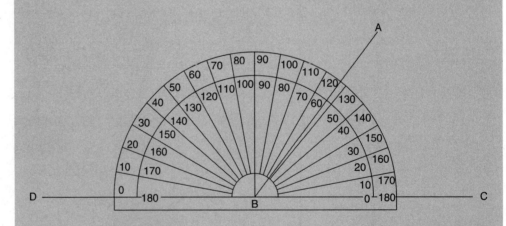

Figure 13.1 Measuring an angle with a protractor

Read off the angle: angle ABC = 53°
                      angle ABD = 127°
Note that a straight line is equivalent to 180°.
An angle of 90° is called a **right angle**.

Worked example 2 | How big is angle XOZ?

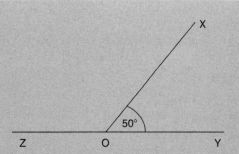

Angle XOY is shown as 50°.
The straight line ZOY is equivalent to 180°.
So angle XOZ = 180° − 50° = 130°
Answer 130°

Worked example 3 | When two straight lines cross then opposite angles are equal.

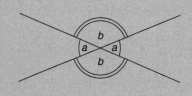

Worked example 4

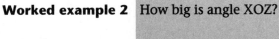

These are parallel lines, i.e. they continue for ever without crossing one another.

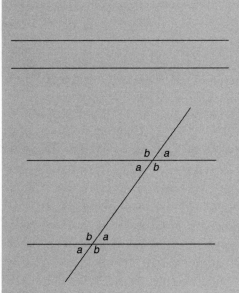

Equal angles are shown using the same letter.

3 Bearings

A bearing indicates how to reach one point (place) from another one by using an angle and a fixed reference line. The fixed reference line is due north and an angle is given from this reference line in a clockwise direction using the full 360° of a circle.

Worked example 5

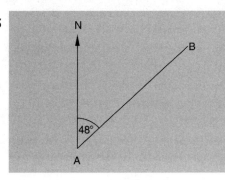

The bearing of B from A is said to be 048°: that is, starting at the fixed reference line you have to go along a course that is at an angle of 48° in a clockwise direction.

Sometimes the direction is given with reference to the points of a compass (north, south, east and west).

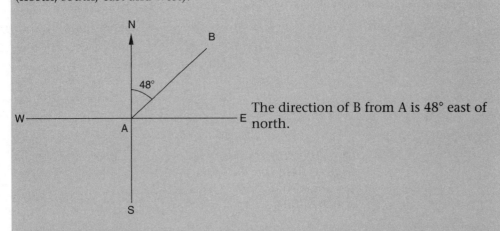

The direction of B from A is 48° east of north.

In this book we shall use the fixed reference line and the full 360°.

Worked example 6

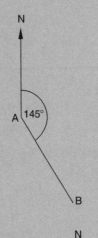

The bearing of B from A is 145°.

Worked example 7

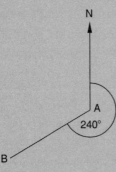

The bearing of B from A is 240°.

Worked example 8 What is the bearing of an aircraft flying *from* B *to* A as shown in the diagram?

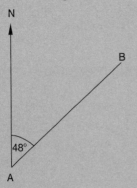

Note how important it is to say which way you are going; compare this with example 5.

To do this example put in a dotted line through B and parallel to the fixed reference line. Call it XY.

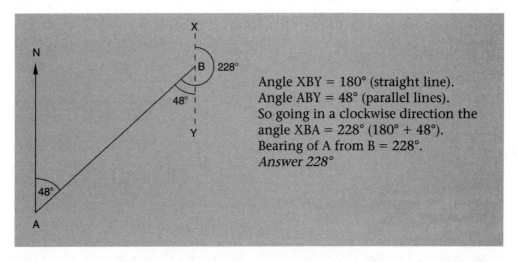

Angle XBY = 180° (straight line).
Angle ABY = 48° (parallel lines).
So going in a clockwise direction the
angle XBA = 228° (180° + 48°).
Bearing of A from B = 228°.
Answer 228°

Exercise 1

1 Measure the angles given below.

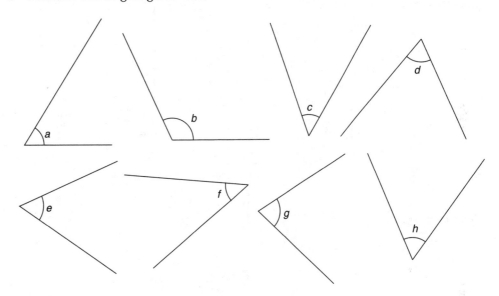

2 Draw the following angles:
 (a) 42° (b) 75° (c) 90° (d) 140°
 (e) 172° (f) 210° (g) 240° (h) 290°

3 How big are angles *a*, *b*, and *c*?

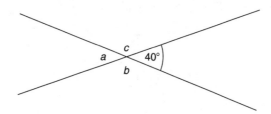

4 Find the sizes of the angles denoted by letters.

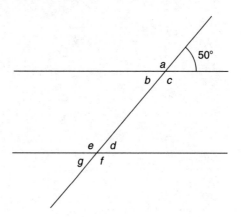

5 What is the bearing of B from A?

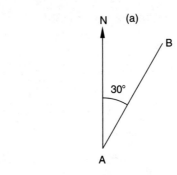

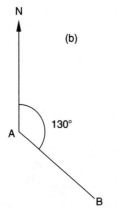

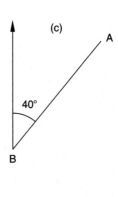

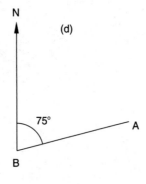

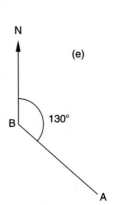

6 Find the sizes of the angles denoted by letters.

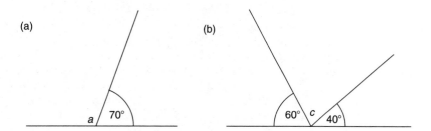

4 Rectangles and Squares

A **rectangle** is a four-sided figure with its opposite sides equal and all four angles equal. The angles are each 90°.

A **square** is a special rectangle in which all four sides are equal.

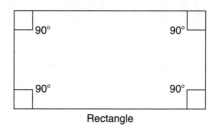

Rectangle   Square

5 Perimeters

The perimeter is the distance all round the sides of a shape.

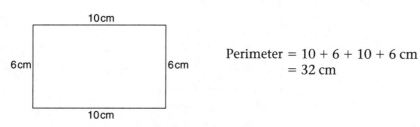

Perimeter = 10 + 6 + 10 + 6 cm
= 32 cm

A diagram often helps in working out a problem.

Worked example 9

A rectangle has one side 15 cm and a perimeter of 80 cm. Find the length of a side of different length.

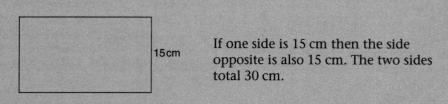

If one side is 15 cm then the side opposite is also 15 cm. The two sides total 30 cm.

Perimeter = 80 cm
Total length of the other two equal sides = 80 cm − 30 cm
= 50 cm

Length of one other side = $\dfrac{50}{2}$ cm   = 25 cm

Answer 25 cm

Worked example 10

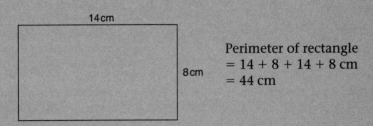

A rectangle has sides of 14 cm and 8 cm. What would be the length of the side of a square having the same perimeter?

14cm

8cm

Perimeter of rectangle
= 14 + 8 + 14 + 8 cm
= 44 cm

A square has four equal sides and its perimeter has to be 44 cm (equal to the rectangle).

Length of side of square = $\dfrac{44}{4}$ cm = 11 cm

Answer 11 cm

6 Area of Rectangles

Area is measured in square units.

1 cm

1 cm

Area within this perimeter is 1 square cm (1 sq cm or 1 cm^2).

For any rectangle, therefore, imagine it to be divided into squares.

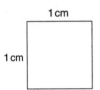

1 cm	1 cm	1 cm	1 cm	1 cm
1 cm^2	1 cm^2	1 cm^2	1 cm^2	1 cm^2	1 cm
1 cm^2	1 cm^2	1 cm^2	1 cm^2	1 cm^2	1 cm
1 cm^2	1 cm^2	1 cm^2	1 cm^2	1 cm^2	1 cm

3 cm

5 cm

Add the squares together.
Area = 15 cm^2
There are five rows with three squares in each row.
$5 \text{ cm} \times 3 \text{ cm} = 15 \text{ cm}^2$

The area of any rectangle is found by multiplying length by breadth.

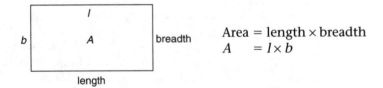

l

b   *A*   breadth

length

Area = length × breadth
$A \quad = l \times b$

Important: The length and breadth must be in the same units, and the answer will then be in square units of the same name.

Worked example 11   A rectangular sheet of paper is 12 cm × 15 cm. Find its area.

First, get into the habit of drawing a diagram.

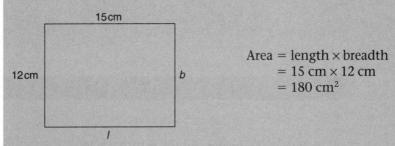

Area = length × breadth
= 15 cm × 12 cm
= 180 cm²

Worked example 12   A square has a side of 8 cm 5 mm. What is its area?

Note: Before multiplying, measurements must be in the same units. 8 cm 5 mm is 8.5 cm or 85 mm

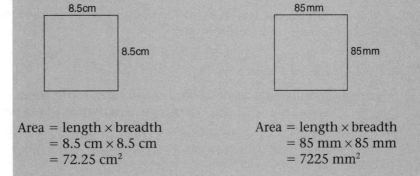

Area = length × breadth
= 8.5 cm × 8.5 cm
= 72.25 cm²

Area = length × breadth
= 85 mm × 85 mm
= 7225 mm²

Worked example 13   Find the area of the shape below.

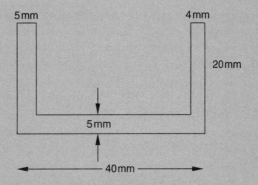

A shape like this is made up of rectangles.

Put in dotted lines to show the rectangles, label each one and find the area of each.

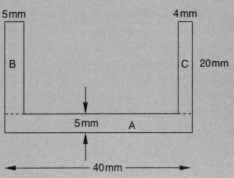

Area of rectangle A = 40 mm × 5 mm = 200 mm²
Area of rectangle B = 15 mm × 5 mm = 75 mm²
Area of rectangle C = 15 mm × 4 mm = 60 mm²
Total area = 200 mm² + 75 mm² + 60 mm²
= 335 mm²

Exercise 2

1   A square has a side of 7 cm. What is the perimeter?

2   A square has a side of 6 cm 4 mm. What is the perimeter?

3   A square has a side of 14 yd 2 ft. What is the perimeter?

4   The perimeter of a square is 1 m 40 cm. What is the length of a side?

5   The perimeter of a square is 10 m 60 cm. What is the length of a side?

6   A rectangle has sides of 14 cm and 8 cm. What is the perimeter?

7   A rectangle has one side 12 cm long and a perimeter of 38 cm. What is the length of the shorter side?

8   A rectangle has sides of 3 yd 1 ft and 6 yd. What would be the length of the side of a square having the same perimeter?

9   A square has a side of 30 cm. A rectangle with the same perimeter has a short side of 22 cm. What is the length of the long side?

10   A square has a perimeter of 8 cm. A rectangle with the same perimeter has one side 1 cm 6 mm. What is the length of the other side of the rectangle?

Exercise 3

Find the areas of the following figures.

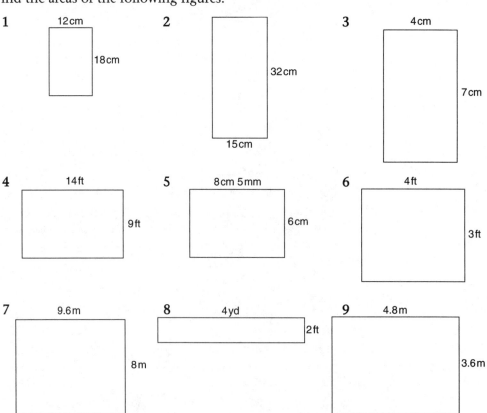

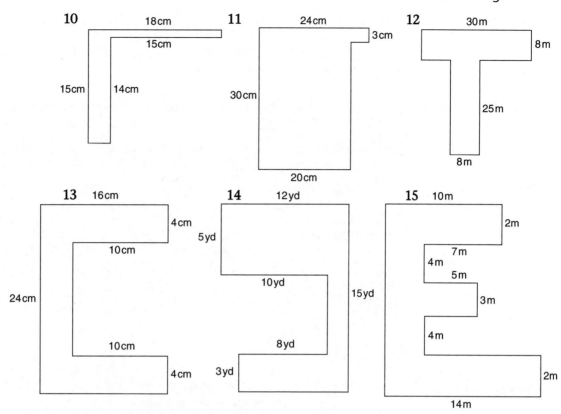

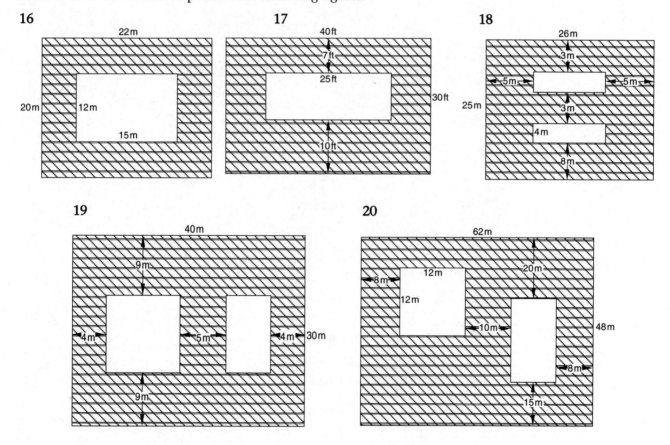

Find the area of the shaded parts in the following figures:

7 Costing

Area is often involved with costs; for example, how much does it cost to paint a surface, how much to sow a lawn, how much to carpet a floor, how much to put glass in window frames, how much to wallpaper a room, how much to tile a wall, how much to make a dress, and so on.

Worked example 14

An area 12 m by 4 m has to be painted. The instructions on the paint tin say that 1 litre should cover 8 m². If one litre of paint costs £2.25 what will it cost to paint the whole surface?

What is the area of the surface?
Area = length × breadth
$\qquad$ = 12 m × 4 m
$\qquad$ = 48 m²
1 litre of paint covers 8 m². How many tins of paint are needed?

Number of tins = $\dfrac{48 \text{ m}^2}{8 \text{ m}^2}$ = 6

One tin costs £2.25
6 tins cost 6 × £2.25 = £13.50
Answer £13.50

Worked example 15

A garden 10 m × 6 m is to be grassed. Best lawn seed costs £2.40 for 500 g and the recommended sowing is 50 g (3 handfuls) per m².
Turf is £1 per m². Find the cost of making a lawn in each case.

Area of garden = length × breadth
$\qquad$ = 10 m × 6 m = 60 m²
Cost of turf at £1 per m² = £60
Cost of using seed:
50 g cover 1 m²
To cover 60 m² needs 60 × 50 g of seed
$\qquad$ = 3000 g
500 g cost £2.40

3000 g will cost $\dfrac{\overset{6}{\cancel{3000}}}{\underset{1}{\cancel{500}}}$ × £2.40 = £14.40

Cost of using seed = £14.40
Answer Cost of turf £60; cost of seed £14.40

Worked example 16

A kitchen 3 m × 4.5 m is to have quarry tiles on the floor. Each tile is 15 cm square. How many tiles are required?

Method 1

Find the area of the floor and divide by the area of each tile.
Area of floor = 3 m × 4.5 m
$\qquad$ = 300 cm × 450 cm
$\qquad$ = 135 000 cm²
Area of one tile = 15 cm × 15 cm
$\qquad$ = 225 cm²

Number of tiles required = $\dfrac{\text{area of floor}}{\text{area of 1 tile}}$ = $\dfrac{135\,000 \text{ cm}^2}{225 \text{ cm}^2}$ = 600

Answer 600

Method 2

Find how many floor tiles are required on each side of the kitchen.

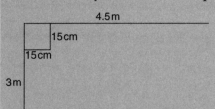

How many tiles (15 cm) are required to go along 4.5 m?

$$\text{Answer} = \frac{4.5 \text{ m}}{15 \text{ cm}} = \frac{450 \text{ cm}}{15 \text{ cm}} = 30$$

How many tiles (15 cm) are required to go along 3 m?

$$\text{Answer} = \frac{3 \text{ m}}{15 \text{ cm}} = \frac{300 \text{ cm}}{15 \text{ cm}} = 20$$

Number of tiles
required $= 30 \times 20 = 600$
Answer 600

Sometimes it is easier to work on 'length runs' such as in floorboards or wallpaper.

Worked example 17   **A wall is 4.68 m long by 2.20 m high. What length of wallpaper is needed to cover the wall if wallpaper is 52 cm wide?**

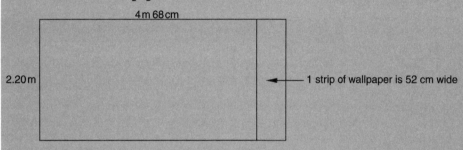

How many strips of wallpaper will cover 4.68 m?

$$\text{Number of strips} = \frac{4.68 \text{ m}}{52 \text{ cm}} = \frac{468 \text{ cm}}{52 \text{ cm}} = 9$$

Each strip is 2.20 m long.
Therefore, 9 strips will be 9×2.20 m long $= 19.80$ m.
Length of wallpaper needed $= 19.80$ m.

Normally, of course, wallpaper is bought as a roll which is just over 10 m long. To cover the wall would need 2 rolls.
Answer 2 rolls

Worked example 18   **A small bungalow is L-shaped with basic floor measurements as shown. How many floorboards 2.5 m × 12 cm are needed to cover the floor (assume no waste)? What is the cost if a floorboard is £1.35?**

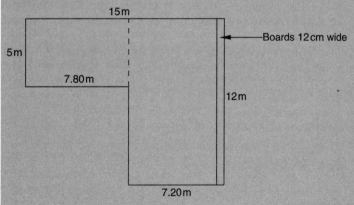

How many boards, side by side, will be needed to go across 7.20 m and then 7.80 m?

Number of boards, side by side, in 7.20 m $= \dfrac{7.20 \text{ m}}{12 \text{ cm}} = \dfrac{720 \text{ cm}}{12 \text{ cm}} = 60$

Length of board required in 12 m side $= 60 \times 12 \text{ m} = 720 \text{ m}$

Number of boards, side by side, in 7.80 m $= \dfrac{7.80 \text{ m}}{12 \text{ cm}} = \dfrac{780 \text{ cm}}{12 \text{ cm}} = 65$

Length of board required in 5 m side $= 65 \times 5 \text{ m} = 325 \text{ m}$
Total length of board required $= 720 \text{ m} + 325 \text{ m} = 1045 \text{ m}$
A floorboard is 2.5 m long

Number of floorboards required $= \dfrac{1045 \text{ m}}{2.5 \text{ m}} = 418$

Each board costs £1.35
Total cost $= £1.35 \times 418$
$\qquad\quad = £564.30$
Answer £564.30
In practice there is waste, and a certain percentage is added on to allow for this.

Exercise 4

1   What length of carpet 200 cm wide is required to cover a floor 4 m × 6 m?

2   Carpet tiles are 300 mm square. How many carpet tiles are needed to cover a room 5 m 10 cm by 6 m?

3   A rectangular room $4\frac{1}{2}$ m by $3\frac{1}{2}$ m has a carpet 4 m by 3 m. What area is not carpeted?

4   Dress material is 114 cm wide and costs £12 per metre run. How much would it cost to buy $2\frac{1}{2}$ metres?

5   What length of wallpaper is required to cover a wall 4 m 32 cm long by 2 m 20 cm high if the wallpaper is 54 cm wide and is put on vertically?

6   Patio flags 300 mm × 300 mm in Yorkstone are £1.45 each. How much does it cost to make a patio 7 m 20 cm by 4 m 20 cm?

7   A $2\frac{1}{2}$ litre tin of white gloss paint costs £9.95 and should cover an area of 40 m². How much would it cost to cover a surface 25 m × 24 m?

8   A roll of wallpaper is 10 m by 54 cm wide. How many rolls are needed to wallpaper a room 5 m 40 cm square and 2 m high, assuming there is no waste and windows and doors are equivalent to one roll?

9   Glass, when cut to size, is charged at £6 per m². What is the cost of glass, cut to size, for a window 1 m 40 cm by 90 cm?

10   A garden is 18 m long and 12 m wide. The cost of laying turf was quoted at £6 per m². The total cost of laying the turf was £720. What area of garden was not turfed?

8 Triangles

A triangle is a three-sided figure.

A triangle with two sides of equal length (or two equal angles) is called an **isosceles triangle**.

A triangle with three sides equal (or three equal angles) is called an **equilateral triangle**.

The three angles of any triangle add up to 180°.

9 Perimeter of Triangles

The perimeter is the distance round all the sides of the triangle.

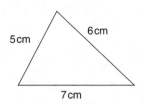

Perimeter = 5 cm + 6 cm + 7 cm
= 18 cm

10 Area of Triangles

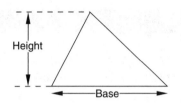

Let the **base** be the side drawn horizontally.

Height is the vertical height of the triangle.

$$\text{Area of triangle} = \frac{\text{base} \times \text{height}}{2}$$

$$A = \frac{b \times h}{2}$$

Worked example 19

Find the area of a triangle of base 25 mm and perpendicular height 40 mm.

(Usually the word 'perpendicular' is missed out.)

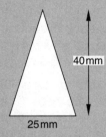

$$\text{Area} = \frac{\text{base} \times \text{height}}{2}$$

$$= \frac{25 \text{ mm} \times 40 \text{ mm}}{2}$$

$$= 500 \text{ mm}^2$$

Worked example 20

Find the area of a triangle of base 1 m 20 cm and height 40 cm.

Before beginning the question make sure all measurements are in the same units:

	1 m 20 cm = 1.20 m	40 cm = 0.40 m
or	1 m 20 cm = 120 cm	40 cm = 40 cm

$$\text{Area} = \frac{\text{base} \times \text{height}}{2}$$

$$= \frac{1.20 \text{ m} \times 0.40 \text{ m}}{2}$$

$$= \frac{0.48 \text{ m}^2}{2}$$

$$= 0.24 \text{ m}^2$$

Answer 0.24 m²

or

$$\text{Area} = \frac{\text{base} \times \text{height}}{2}$$

$$= \frac{120 \text{ cm} \times 40 \text{ cm}}{2}$$

$$= \frac{4800 \text{ cm}^2}{2}$$

$$= 2400 \text{ cm}^2$$

Answer 2400 cm²

Worked example 21

A triangle has an area of 120 cm². If the height is 20 cm how long is the base?

$$\text{Area} = \frac{\text{base} \times \text{height}}{2}$$

$$120 = \frac{\text{base} \times 20}{2}$$

$$120 = \text{base} \times 10$$

$$\frac{120}{10} = \text{base}$$

Cancelling by 2.

$12\text{ cm} = \text{base}$
Answer 12 cm

Exercise 5

1 Find the perimeter of a triangle whose sides are 5 cm, 8 cm and 9 cm.

2 Find the perimeter of a triangle whose sides are 4 cm 7 mm, 7 cm 2 mm and 10 cm 9 mm.

3 An isosceles triangle has a perimeter of 30 cm. If the length of one of the equal sides is 9 cm 8 mm, what is the length of the unequal side?

4 An equilateral triangle has a perimeter of 40 cm 8 mm. What is the length of one side?

5 An isosceles triangle has sides of 10 cm and 8 cm. What could be the perimeter of the triangle?

6 Find the area of the following triangles:
   (a) base = 6 cm   height = 10 cm
   (b) base = 4 cm   height = 6 cm
   (c) base = 12 cm   height = 8 cm
   (d) base = 25 mm   height = 18 mm
   (e) base = 8 m   height = 3.5 m

7 Find the area of the following triangles:
   (a) base = 4 cm 2 mm   height = 5 cm
   (b) base = 10 cm 4 mm   height = 8 cm
   (c) base = 2 ft 4 in   height = 1 ft 2 in
   (d) base = 6 m 30 cm   height = 3 m
   (e) base = 3 cm 2 mm   height = 2 cm 4 mm

8 Find the base or height measurement in the following triangles:
   (a) area = 30 cm^2 height = 10 cm
   (b) area = 72 cm^2 height = 8 cm
   (c) area = 45 cm^2 height = 18 cm
   (d) area = 105 m^2 height = 14 m
   (e) area = 43.2 m^2 height = 6 m

9 Find the area of the following figures. (*Hint:* Where a shape looks awkward split it up into triangles and rectangles.)

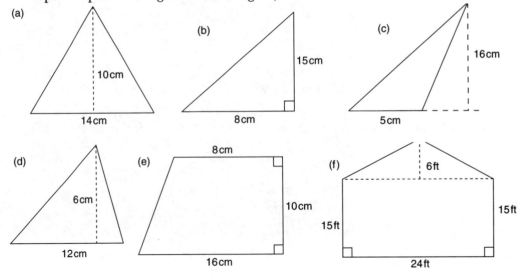

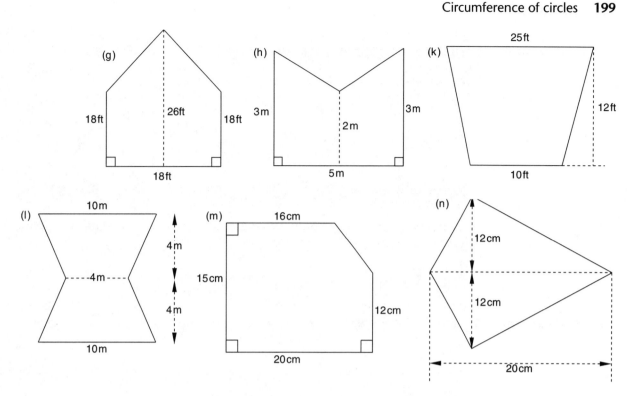

11 Circles

The most common terms in connection with a circle are as follows:

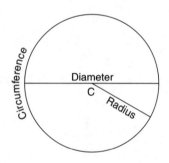

The **circumference** of the circle is the distance all the way round it, i.e. it is the perimeter.

The **diameter** is the distance from circumference to circumference through the centre of the circle, C.

The **radius** is the distance from the circumference to the centre.

Diameter = twice the radius: if D = diameter and R = radius then $D = 2 \times R = 2R$.

12 Circumference of Circles

Circumference = π (pi) $\times D$ or $\pi \times 2R$.

What is π? It is the number of times the diameter will divide into the circumference of a circle; no matter what the size of the circle the value is always the same. The value of π to be used will be given for any question. It is usually given as $\frac{22}{7}$ ($3\frac{1}{7}$) or as 3.14.

Worked example 22

Find the circumference of a circle whose diameter is 21 cm (Take $\pi = \frac{22}{7}$.)

Circumference = $\pi \times$ diameter

$$= \frac{22}{\overset{}{\underset{1}{7}}} \times \overset{3}{21} \text{ cm}$$

$$= 66 \text{ cm}$$

Worked example 23   Find the circumference of a circle of radius 4 cm. (Take $\pi = \frac{22}{7}$.)

Circumference $= \pi \times$ diameter (diameter $= 2 \times$ radius)

$$= \frac{22}{7} \times 2 \times 4 \text{ cm}$$

$$= \frac{176}{7} \text{ cm}$$

$$= 25\frac{1}{7} \text{ cm}$$

When you have written down the relationship between circumference and diameter often enough, it becomes a habit to write

$$C = \pi \times D \qquad \text{or} \qquad C = 2 \times \pi \times R$$

Worked example 24   Find the circumference of a circle of radius $5\frac{1}{4}$ in. (Take $\pi = \frac{22}{7}$.)

$C = 2 \times \pi \times R$

$$= 2 \times \frac{22}{7} \times 5\frac{1}{4} \text{ in}$$

$$= \overset{1}{2} \times \frac{\overset{11}{22}}{\underset{1}{7}} \times \frac{\overset{3}{21}}{\underset{\underset{1}{2}}{4}} \text{ in}$$

$$= 33 \text{ in}$$

Worked example 25   Find the circumference of a circle of diameter 80 cm. (Take $\pi = 3.14$.)

$C = \pi \times D$
$= 3.14 \times 80 \text{ cm}$
$= 251.2 \text{ cm}$

Worked example 26   Find the diameter of a circle if the circumference is 99 cm. (Take $\pi = \frac{22}{7}$.)

$C = \pi \times D$
Substitute the values given:

$$99 = \frac{22}{7} \times D$$

To remove fractions multiply both sides of the equation by 7:

$$99 \times 7 = \overset{1}{7} \times \frac{22}{\underset{1}{7}} \times D$$

$$693 = 22D$$

To find D, now divide by 22:

$$\frac{\overset{63}{693}}{\underset{2}{22}} = D$$

$$31\frac{1}{2} \text{ cm} = D$$

Answer $31\frac{1}{2}$ cm

Worked example 27   Find the radius of a circle if the circumference is 132 cm. (Take $\pi = \frac{22}{7}$.)

$C = 2 \times \pi \times R$

$132 = 2 \times \dfrac{22}{7} \times R$ | Multiply both sides by 7. |

$7 \times 132 = 2 \times 22 \times R$

$\qquad 924 = 44R$

$\dfrac{924}{44} = R$

Answer 21 cm

Exercise 6

For all questions in this exercise assume $\pi = \frac{22}{7}$.

Find the circumference of the following circles:
1 Diameter = 7 cm	**2** Diameter = 21 in	**3** Diameter = 14 ft
4 Diameter = 42 m	**5** Diameter = 35 m	**6** Diameter = 10.5 cm
7 Radius = 7 in	**8** Radius = 63 m	**9** Radius = 42 cm
10 Radius = 17.5 cm	**11** Radius = 3.5 m	**12** Radius = 8 cm

Find the diameter of the following circles:
13 Circumference = 132 cm	**14** Circumference = 110 m
15 Circumference = 242 m	**16** Circumference = 88 ft
17 Circumference = 33 cm	**18** Circumference = 66 m

Find the radius of the following circles:
19 Circumference = 44 cm	**20** Circumference = 55 m
21 Diameter = 8.6 m	**22** Diameter = 24.2 cm
23 Circumference = 165 ft	**24** Circumference = 99 mm

25   A piece of wire is 44 m long. It is bent to form a circle. What is the diameter of the circle formed?

26   A piece of wire is a circle of radius 21 cm. It is made into a square shape. What is the size of one side of the square?

What is the perimeter of the following shapes?

27
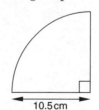
14 cm

28
10.5 cm

29
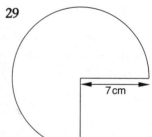
7 cm

30   Find the perimeter of the running track shown

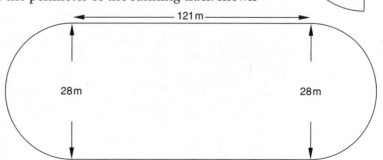
121 m

28 m   28 m

13 Area of Circles

The formula for calculating the area of a circle is $\pi \times R^2$.

π is the same symbol as used to find the circumference.

R^2 ('R squared') means $R \times R$; see Chapter 12, section 10.

It will probably help your working out if you write down the meaning each time.

Worked example 28

Find the area of a circle whose radius is 14 cm. (Take $\pi = \frac{22}{7}$.)

$$
\begin{aligned}
\text{Area of circle} &= \pi R^2 \\
&= \pi \times R \times R \\
&= \frac{22}{\underset{1}{\cancel{7}}} \times \cancel{14}^{2} \times 14 \text{ cm}^2 \\
&= 616 \text{ cm}^2
\end{aligned}
$$

Answer 616 cm²

Note: The units of area are square units.

Worked example 29

Find the area of a circle of radius 4 cm. (Take $\pi = \frac{22}{7}$.)

$$
\begin{aligned}
\text{Area of circle} &= \pi R^2 \\
&= \pi \times R \times R \\
&= \frac{22}{7} \times 4 \times 4 \text{ cm}^2 \\
&= \frac{352}{7} \text{ cm}^2 \\
&= 50\frac{2}{7} \text{ cm}^2
\end{aligned}
$$

Answer 50$\frac{2}{7}$ cm²

Worked example 30

Find the area of a circle of diameter 20 cm. (Take $\pi = 3.14$.)

If the diameter is given then divide it by 2 in order to find the radius.

$D = 20$; $R = 10$.

$$
\begin{aligned}
\text{Area of circle} &= \pi R^2 \\
&= \pi \times R \times R \\
&= 3.14 \times 10 \times 10 \text{ cm}^2 \\
&= 3.14 \times 100 \text{ cm}^2 \\
&= 314 \text{ cm}^2
\end{aligned}
$$

Answer 314 cm²

Worked example 31

Find the area of the following shape, which is a semicircle ($\pi = \frac{22}{7}$).

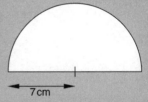

7 cm

First, find the area of the whole circle, then divide by 2 to find the area of the semicircle.

$$
\begin{aligned}
\text{Area of circle} &= \pi R^2 \\
&= \pi \times R \times R \\
&= \frac{22}{7} \times 7 \times 7 \text{ cm}^2 \\
&= 154 \text{ cm}^2
\end{aligned}
$$

This is the area of the whole circle: therefore

$$\text{Area of semicircle} = \frac{154}{2} = 77 \text{ cm}^2$$

Answer 77 cm²

Worked example 32   Find the area of the shape below. (Take $\pi = \frac{22}{7}$.)

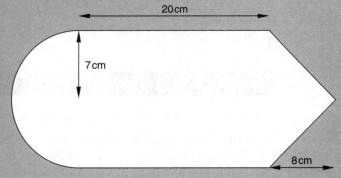

Split the shape into shapes you already know:

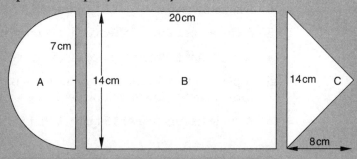

A is a semicircle, B a rectangle, C a triangle.

$$\begin{aligned}
\text{Area of triangle C} \quad &= \tfrac{1}{2} \text{ base} \times \text{height} \\
&= \tfrac{1}{2} \times 14 \times 8 \text{ cm}^2 \\
&= 56 \text{ cm}^2 \\
\text{Area of rectangle B} \quad &= \text{length} \times \text{breadth} \\
&= 20 \times 14 \text{ cm}^2 \\
&= 280 \text{ cm}^2 \\
\text{Area of semicircle A} &= \tfrac{1}{2} \text{ area of whole circle} \\
&= \tfrac{1}{2} \times \pi R^2 \\
&= \tfrac{1}{2} \times \pi \times R \times R \\
&= \frac{1}{\underset{1}{2}} \times \frac{\overset{11}{22}}{\underset{1}{7}} \times \overset{1}{\cancel{7}} \times 7 \text{ cm}^2 \\
&= 77 \text{ cm}^2 \\
\text{Area of whole shape} &= 56 \text{ cm}^2 + 280 \text{ cm}^2 + 77 \text{ cm}^2 \\
&= 413 \text{ cm}^2
\end{aligned}$$

Answer 413 cm²

Worked example 33   Find the area of the shaded portion if it is 7 cm wide ($\pi = \frac{22}{7}$).

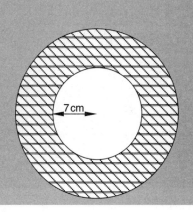

Treat the figure as two circles and take the area of the small circle away from the area of the large circle.

$$\begin{aligned}
\text{Area of small circle} \quad &= \pi R^2 \\
&= \pi \times R \times R \\
&= \frac{22}{\underset{1}{\cancel{7}}} \times 7 \times \overset{1}{\cancel{7}} \text{ cm}^2 \\
&= 154 \text{ cm}^2
\end{aligned}$$

Area of large circle	$= \pi R^2$
	$= \pi \times R \times R$
	$= \dfrac{22}{\cancel{7}_1} \times 14 \times \cancel{14}^2 \text{ cm}^2$
	$= 616 \text{ cm}^2$
Area of shaded portion	$= 616 - 154 \text{ cm}^2$
	$= 462 \text{ cm}^2$

Answer 462 cm²

Exercise 7

For all questions in this exercise assume $\pi = \frac{22}{7}$.

Find the area of the following circles:

1	Radius = 14 cm	**2**	Radius = 21 cm	**3**	Radius = 63 ft
4	Radius = 10.5 m	**5**	Radius = 35 in	**6**	Radius = $3\frac{1}{2}$ cm
7	Diameter = 10 cm	**8**	Diameter = $5\frac{1}{4}$ in	**9**	Diameter = 2 m
10	Diameter = $3\frac{1}{2}$ m	**11**	Diameter = 5 cm	**12**	Diameter = $17\frac{1}{2}$ m

13 A circle has a circumference of 33 cm. What is its area?

14 A circle has a circumference of 154 ft. What is its area?

15 A piece of wire in the form of a square has a side of 11 cm. It is made to form a circle. How much bigger is the area of this circle than the square?

16 A circle has an area of 154 cm². What is its radius?

Exercise 8

For all questions in this exercise assume $\pi = \frac{22}{7}$.

Find the areas of the figures given:

1

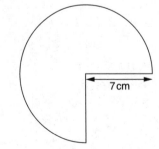

28 cm

2

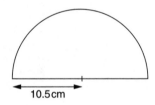

10.5 cm

3

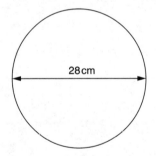

7 cm

4

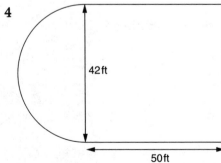

42 ft

50 ft

5

6

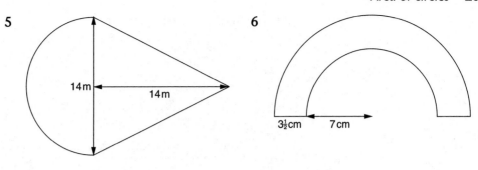

7

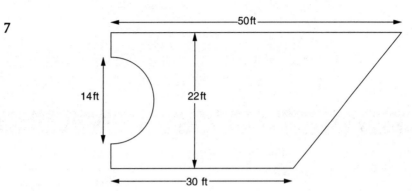

8 Find the area of the unshaded portion.

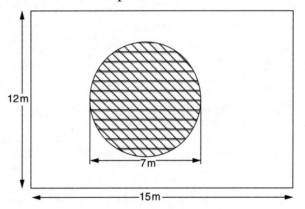

9 Find the area of the shaded part if it is 10.5 cm wide.

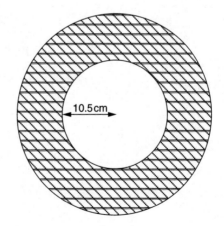

10 Find the area of the unshaded part.

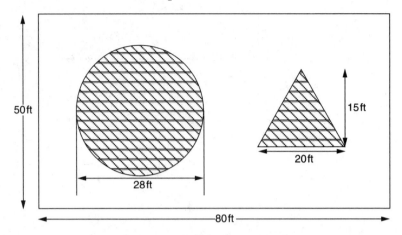

Exercise 9 Multiple choice questions

Work out which is the correct answer in the following questions (where required take $\pi = \frac{22}{7}$):

1 The angle X is equal to
  A 100°   **B** 80°   **C** 50°   **D** 30°

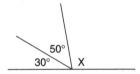

2 The bearing of an aircraft flying from X to Y is
  A 60° S   **B** 60° E of N
  C 60° W of N   **D** 60° N

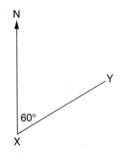

3 The bearing of an aircraft flying from X to Y is
  A 070°   **B** 020°   **C** 110°   **D** 250°

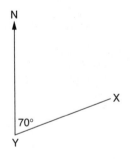

4 A rectangle has sides of 22 cm and 18 cm. The side of a square of equal perimeter is
  A 40 cm   **B** 20 cm   **C** 36 cm   **D** 22 cm

5 A square of side 12 cm has a piece cut away equivalent to 16 cm². The area left is
  A 128 cm²   **B** 32 cm²
  C 56 cm²   **D** 256 cm²

6 Kitchen tiles 18 cm by 18 cm are laid on a floor 3 m 24 cm by 4 m 32 cm. The floor will need
  A 84 tiles   **B** 324 tiles
  C 432 tiles   **D** 576 tiles

7 A triangle has an area of 96 cm². The base is 12 cm. The height is
  A 8 cm   **B** 4 cm   **C** 12 cm   **D** 16 cm

8 The perimeter of a square is 44 cm. The area is
  A 176 cm²   **B** 11 cm²
  C 121 cm²   **D** 44 cm²

9 A circle has an area of 616 cm². The diameter is
  A 7 cm   **B** 28 cm   **C** $15\frac{4}{7}$ cm   **D** 14 cm

10 A circle has a diameter of 14 cm. The circumference is
  A 176 cm   **B** 44 cm
  C 14 cm   **D** 28 cm

11 A quarry tile is 20 cm square and costs £1.50. The cost to tile a floor 3 m 20 cm by 2 m 80 cm is
  A £44   **B** £284   **C** £336   **D** £84

12 A piece of metal sheet 30 cm by 20 cm has two circles of $3\frac{1}{2}$ cm radius stamped out of it. The area of metal sheet left is
  A 523 cm²   **B** 593 cm²
  C 586 cm²   **D** 484 cm²

14 More Use of the Calculator

1 Use of Memory Electronic calculators have a memory facility, indicated by the keys MR, M+ and M-.

The M+ key transfers the number displayed to the memory and *automatically adds it* into the memory.

The M- key transfers the number displayed to the memory and *automatically subtracts it* from the memory.

When a number is stored in the memory an 'M' sign appears in the display window to remind you that you are using the memory facility.

The MR key recalls the result of everything that has gone into the memory.

Read the instructions supplied with your calculator about clearing the calculator *before* a memory calculation. In the Casio SL 450 (see Chapter 5) it is AC. On other calculators it may be CE, or you may have to switch off.

Worked example 1 $3 \times 12 + 7 \times 9$

AC 3 ☒ 12 M+	(36)
7 ☒ 9 M+	(63)

MR 99
Answer 99
AC makes sure the calculator is completely clear before beginning a memory calculation.

Worked example 2 $(15.6 \times 2.34) + 10 \div 4.2$

AC 15 ⊡ 6 ☒ 2 ⊡ 34 M+	(36.504)
10 ÷ 4 ⊡ 2 M+	(2.380 952 3)

MR 38.884 952
Answer 38.88 correct to two decimal places

Worked example 3 $(13.2 \times 0.64) - (2.69 \div 1.25)$

AC 13 ⊡ 2 ☒ 0 ⊡ 64 M+	(8.448)
2 ⊡ 69 ÷ 1 ⊡ 25 M-	(2.152)

MR 6.296
Answer 6.296

Worked example 4   Find the total cost of 2 lb of bacon at 132p a lb, 3 loaves at 26p a loaf, 3 pkts of cornflakes at 81p a pkt, and 6 oranges at 8p each

[AC] 2 [×] 132 [M+]
   3 [×] 26 [M+]
   3 [×] 81 [M+]
   6 [×]   8 [M+]
[MR] 633

The display shows 633; all calculations were done in pence, so the answer is 633p, or £6.33.
Answer £6.33

Worked example 5 $$\frac{7.32 \times 15.6 - 3.25 \times 14.28}{4.68}$$

[AC] 7 [.] 32 [×] 15 [.] 6 [M+]
   3 [.] 25 [×] 14 [.] 28 [M-]
[MR] [÷] 4 [.] 68 [=] 14.48
Answer 14.48

Sometimes, even using the memory, you have to write a number on a piece of paper before you can complete the calculation. For example:

Worked example 6 $$\frac{(15.6 \times 2.42) + (3.25 \times 6.54)}{27.08 - 19.71}$$

The result of the *bottom line* needs to be written on a piece of paper.

27 [.] 08 [-] 19 [.] 71 [=] 7.37 | Remember this figure. |
15 [.] 6 [×] 2 [.] 42 [M+]
3 [.] 25 [×] 6 [.] 54 [M+]
[MR] [÷] 7 [.] 37 [=] 8.00
Answer 8.00
Or:
15 [.] 6 [×] 2 [.] 42 [M+]
3 [.] 25 [×] 6 [.] 54 [M+]
Now do the bottom line:
27 [.] 08 [-] 19 [.] 71 [=] 7.37
Write 7.37 on a piece of paper.
Bring back the memory [MR] and ÷7.37:
[MR] [÷] 7 [.] 37 [=] 8.00
Answer 8.00

Exercise 1

Give answers correct to 2 decimal places.

1   $(46 \times 84) + (17 \times 19)$ 2 $(9.62 \times 8.48) + (11.24 \times 5.03)$
3   $(75 \times 18) - (38 \times 29)$ 4 $(58.24 \times 6.07) - (24.23 \times 5.09)$
5   $(24.61 \div 0.014) - (9.26 \times 53.5)$ 6 $11.1 \times 7.4 + 63 \times 9.7 + 15.6 \times 8.3$

7   $13.24 + 26.04 \times 8.51 + 16.23 \times 0.52$

8   $32.52 \times 17.41 + 18.32 \times 9.6 - 17.07 \times 32.16$

9   $56.41 \div 6.87 + 9.24 \times 6.52 - 324.08 \times 0.57$

10   $97 - 14.1 \times 0.57 + 13.8 \times 0.34$

11 $17.2 \div 8.5 - 13 \times 5.06 - 94.8 \div 25.2$

12 $\dfrac{24.1 \times 9.47 + 0.74 \times 38.6}{23}$

13 $\dfrac{15.25 \times 11.14 - 28.61 \times 3.59}{24.75}$ 14 $\dfrac{47.24 \div 9.58 \times 6.48}{3.07}$

15 $\dfrac{79.24 \times 8.56 \div 2.07}{58.04 - 17.59}$ 16 $\dfrac{942.7}{74.65 - 13.64 \times 3.28}$

2 Using a Constant

There are times when we want to use the same constant number continuously, say π, for a series of multiplications, additions etc.

When a number is set up as a constant a 'K' sign may appear in the display window; again, look at the instructions for the calculator.

The following examples are of the use of a constant on a Casio SL 450.

Worked example 7

Multiply the following numbers by 3.14: 6, 8, 11, 14.6, 15.2.

Key as follows:

3 [.] 14 [×] [×] 6 [=] 18.84
                8 [=] 25.12
               11 [=] 34.54
            14 [.] 6 [=] 45.844
            15 [.] 2 [=] 47.728

Note: The double command [×] [×] keys in the constant 3.14.

Worked example 8

Divide the following numbers by 3.14: 14, 21, 30, 45.

3 [.] 14 [÷] [÷] 14 [=] 4.46
                21 [=] 6.69
                30 [=] 9.55
                45 [=] 14.33

Figures are correct to 2 decimal places.

Worked example 9

Add 19.07 to the following numbers: 5.62, 9.42, 13.07, 18.25.

The constant is 19.07.

19 [.] 07 [+] [+] 5 [.] 62 [=] 24.69
                   9 [.] 42 [=] 28.49
                  13 [.] 07 [=] 32.14
                  18 [.] 25 [=] 37.32

If you want to keep multiplying (or dividing or adding or subtracting) the same constant by itself, just keep pressing the [=] key.

Worked example 10

Multiply 7×7 and so on.

7 [×] [×] 7 [=] 49
          [=] 343 $(7 \times 7 \times 7)$
          [=] 2401 $(7 \times 7 \times 7 \times 7)$
          [=] 16 807 $(7 \times 7 \times 7 \times 7 \times 7)$

Worked example 11 | From 200 keep taking 13.625.

The constant is 13.625:

13 ⊡ 625 ⊟ ⊟ 200 ⊜ 186.375
⊜ 172.75
⊜ 159.125
⊜ 145.5

Some calculators (for example, the Texet Senator) require the command function to be pressed once only and then the ⊜ key continuously without any other command.

Worked example 12 | Multiply 3.14 by 5, 6, 7, 8.

3 ⊡ 14 ⊠ 5 ⊜ 15.7
6 ⊜ 18.84
7 ⊜ 21.98
8 ⊜ 25.12

Notice the command position for division.

Worked example 13 | Divide the following numbers by 3:
9, 18, 63, 96

9 ⊟ 3 ⊜ 3
18 ⊜ 6
63 ⊜ 21
96 ⊜ 32

Exercise 2

1   Add 17.08 to the following numbers:
   (a) 96.24   (b) 48.03   (c) 56.65   (d) 132.17
   (e) 42.88   (f) 31.19   (g) 327.39   (h) 80.03

2   Subtract 11.87 from the following numbers:
   (a) 30.1   (b) 20.09   (c) 46.25   (d) 182.9
   (e) 49.08   (f) 40.09   (g) 258.52   (h) 90.03

3   Multiply the following numbers by 3.14:
   (a) 9   (b) 7.5   (c) 8.23   (d) 25.06
   (e) 18.95   (f) 7.07   (g) 20.03   (h) 35

4   Divide the following numbers by 3.14 (answers correct to 2 decimal places):
   (a) 6   (b) 13   (c) 9.32   (d) 46.05
   (e) 18.28   (f) 50   (g) 76.04   (h) 20.07

5   The circumference of a circle is found by multiplying the diameter by π. If $\pi = 3.14$ find the circumference of circles with a diameter of
   (a) 4 cm   (b) 15 cm   (c) 65 cm   (d) 25 in
   (e) 19 ft   (f) 7.5 cm   (g) 13.8 m   (h) 400 mm

6   $D = \dfrac{C}{\pi}$ where D = diameter C = circumference

If $\pi = 3.14$ find the diameter of a circle, correct to 2 decimal places, when the circumference is
   (a) 20 cm   (b) 8 ft   (c) 17 m   (d) 155 cm
   (e) 32.6 ft   (f) 96.2 cm   (g) 18 in   (h) 326.9 cm

3 Square Root

The square root of a number is the figure that, multiplied by itself, will give you the number.

$9 = 3 \times 3$, 3 is said to be the square root of 9;
or $\sqrt{9} = 3$.

On a calculator this is very simple; press the $\boxed{\sqrt{}}$ key to find the square root of the number displayed.

Worked example 14

Find the square root of 625.

$625 \boxed{\sqrt{}} \rightarrow 25$

Answer 25

No need to press $\boxed{=}$.

Worked example 15

Find the square root of 349.69.

$349 \boxed{.} 69 \boxed{\sqrt{}} \rightarrow 18.7$

Answer 18.7

Exercise 3

1   Find the square root of the following numbers
    (a)   4096   (b)   1369   (c)   29.16
    (d)   152.5225   (e)   334.89   (f)   640.09
    (g)   0.0441   (h)   0.004 225

2   $r = \sqrt{\dfrac{A}{\pi}}$ where r = radius of a circle
                                     A = area of a circle
    and assume $\pi = 3.14$

    Find r when
    (a) $A = 216 \text{ cm}^2$ (b) $A = 84 \text{ cm}^2$ (c) $A = 9.2 \text{ cm}^2$
    (d) $A = 60 \text{ cm}^2$ (e) $A = 176 \text{ ft}^2$ (f) $A = 100 \text{ cm}^2$
    (g) $A = 50 \text{ cm}^2$ (h) $A = 320 \text{ m}^2$

Exercise 4 Multiple choice questions

Work out which is the correct answer in the following questions:

1   The answer to $18.5 + 2.5 \div 7$ is
    A 3   B 0.36   C 18.86   D 15.24

2   The answer to $\dfrac{17.5 \times 5.6 - 3.2 \div 0.8}{5.4}$ is

    A 97.6   B 9.72   C 26.28   D 17.41

3   A meal costs £12.60 plus 15% service charge. The total cost is
    A £14.49   B £27.60   C £14.40   D £15.00

4   Ford offers a 12% discount on a Mondeo car where there is no trade-in. The Mondeo costs £13 500. The discount price is
    A £13 338   B £15 120
    C £12 400   D £11 880

5   A number when multiplied by itself is 361. The number is
    A 180.5   B 19   C 10   D 17

6   A house has a floor area of 1200 ft². An extension is built that provides an extra 24% of floor area. The cost of the extension is calculated at £64 per ft². The extension costs
    A £76 800   B £15 364
    C £18 432   D £16 400

7   The volume of a cylinder is given by $V = \pi r^2 h$, where V = volume of cylinder, r = radius of cylinder, h = height of cylinder and $\pi = 3.14$. For a volume of 100 cm³ and height 10 cm the radius is
    A 3.18 cm   B 1.54 cm
    C 1.78 cm   D 2 cm

8 A person earning £17 700 a year is given a rise of 3.0%. The amount extra earned per month is

A £45   B £47.25
C £53.10   D £44.25

9 A floor is 6 m 12 cm by 4 m 86 cm. The number of tiles 18 cm square required to cover this floor is

A 918   B 1216   C 868   D 948

10 In a right-angled triangle $a^2 = b^2 + c^2$ where a = the length of the side opposite the right angle, and b and c are the lengths of the other two sides of the triangle. If $b = 5$ and $c = 12$ then a is

A 17 cm   B 13 cm   C 7 cm   D 8.5 cm

15 Space Shapes

1 Volume

Volume is a measure of space taken up.

Space is taken up or occupied by houses, bricks, factories, footballs, buses, rivers, mountains, planets, and so on. All have a certain volume.

2 Measurement of Volume

Volume is measured in cubic units.

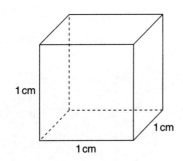

This would be 1 cubic cm (1 cm³).

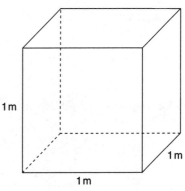

1 cubic metre (1 m³).

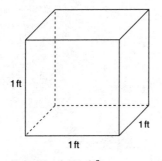

1 cubic ft (1 ft³).

This book is concerned only with finding the volumes of regular shapes called **right prisms**.

3 Volumes of Right Prisms

A right prism has all its sides vertical to the base, and they are all the same length.

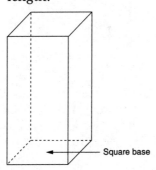

Square prism

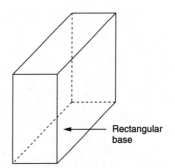

Rectangular prism

The two shapes above are often called **cuboids** or simply **box shapes**.

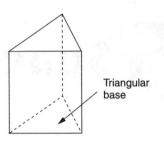

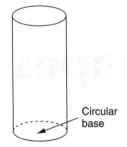

Circular base

Circular prism (cylinder)

Triangular base

Triangular prism

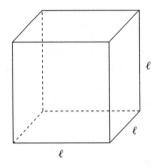

ℓ

ℓ

ℓ

Cube

A cube is a square prism, but its height is equal to the length of one of the sides of the base.

In every case of a right prism

volume = area of base × height

All measurements must be in the same units.

Worked example 1   Find the volume of a small box 10 cm × 8 cm × 6 cm.

Get into the habit of drawing a diagram of what you think the box looks like.

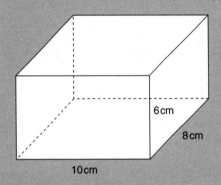

6 cm

8 cm

10 cm

Volume = area of base × height.
Area of base = length × breadth
$\qquad$ = 10 cm × 8 cm
$\qquad$ = 80 cm²
Volume = area of base × height
$\qquad$ = 80 cm² × 6 cm
$\qquad$ = 480 cm³
Answer 480 cm³

Worked example 2   Find the volume of a trinket box that measures
12 cm × 8 cm 5 mm × 6 cm 5 mm.

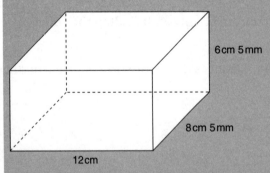

6 cm 5 mm

8 cm 5 mm

12 cm

Measurements must be in the same units:
8 cm 5 mm = 8.5 cm
6 cm 5 mm = 6.5 cm
Volume = area of base × height
Area of base = length × breadth
$\qquad$ = 12 cm × 8.5 cm
$\qquad$ = 102 cm²

Volume = area of base × height
$\qquad$ = 102 cm² × 6.5 cm
$\qquad$ = 663 cm³
Answer 663 cm³

Worked example 3   Find the volume of a cardboard box 3 ft × 2 ft 6 in by 1 ft 3 in.

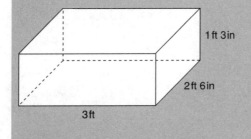

Measurements must be in the same units:

3 ft   = 36 in
2 ft 6 in = 30 in
1 ft 3 in = 15 in

Volume = area of base × height
Area of base = length × breadth
$\qquad\qquad\quad$ = 36 in × 30 in
$\qquad\qquad\quad$ = 1080 in²

Volume = area of base × height
$\qquad\quad$ = 1080 in² × 15 in
$\qquad\quad$ = 16 200 in³

Answer 16 200 in³

Worked example 4   Find the volume of a circular prism (cylinder) of radius 7 cm and height 20 cm $(\pi = \frac{22}{7})$.

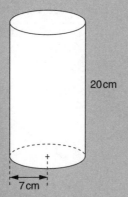

Volume = area of base × height
Area of base = πR^2
$\qquad\qquad\quad$ = $\pi \times R \times R$
$\qquad\qquad\quad$ = $\frac{22}{7} \times 7$ cm × 7 cm
$\qquad\qquad\quad$ = 154 cm²

Volume = area of base × height
$\qquad\quad$ = 154 cm² × 20 cm
$\qquad\quad$ = 3080 cm³

Answer 3080 cm³

Worked example 5   Find the volume of a cylinder of radius 2 cm and height 10 cm ($\pi = 3.14$).

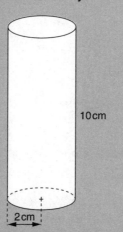

Volume = area of base × height
Area of base = πR^2
$\qquad\qquad\quad$ = $\pi \times R \times R$
$\qquad\qquad\quad$ = 3.14 × 2 cm × 2 cm
$\qquad\qquad\quad$ = 12.56 cm²

Volume = area of base × height
$\qquad\qquad\quad$ = 12.56 cm² × 10 cm
$\qquad\qquad\quad$ = 125.6 cm³

Answer 125.6 cm³

Worked example 6   Find the volume of the piece of steel shown:

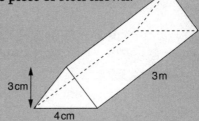

The sides do not go up vertically from the base but by standing it on the triangular side they will.

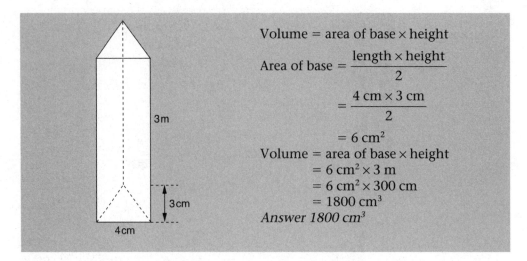

$$\text{Volume} = \text{area of base} \times \text{height}$$

$$\text{Area of base} = \frac{\text{length} \times \text{height}}{2}$$

$$= \frac{4\,\text{cm} \times 3\,\text{cm}}{2}$$

$$= 6\,\text{cm}^2$$

$$\text{Volume} = \text{area of base} \times \text{height}$$
$$= 6\,\text{cm}^2 \times 3\,\text{m}$$
$$= 6\,\text{cm}^2 \times 300\,\text{cm}$$
$$= 1800\,\text{cm}^3$$

Answer 1800 cm³

The method of worked example 6 can apply to any shape that has the same cross-section along the whole length.

Worked example 7 Find the volume of an angle iron having the following measurements:

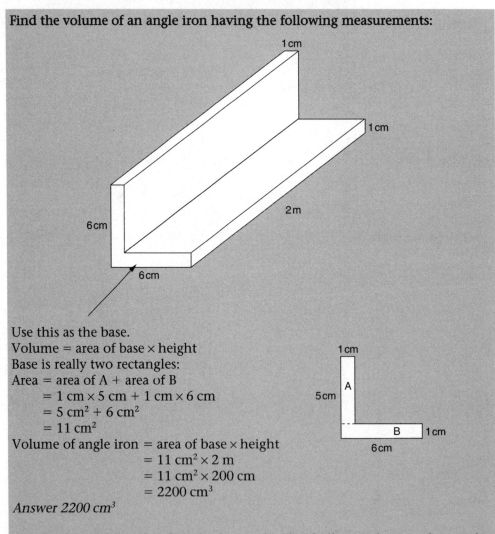

Use this as the base.
Volume = area of base × height
Base is really two rectangles:
Area = area of A + area of B
     = 1 cm × 5 cm + 1 cm × 6 cm
     = 5 cm² + 6 cm²
     = 11 cm²
Volume of angle iron = area of base × height
                     = 11 cm² × 2 m
                     = 11 cm² × 200 cm
                     = 2200 cm³

Answer 2200 cm³

Worked example 8 A swimming pool is 15 m long by 8 m wide. The shallow end is 1 m deep and it slopes gradually to the deep end, which is 2 m deep. What volume of water does the pool hold?

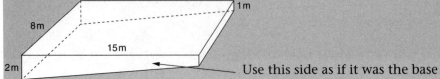

Use this side as if it was the base

Volume of the pool = area of side shown × width
To calculate the area of the side split it into two simple shapes, a rectangle A and a triangle B:

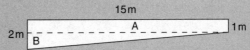

Area of rectangle = length × breadth
$$= 15 \text{ m} \times 1 \text{ m}$$
$$= 15 \text{ m}^2$$

$$\text{Area of triangle} = \frac{\text{base} \times \text{height}}{2}$$

$$= \frac{1 \text{ m} \times 15 \text{ m}}{2}$$

$$= 7\tfrac{1}{2} \text{ m}^2$$

Total area of side $= 15 \text{ m}^2 + 7\tfrac{1}{2} \text{ m}^2$
$$= 22\tfrac{1}{2} \text{ m}^2$$

Volume of pool = area of side × width
$$= 22\tfrac{1}{2} \text{ m}^2 \times 8 \text{ m}$$
$$= 180 \text{ m}^3$$

Answer 180 m³

Worked example 9 A garden shed has a shape and measurements as shown. What is its volume?

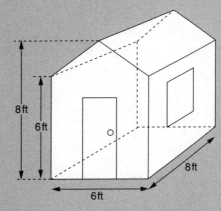

The front end of the shed continues in this shape throughout its length.
Volume of shed = area of end × length
Area of end:

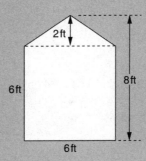

The shape consists of a rectangle and a triangle.

$$\text{Area of end} = 6\,\text{ft} \times 6\,\text{ft} + \frac{6\,\text{ft} \times 2\,\text{ft}}{2}$$

$$= 36\,\text{ft}^2 + 6\,\text{ft}^2$$
$$= 42\,\text{ft}^2$$

$$\text{Volume of shed} = \text{area of end} \times \text{length}$$
$$= 42\,\text{ft}^2 \times 8\,\text{ft}$$
$$= 336\,\text{ft}^3$$

Answer 336 ft³

The same type of working applies to shapes such as pipes.

Worked example 10 A metal pipe has an internal diameter of 20 mm and an external diameter of 40 mm. Find the volume of metal in a pipe 3 m long ($\pi = 3.14$).

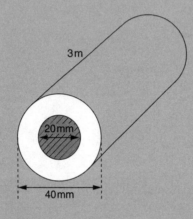

In this case find the area of metal at the end and then multiply by the length.

Volume of metal in pipe = area of metal at end × length
Area of metal at end:

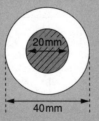

If $D = 20$ mm, $R = 10$ mm
$\qquad\qquad\qquad\quad = 1$ cm
$D = 40$ mm, $R = 20$ mm
$\qquad\qquad\qquad\quad = 2$ cm

To find the area of the end, unshaded part, first find the area of the outer circle and subtract from it the area of the inner circle.

$$\text{Area of outer circle} = \pi R^2$$
$$= \pi \times R \times R$$
$$= 3.14 \times 2\,\text{cm} \times 2\,\text{cm}$$
$$= 12.56\,\text{cm}^2$$

$$\text{Area of inner circle} = \pi R^2$$
$$= 3.14 \times 1\,\text{cm} \times 1\,\text{cm}$$
$$= 3.14\,\text{cm}^2$$

$$\text{Area of end} = 12.56\,\text{cm}^2 - 3.14\,\text{cm}^2$$
$$= 9.42\,\text{cm}^2$$

$$\text{Volume of metal in pipe} = \text{area of end} \times \text{length}$$
$$= 9.42\,\text{cm}^2 \times 3\,\text{m}$$
$$= 9.42\,\text{cm}^2 \times 300\,\text{cm}$$
$$= 2826\,\text{cm}^3$$

Answer 2826 cm³

4 Surface Area Each of the prisms so far, whether solid or hollow, also has a surface area. It is this surface area that encloses the space, so giving a volume.

It will help to draw a diagram and then try and imagine what the object would look like if it was flattened out.

Worked example 11 A cube has a side of 5 cm. Find the total surface area of the cube.

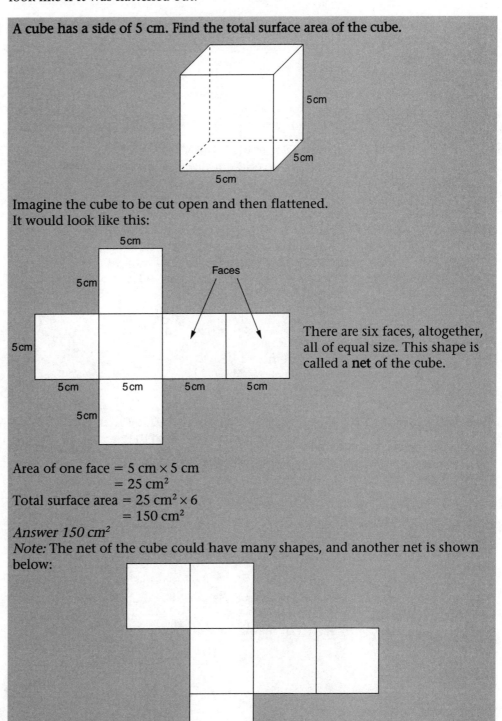

Imagine the cube to be cut open and then flattened.
It would look like this:

There are six faces, altogether, all of equal size. This shape is called a **net** of the cube.

Area of one face = 5 cm × 5 cm
$\qquad\qquad\qquad$ = 25 cm^2
Total surface area = 25 cm^2 × 6
$\qquad\qquad\qquad\qquad$ = 150 cm^2
Answer 150 cm^2
Note: The net of the cube could have many shapes, and another net is shown below:

5 Importance of Surface Area Most containers for storage and packing are made from sheet cardboard, sheet wood, or sheet metal. These are used to make 'box' shapes, cylinder shapes, or pipe shapes, and so buying the material in sheets enables a costing to be done for making a container.

In other words, costs are usually calculated from surface area and not from volume.

Worked example 12

A house is heated by oil contained in a metal tank, which is 2 m by 1.5 m by 1 m. The sheet metal from which the tank was made cost £10 per m². What was the cost of the metal needed to make the tank?

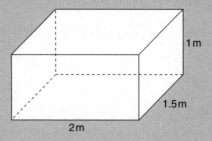

Without flattening it out you may be able to see that
      the top and bottom will be of equal size
      the two sides will be of equal size
and   the two ends will be of equal size
Area of bottom = 2 m × 1.5 m = 3 m²
Area of top and bottom = 6 m²
Area of one side = 2 m × 1 m = 2 m²
Area of two sides = 4 m²
Area of one end = 1.5 m × 1 m = 1.5 m²
Area of two ends = 3 m²
Total surface area = 6 m² + 4 m² + 3 m²
                = 13 m²
Cost is £10 per m²
Cost of 13 m² = £10 × 13
            = £130
Answer £130

Worked example 13

A large tin of Heinz baked beans is 110 mm tall and has a diameter of 74 mm. What area of sheet tin goes into the making of one tin? (Take $\pi = 3.14$.)

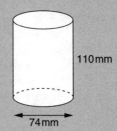

Imagine the two ends to be lifted up and the remaining part of the tin cut and then flattened.
The net of the tin could look like this:

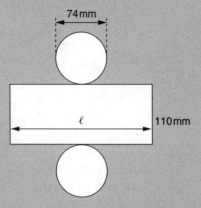

The flattened-out part of the tin will be the same length as the circumference of the top or bottom lid.

Area of top lid = πR^2
$\qquad\qquad$ = 3.14 × 3.7 cm × 3.7 cm $\qquad$ | 3.7 cm = 37 mm. |
$\qquad\qquad$ = 3.14 × 13.69 cm²
$\qquad\qquad$ = 42.99 cm²

Area of bottom lid is also 42.99 cm²
Area of flattened metal = ℓ × 11 cm
$\qquad\qquad\qquad\quad$ = πD × 11 cm
$\qquad\qquad\qquad\quad$ = 3.14 × 7.4 cm × 11 cm $\qquad$ | 110 mm = 11 cm;
$\qquad\qquad\qquad\quad$ = 255.60 cm² $\qquad\qquad\qquad$ | 74 mm = 7.4 cm.

Total area = 42.99 cm² + 42.99 cm² + 255.60 cm²
$\qquad\qquad$ = 341.58 cm²
Answer 341.58 cm² of sheet tin

Exercise 1

Find the volumes of the following shapes and, where needed, take $\pi = \frac{22}{7}$.

1
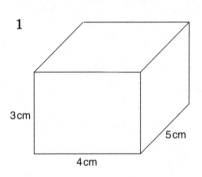
3 cm, 4 cm, 5 cm

2
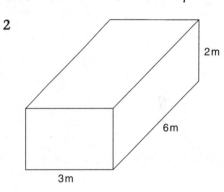
2 m, 6 m, 3 m

3
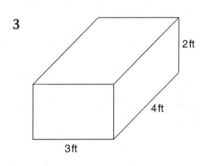
2 ft, 4 ft, 3 ft

4
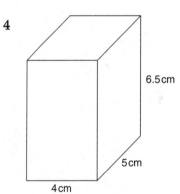
6.5 cm, 5 cm, 4 cm

5
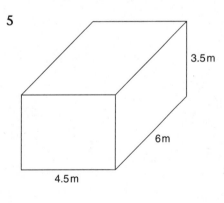
3.5 m, 6 m, 4.5 m

6
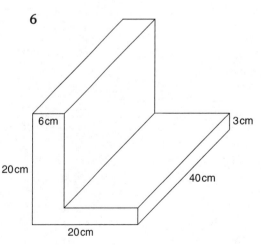
6 cm, 3 cm, 20 cm, 40 cm, 20 cm

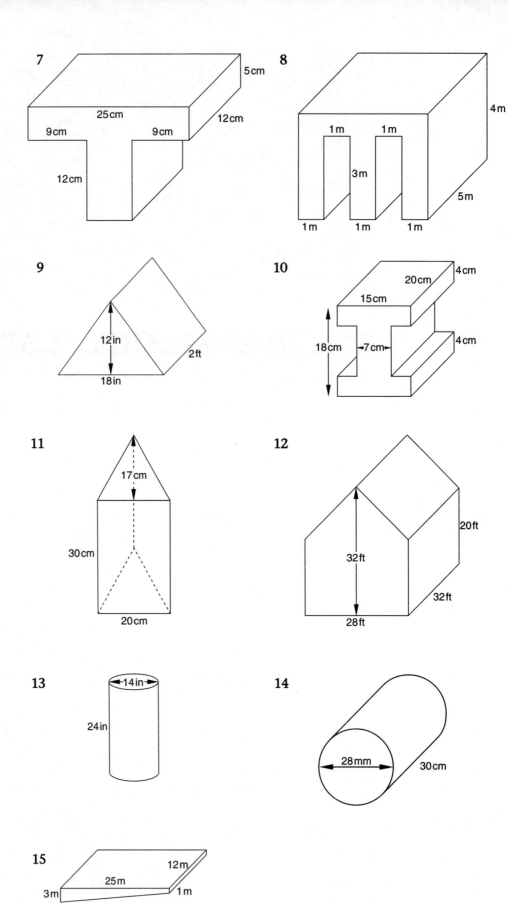

16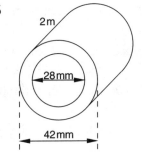

17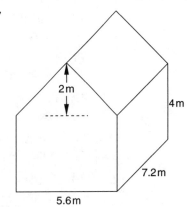

18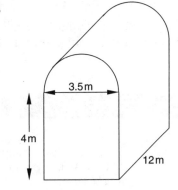

19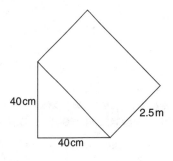

20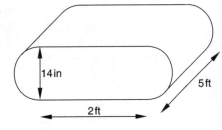

Exercise 2

Where required use $\pi = \frac{22}{7}$.

1 Find the volume of a cassette box that measures $1\frac{1}{2}$ cm by 7 cm by 11 cm.

2 Find the volume of a document box that measures 42 cm by 25 cm by 14 cm.

3 Find the volume of a book that measures 16 cm by 11 cm by 2 cm.

4 Find the volume of a cupboard that measures 5 ft by 2 ft 6 in by 1 ft 6 in.

5 Find the volume of a chest of drawers that measures 2 ft 6 in by 2 ft by 1 ft 6 in.

6 Find the volume of a water tank 3 ft by 2 ft by 2 ft.

7 A rectangular prism has a base of 18 cm². It is 25 cm high. What is its volume?

8 A rectangular prism has a volume of 540 cm³. Its height is 18 cm. What is the area of the base of the prism?

9 A tent is in the form of a triangular prism. The base is 8 ft by 6 ft. If the height of the ridge is 4 ft what is the volume occupied by the tent?

10   Find the volume of a cylinder that is 15 cm high and has a base of radius 7 cm.

11   Find the volume of a cylindrical toilet roll that measures 11 cm high and 14 cm across the base.

12   Find the volume of a cylindrical tin of hair spray if it measures 18 cm high and 5 cm across the base.

13   A water tank is 4 ft by 3 ft by 2 ft 6 in. How many gallons does it hold if 1 ft^3 holds $6\frac{1}{4}$ gallons?

14   A quarter of an inch of rain fell on a bowling green measuring 45 yd by 45 yd. What volume of water fell on the bowling green? (Answer in ft^3.)

15   Find the volume of a cube of side 6.5 cm.

16   A petrol tanker delivers petrol to a garage in a cylindrical container 24 ft long and 7 ft across. How many gallons does it hold when full if 1 ft^3 holds $6\frac{1}{4}$ gallons?

Exercise 3 Multiple choice questions

Work out which is the correct answer in the following questions (where necessary assume $\pi = \frac{22}{7}$):

1   A cube has a side of length 5 cm. Its volume is
   A 20 cm^3 B 125 cm^3 C 15 cm^3 D 75 cm^3

2   A rectangular box is 40 cm by 25 cm by 15 cm. Its volume is
   A 2.5 m^3 B 80 cm^3
   C 15 000 cm^3 D 12 000 cm^3

3   A rectangular box is 2 m × 60 cm × 40 cm. Its volume is
   A 0.48 m^3 B 4800 cm^3
   C 3.0 m^3 D 48 000 cm^3

4   A cube has a volume of 216 cm^3. The length of one side is
   A 72 cm   B 8 cm   C 36 cm   D 6 cm

5   A dice in the form of a cube has a side of 1 cm. The number of dice that will fit into a box 12 cm by 10 cm by 4 cm is
   A 26   B 480   C 120   D 360

6   A triangular prism has a volume of 360 cm^3. It is 18 cm high. The area of the end of the prism is
   A 40 cm   B 10 cm   C 20 cm   D 15 cm

7   Gold weighs 19 g for every cm^3. A gold ingot 8 cm × 4 cm × 12 cm weighs
   A 2.5 kg   B 20.21 g
   C 7296 g   D 3.21 kg

8   A rectangular metal box with top measures 12 cm × 10 cm × 4 cm. The metal surface area is
   A 416 cm^2 B 480 cm^2
   C 26 cm^2 D 324 cm^2

9   A small tin of baked beans is 6 cm high and has a diameter of 7 cm. The area of sheet tin that goes into its making is
   A 252 cm^2 B 42 cm^2
   C 294 cm^2 D 209 cm^2

10   An oat bran flake packet is 25 cm by 20 cm by 5 cm. The number of packets that can go into a cardboard box 1 m × 1 m × 80 cm is
   A 240   B 600   C 80   D 320

11   A water tank in the loft measures 1 m by 1 m by 80 cm. If 1 cm^3 of water weighs 1 g, the weight of water in the tank when it is full is
   A 8 kg   B 80 kg
   C 800 kg   D 8000 kg

12   Cylindrical tins 6 cm in diameter and 10 cm high are packed into a box 1 m by 72 cm by 60 cm. The maximum number of tins in the box is
   A 1200   B 960   C 1440   D 232

16 Assignments

1 Introduction

The purpose of this chapter is to present a number of situations showing that mathematics and its applications are always with us. The assignments do not demand a higher level of mathematics than that already attempted in this book.

The assignments may be regarded as being in order of difficulty.

Students should go carefully through all the information given in each assignment and try and establish what is being asked for and, therefore, what needs to be worked out.

As a major stumbling block in attempting to answer a problem is often 'Where do I start?', each assignment has hints relating to the order in which the working out may be attempted, though this does not mean it is the only way or the easiest way.

2 Equality or Not

Table 16.1 gives figures from HM Statistical Office, relating to the average hourly pay of adult men and women manual full-time employees over the years 1990–1994 in the various sectors stated (the pay is unaffected by absence).

Table 16.1 Average hourly pay of adult men and women manual full-time employees

	Energy and water supply	Extraction of minerals/ manufacture of metals/ mine products/ chemicals	Metal goods engineering and vehicles	Other manufacturing industries	Distribution/ hotel and catering	Transport and communication	Banking/ finance/ insurance	Service industries
Men								
1990	6.83	5.81	5.58	5.36	4.51	5.22	5.12	4.85
1991	7.50	6.19	6.08	5.74	4.83	5.71	5.42	5.28
1992	8.22	6.61	6.45	6.08	5.10	5.99	5.67	5.56
1993	8.54	6.81	6.68	6.29	5.21	6.23	5.60	5.72
1994	8.82	7.01	6.85	6.42	5.32	6.31	5.66	5.81
Women								
1990		4.06	3.86	3.67	3.29	4.68	4.59	3.64
1991	not available	4.38	4.18	3.93	3.60	5.21	4.95	3.97
1992		4.71	4.50	4.19	3.71	5.46	5.02	4.22
1993		4.90	4.64	4.40	3.83	5.74	5.04	4.32
1994		5.04	4.78	4.42	3.99	5.90	5.01	4.46

1 Which group, male or female, had the biggest percentage increase over the years 1990–1994? By how much?

2 Which group, male or female, had the smallest percentage increase over the years 1990–1994? By how much?

3 Which male group had the biggest percentage difference over their female colleagues in 1994? By how much?

4 Which male group had the smallest percentage difference over their female colleagues in 1994? By how much?

5   What was the percentage difference in 1994 between male employees in energy/water and hotel/catering, and what was it in 1990?

6   What was the percentage difference in 1994 between female employees in transport/communication and hotel/catering, and what was it in 1990?

Hints

When working out the percentages, first find the difference in money, then the fractional increase, and then the percentage increase. For example, finding the percentage increase in male pay for banking/finance between 1990 and 1994:

Hourly rate in 1990 = £5.12
        in 1994 = £5.66
Increase = £0.54

$$\text{Fractional increase in 1994 over 1990} = \frac{£0.54}{£5.12}$$

$$\text{Percentage increase} = \frac{0.54}{5.12} \times 100\%$$

$$= 10.55\%$$

Using this type of format, work out the other questions asked.

3 Business Studies Students' Christmas Party

The 2nd-year business studies students have the task each year of organising the Christmas party for 1st-, 2nd- and 3rd-year business studies students.

This year it was held on 12 December from 8.00 p.m. to 1.00 a.m. Tickets, including buffet refreshments, were £3 for each student and £5 for any guests.

The DJ charged £25 an hour before midnight and £40 an hour after. £1.50 was spent on buffet refreshments for each person. Drinks, on sale or return, cost £240 for wine, £420 for beer, and £60 for soft drinks. Profit on wine was to be 30%, beer 25% and soft drinks 60%. Returns were £40 wine, £64 beer and no soft drinks.

280 students and 66 guests attended.

Profit to be split as follows: £50 to business studies social fund, and of the remaining profit 40% to the local hospice, 35% to cancer research, and 25% to Greenpeace.

Find how much money was given to the local hospice, how much to cancer research, and how much to Greenpeace.

Hints

Find total income collected on tickets; subtract fixed expenditure of DJ and buffet costs.
Find profit on wine, beer and soft drinks, remembering there were some returns. Now find total profit.
Split up as agreed.

4 Careful Driving

Remember that the 15–19 and 20–24 groups are more vulnerable to road accidents than other ages. In fact, in 1993, 27.4% of all people killed and seriously injured in road accidents were from the 15–24 age group.

The *Highway Code* gives the *shortest* stopping distances for cars travelling at different speeds, allowing a small amount of stopping distance for thinking. (Large vehicles and motorcycles need more time to stop than cars.)

The speeds and shortest stopping distances are given in Table 16.2, and apply to a dry road and the car having good brakes and tyres.

Table 16.2 Relationship between speed of cars and shortest stopping distances on dry roads with good brakes and tyres

Speed (mile/h)	20	30	40	50	60	70
Shortest stopping distance (ft)	40	75	120	175	240	315

Draw a curved graph to illustrate this information, with speed on the *x*-axis and distance on the *y*-axis. Leave enough room on the *x*-axis to extend the speed to 90 mile/h and on the *y*-axis distance to 600 ft.

From the graph what do you estimate the shortest stopping distance is for a speed of

1 10 mile/h?   2 35 mile/h?   3 65 mile/h?

Estimate what speed you are doing to have a shortest stopping distance of

4 100 ft   5 200 ft   6 300 ft

By extending the curve of the graph what do you estimate to be the shortest stopping distance for cars travelling at

7 80 mile/h?   8 90 mile/h?

Hints

Use a scale for the *x*-axis, say from 0 to 100, so that it covers most of the graph paper. Choose a scale for the *y*-axis, say from 0 to 600, so that it covers most of the paper. Plot the points given. Draw the best curve you can so that it goes through these points and also through 0, 0. (If you are not moving there is no stopping distance required!) From the graph, answer the questions.

5 Timetables

1 Using the timetables below find
   (a) How often does flight LC680 operate from Kirkwall?
   (b) How long does it take on the morning flight from Kirkwall to Edinburgh?
   (c) On which day does flight number BA4793 not operate from Edinburgh to London?
   (d) What is the longest time taken to fly from Gatwick to Plymouth?
   (e) What is the earliest time you can reach Plymouth by leaving Papa Westray on a Thursday morning at 0904 hours going via Kirkwall, Edinburgh and London Heathrow?

ORKNEY INTERNAL AIR SERVICE

Reservations: Telephone: Kirkwall 2494

Operating   25th MARCH 1985 to 27th OCTOBER 1985

Days		Monday & Wednesday							Tuesday & Thursday					
Flight No. LC		610	612	614	680	611	613	615	620	622	624	621	623	625
Kirkwall	dep	0830	0935	1025	1200	1430	1535	1620	0830	0930	1030	1430	1530	1630
Westray	arr dep		0947 0957				1547 1557		0842 0852			1442 1452		
Papa Westray	arr dep								0854 0904			1454 1504		
Stronsay	arr dep			1033 1043	1208 1216			1628 1638	0938 0948				1538 1548	
Eday	arr dep			1048 1058				1643 1653	0953 1003				1553 1603	
Sanday	arr dep	0841 0851		No Eday	1221 1229	1441 1451		No Eday		1041 1051				1641 1651
North Ronaldsay	arr dep	0856 0906		Call on Wed		1456 1506		Call on Wed						
Stronsay	arr dep													
Kirkwall	arr	0919	1009	1106	1240	1519	1609	1701	0916	1011	1102	1516	1611	1702

Days		Friday						Saturday				
Flight No. LC		630	632	634	631	633	635	650	651	652	653	654
Kirkwall	dep	0830	0930	1020	1415	1515	1605	0830	0920	1330	1430	1520
Westray	arr dep		0941 0951			1527 1537			0932 0940		1442 1540	
Papa Westray	arr dep								0854 0950		1458	1454
Stronsay	arr dep				1423 1433					1338 1346		
Eday	arr dep			1028 1038			1613 1623	0956 1004				
Sanday	arr dep	0841 0851			1438 1448			0841 0849				1531 1539
North Ronaldsay	arr dep			1044 1054			1629 1639		1352 1400			
Stronsay	arr dep	0856 0906						0854 0902				
Kirkwall	arr	0914	1003	1107	1459	1549	1652	0910	1012	1414	1510	1550

NOTE: LC680 OPERATES ONLY WHEN ALTERNATIVE FLIGHTS ARE FULL.

Part of British Airways' summer timetable

EDINBURGH—WICK—KIRKWALL
Reservations: Telephone: 031-344 3341/3247

Operating		25 Mar–26 Oct	26 Mar–24 Oct
Days Aircraft		Mon, Fri, Sat SH6	Tu, We, Th DHT
Flight No.		LC333	LC333
Edinburgh	dep	1040	0835
Wick	arr dep	1145 1200	0950 1005
Kirkwall	arr	1215	1020
Flight No.		LC334	LC334
Kirkwall	dep	1235	1040
Wick	arr dep	1250 1305	1055 1110
Edinburgh	arr	1410	1225

Part of British Airways' summer timetable

From	To	Days 1234567	Depart	Arrive	Flight No	Air- craft	Class Stops	Arr.	Airport	Dep.	Flight	Aircraft	Class
									-Transfer -				

From EDINBURGH   continued

► London

		123456-	0710	0820	BA4713	EQV	M 0	Super Shuttle
		12345--	0810	0920	BA4723	TRD5	M 0	Super Shuttle
		Daily	0910	1020	BA4733	TRD5	M 0	Super Shuttle
		Daily	1110	1220	BA4753	EQV	M 0	Super Shuttle
		Daily	1310	1420	BA4773	7575	M 0	Super Shuttle
		12345-7	1510	1620	BA4793	EQV	M 0	Super Shuttle
		12345--	1610	1720	BA4803	B115	M 0	Super Shuttle
		Daily	1710	1820	BA4813	7575	M 0	Super Shuttle
		Daily	1910	2020	BA4833	7575	M 0	Super Shuttle

Part of British Airways' Worldwide Timetable

Flight No.	Frequency	Dep.	Arr.	Route	Service
FROM LONDON GATWICK					
to Birmingham					
BC 203	12345	0835	0920	Direct	CB/BA
BC 205	12345	1130	1215	Direct	BA
BC 207	12345	1925	2010	Direct	LR/BA
BC 209	67	1045	1130	Direct	CB/BA
BC 211	7	1945	2030	Direct	LR/BA
to Exeter					
BC 702	123456	0845	0945	Direct	HD
BC 722	123456	1900	2005	Direct	HD
BC 704	7	0955	1100	Direct	HD
to Isles of Scilly					
BC 702/511•	123456	0845	1130	EXT/PLH	HD
to Plymouth					
BC 702	123456	0845	1015	EXT	HD
BC 722	123456	1900	2030	EXT	HD
BC 704	7	0955	1130	EXT	HD
FROM LONDON HEATHROW					
to Isles of Scilly					
BC 803/511•	12345	0915	1130	PLH	HD/BA
BC 805/515•	12345	1245	1530	PLH/NQY	HD/BA
to Newquay					
BC 803	12345	0915	1050	PLH	CB/BA
BC 805	12345	1245	1420	PLH	HD/BA
BC 807	12345	1615	1750	PLH	HD/BA
BC 809	12345	1940	2110	PLH	LR/BA
BC 813	6	1015	1125	Direct	CB/BA
BC 819	7	1940	2050	Direct	LR/BA
to Plymouth					
BC 803	12345	0915	1020	Direct	CB/BA
BC 805	12345	1245	1350	Direct	HD/BA
BC 807	12345	1615	1715	Direct	HD/BA
BC 809	12345	1940	2045	Direct	LR/BA
BC 813	6	1015	1155	NQY	CB/BA
BC 819	7	1940	2125	NQY	LR/BA

ADDITIONAL NOTES:

•Services to Isles of Scilly operate on the following days:
Mondays - 3rd June to 2nd Sept. Tues/Wed/Thurs. - 14th May to 26th Sept.
Fri/Sats. - April to Oct.

HD – Hot Drinks   LR – Light Refreshments   BA – Bar Service   CB – Continental Breakfast

1 — Monday. 2 — Tuesday. 3 — Wednesday. 4 — Thursday.
5 — Friday.   6 — Saturday. 7 — Sunday.

Part of British Airways' summer timetable

2 Please look at railway timetables numbers 23, 49 and 75. From the tables find
   (a) On Mondays to Fridays, what is the frequency of trains from Manchester Piccadilly to Liverpool Lime Street? Which train takes longest?
   (b) On Saturdays, how long does the 1123 train from Shrewsbury wait in Machynlleth?
   (c) What is the quickest time by train, Monday to Friday, from London Kings Cross to Knebworth? What time does it leave Kings Cross? Between which stations does it seem to gain a minute?
   (d) A salesman has to travel on Tuesday from Huntingdon to Aberystwyth in time to attend a 2.00 p.m. meeting in Aberystwyth. If he goes via Peterborough and Birmingham find the latest time he can leave Huntingdon to be at Aberystwyth in time for the meeting. How long will he have to wait for the meeting?

Table 23 **Mondays to Fridays**

London → Royston, Cambridge and Peterborough

Miles	Miles			MX	MX [1]	MX [1]	MO [1]	MX	MX [1]	[1]	[1]	[1]	[1]	[1]	[1]	[1] A	[1]	[1] A	[1]	[1]	[1]	[1]	[1] A	[1]
0	0	**London Kings Cross §**	⊖ 20, 24, 26 d	23p02	23p08	23p23	23p23		23p38	00 08	00 38	01 08	01 38	05 20	05 48	06 08	06 38	06 52	07 08	07 12		07 38	07 43	
2½	2½	Finsbury Park	⊖ 24 d	23p07	23p13		23p28		23p43	00 13	00 43	01 13	01 43	05 25	05 53	06 13	06 43	06 57	07 13	07 17		07 43		
12¾	12¾	Potters Bar	24 d		23p23		23p38		23p59		00 59		01 57	05 37	06 02	06 23	06 53		07 23			07 53		←
17¾	17¾	Hatfield	24 d		23p29		23p44		00 05		01 05		02 03	05 43	06 08	06 29	06 59		07 29		←	07 59		07 59
20¼	20¼	Welwyn Garden City	24 d		23p33		23p48		00 09		01 09		02 07	05 47	06 12	06 33	07 03		07 33		07 33	→		08 03
22	22	Welwyn North	24 d		23p36		23p51		00 13		01 13		02 11	05 50	06 15	06 36	07 06		→		07 36			08 06
25	25	Knebworth	24 d		23p40		23p55	←	00 17		01 17		02 15	05 54	06 19	06 40	07 10				07 40			08 10
—	—	Hertford North	24 d	23p41				23p41		00 39		01 39								*07 12*				
27½	27½	**Stevenage**	24, 26 d	→	23p44	23p48	23p59	23p54	00 21	00 50	01 21	01 50	02 19	05 58	06 23	06 44	07 14	07 18		07 37	07 44		08 06	08 14
31¾	31¾	Hitchin	24 d		23p51	23p54	00 05	00 02	00 33	00 58	01 26	01 58	02 24	06b10	06 32	06 51	07 20	07 24		07 42	07 50		08 11	08 20
34¾	—	Letchworth	24 d		23p58			00a22	00a37	01 03		02a18		06 14		06 55		07 28			07 55		08 16	
36¾	—	Baldock	d		00 01					01 06				06 18		06 58		07 31			07 58		08 19	
41	—	Ashwell & Morden	d		00 07					01 12				06 23		07 04		07 37			08 04		08 25	
45	—	**Royston**	a		00s15					01s32				06 28		07 09		07 42			08 09		08 30	
—	—		d											06 28		07 09		07 42			08 09		08 30	
48	—	Meldreth	d		00s19					01s36				06 32		07 13		07 47			08 13			
50	—	Shepreth	d		00s22					01s39				06 36		07 16		07 51			08 16			
51	—	Foxton	d		00s25					01s42				06 38		07 19		07 53			08 19			
58	—	**Cambridge**	20 a		00 49					02 06				06 52		07 30		08 05			08 32		08 47	
—	37	Arlesey	d			23p59	00 10								06 37		07 25			07 47				08 25
—	41	Biggleswade	d			00 04	00 15				01 36		02 34		06 42		07 30			07 52				08 30
—	44	Sandy	d			00 08	00 19								06 46		07 34			07 56				08 34
—	51½	St Neots	d			00 15	00 26				01 46		02 44		06 53		07 41			08 04				08 41
—	58¾	Huntingdon	26 a			00 26	00 36				01 56		02 54		07 03		07 51			08 14				08 51
—	—		d			00 26	00 36				01 56		02 54		07 04		07 51			08 14				08 51
—	76¼	**Peterborough [8]**	26 a			00 47	00 56				02 29		03 27		07 19		08 10			08 31				09 10

Table 75 **Mondays to Fridays**

Shrewsbury → Aberystwyth

Miles			RR		RR		A			A		◇ RR ⌶			A		◇ RR ⌶			◇ RR ⌶		◇ RR			
—	London Euston	74 d					*05 34*			*08 15*		*10 15*			*12 15*		*14 15*			*15 45*		*18 15*			
—	Birmingham New Street [15]	74 d					08 17			10 17		12 17			14 17		16 17			18 06		20 19			
—	Wolverhampton [10]	74 d					08 38			10u38		12u38			14u38		16u38			18u27		20u43			
—	Cardiff Central	131 d					*07 19*			*08 45*		*10 45*			*12 45*		*14 45*			*16 45*		*18 45*			
—	Liverpool Lime Street	79, 131 d					*07***b***27*			*09 18*		*10***b***49*			*13 18*		*15***b***10*			*16***b***45*		*18***b***54*			
—	Manchester Piccadilly	81, 131 d					*07***b***35*			*09***b***05*		*11 33*			*13***b***05*		*15 33*			*17 33*		*19 33*			
—	Crewe [12]	131 d					*08 39*			*10 30*		*12 13*			*14 13*		*16 13*			*18 17*		*20 20*			
—	Chester	74 d					*07 09*			*10 00*		*11 28*			*13 27*		*15 24*			*17 29*		*20 12*			
0	**Shrewsbury**	d					09 25			11 23		13 25			15 25		17 25			19 25		21 31			
19¾	Welshpool	d					09 48			11 48		13 48			15 48		17 48			19 48		21 54			
33¾	Newtown	d					10 04			12 04		14 04			16 04		18 04			20 04		22 10			
39½	Caersws	d					10 11			12 11		14 11			16 11		18 11			20 11		22 17			
61	Machynlleth	76 a					10 42			12 42		14 42			16 42		18 43			20 46		22 48			
—		76 d	06 20		08 15		10 43			12 45		14 43			16 43		18 44			20 47		22 49			
65	Dovey Junction	76 d	06 27		08 22		10 50			12 52		14 50			16 54		18 51			20 54		22 56			
86½	**Barmouth**	76 a	*07 31*		*09 54*					*13 43*					*17 57*					*21 49*					
118½	Pwllheli	76 a	*09 20*		*11 19*					*14 47*					*19 01*					*22 58*					
73½	Borth	d	06 37		08 32		11 01			13 03		15 01			17 04		19 02			21 05		23 07			
81½	**Aberystwyth**	a	06 49		08 44		11 12			13 14		15 12			17 16		19 13			21 16		23 18			

		RR	RR	𝒜	𝒜	RR ♦ ♓	𝒜	RR ♦ ♓	RR ♦ ♓	RR ♦		
London Euston	74 d				08 05	10 05	12 05	14 05	15 35	17 35		
Birmingham New Street 🔟	74 d			08 17	08 05	10 17	12 17	14 17	16 17	18 06	20 19	
Wolverhampton 🔟	74 d			08 38	10u38	12u38	14u38	16u38	18u27	20u43		
Cardiff Central	131 d			07 19	08 45	10 45	12 45	14 45	16 45	18 45		
Liverpool Lime Street	79, 131 d			07b45	09 18	10b49	13 18	15b05	16b48	18b54		
Manchester Piccadilly	81, 131 d			07b35	09b05	11 33	13b05	15 33	17 33	19 33		
Crewe 🔟	131 d			08 39	10 30	12 13	14 13	16 13	18 17	20 20		
Chester	74 d			07 09	10 00	11 28	13 27	15 24	17 29	20 12		
Shrewsbury	d			09 25	11 23	13 25	15 25	17 25	19 25	21 31		
Welshpool 🖪	d			09 48	11 48	13 48	15 48	17 48	19 48	21 54		
Newtown	d			10 04	12 04	14 04	16 04	18 04	20 04	22 10		
Caersws	d			10 11	12 11	14 11	16 11	18 11	20 11	22 17		
Machynlleth	76 a		06 20	08 15	10 42	12 42	14 42	16 42	18 43	20 46	22 48	
Dovey Junction	76 d	06 27	08 22	10 50	12 52	14 50	16 54	18 51	20 54	22 56		
Barmouth	76 a	07 31	09 54	13 43	15 49	17 57	21 49					
Pwllheli	76 a	09 20	11 19	14 47	17 08	19 01	22 58					
Borth	d	06 37	08 32	11 01	13 03	15 01	17 04	19 02	21 05	23 07		
Aberystwyth	a	06 49	08 44	11 12	13 14	15 12	17 16	19 13	21 16	23 18		

Table 49

East Anglia → East Midlands →
Birmingham and North West England

		♦ RR	𝒜	𝒜	♦ RR	♦ RR	𝒜	♦ RR	𝒜	RR	𝒜	♦ RR	𝒜	RR	𝒜	RR	♦ RR	𝒜
Norwich	d				05 52		07 00		07 53		09 00		09 58		11 02		11 48	
Thetford	d				06 25		07 27		08 26		09 27		10 31		11 29		12 21	
Harwich International	d								07 40				09k00					
Ipswich	d								08 06			08 16	09 43					
Stowmarket	d								08 18			08 32	09 57					
Bury St Edmunds	d								08 35			08 53	10 14					
Cambridge	d		05 20	06 30	06 35		07 35	07 54	08 06	09 05		10 05	10 38	11 05	11 38	12 05	12 38	
Ely	d		05 37	06 47	06 55	07 04	07 54	08 11	08 57	09 22	09 53	10 24	11 02	11 22	11 55	12 23	12 58	
March	d		05 53	07 03	07 12	07 23	08 10	08 27		09 38		10 40	11 38			12 39	13 14	
Peterborough 🖪	a		06 14	07 23	07 32	07 43	08 27	08 45	09 29	09 57	10 25	11 03	11 34	11 56	12 27	12 59	13 32	
Leeds 🔟	a		09c14			09 28		10 41	11 34	12c01	12 33		13 34	14c01	14 33	15c01	15 34	
York 🖪	a		08 31			09c25	09 34		10 59	11 31	11 51		12 24	12 59	13 31	13 54	14 32	
Newcastle 🖪	a		09 35			10c29	10 50		11 59	12 37	12 45		13 19	13 59	14 36	14 49	15 37	
Edinburgh 🔟	a		11 09				12 16		13 42		14 12		14 51	15 32		16 25	17a25	
Glasgow Queen Street	a		12e20				13h19		14e50		15h19		16e20	16h45		17e50	18q50	
London Kings Cross ⊖ 23, 26 d						07 00	07 12		08 20	09 00	09 30		10 00	10 30	11 00		11 30	12 00	12 30
Peterborough 🖪	d		06 16	07 25	07 34	07 47	08 27	08 46	09 31	09 58	10 30		11 04	11 36	11 57	12 29	13 01	13 33
Stamford	d		06 28	07 37		08 00		08 59		10 11			11 16		12 09		13 13	
Oakham	d		06 47	07 51		08 14		09 13		10 25			11 30		12 23		13 27	
Melton Mowbray	d		06 57	08 01		08 24		09 23		10 35			11 41		12 34		13 37	
Leicester	a		07 17	08 21		08 47		09 43		10 54			12 03		12 54		13 55	
Hinckley	a		07 38			09 32		10 09		11 35			12 44		13 36		14 43	
Nuneaton	a		07 47	08 44		09 09		10 18		11 17			12 23		13 16		14 17	
Coventry	a		08 47			10 11		11 02		12 09			13 00		14 15		15 03	
Birmingham New Street 🔟	a		08 22	09 20		09 42		10 49		11 50			12 55		13 50		14 50	
Grantham	d		06 52		08 03		09 01		10 00		11 01		12 09		12 59		14 06	
Loughborough	d		08103	08155		09137		10120		11122		13110		13122		14132		
Nottingham 🖪	a		08g40	09g29	08 42		09g53	09 35	10g40	10 34	11g42	11 36	12g55	12 43	13g45	13 32	14g44	14 39
	d	05 24	06 33	07 34	08 43		09 43		10 45		11 46		12 44		13 37		14 41
Derby 🔟	a			08 41		09g14	09 40	10g14	10 25	11g14	11 43	12g12	12 26	13g14	13 42	14g18	14 14	15g12	15 45
	d			07b40		08b43		09b24		10b38		11b24		12b24		13b41		14b24
Langley Mill	d		06 49	07 51		09 00		09 59		11 08		12 08		13 00		13 58		14 58
Alfreton	d		06 57	07 59		09 08		10 07		11 15		12 15		13 08		14 15		15 06
Chesterfield	d	05 59	07 14	08 15		09 24		10 24		11 25		12 25		13 25		14 15		15 23
Sheffield 🖪	a	06 14	07 32	08 33		09 39		10 39		11 40		12 40		13 40		14 32		15 38
Stockport	d	06 17	07 35	08 42		09 43		10 43		11 43		12 43		13 43		14 36		15 42
Manchester Piccadilly	a	07 25	08 25	09 25		10 25		11 25		12 25		13 25		14 25		15 25		16 25
Manchester Oxford Road	a	07 36	08 36	09 36		10 36		11 36		12 36		13 36		14 36		15 36		16 36
Warrington Central	a	07 39	08 39	09 39		10 39		11 39		12 39		13 39		14 39		15 39		16 39
Widnes	a	07 57	08 57	09 57		10 57		11 57		12 57		13 57		14 57		15 57		16 57
Liverpool Lime Street	a	08 05	09 05	10 05		11 05		12 05		13 05		14 05		15 05		16 05		17 05
	a	08 32	09 29	10 29		11 29		12 29		13 29		14 29		15 29		16 29		17 29

For general notes see front of timetable

b	Change at Sheffield	h	Glasgow Central
c	Change at Doncaster	j	Change at Ely
e	Change at Edinburgh	k	Change at Manningtree and Ipswich
f	Arrival time, change at Leicester	n	Change at Newcastle
g	Change at Leicester	q	Change at Newcastle and Edinburgh

3 Using the timetables opposite find
  (a) How long does it take to travel from the Corporation Arms, Longridge to Blackburn on the bus leaving Preston bus station at 1222?
  (b) If you leave Burnley at 1230, how long does it take by bus to reach Heathrow, Terminal 4?
  (c) What is the quickest journey by bus from Burnley to Heathrow, Terminal 4?
  (d) What wait do you have in Manchester if travelling by the 1050 bus from Blackpool to Sheffield?

(e) A person living near Longridge post office wants to travel by bus to Rotherham and is prepared to travel on the 0723 bus to Blackburn. She sees that by changing in Manchester and going to Sheffield and then on to Rotherham the journey could be done in one day. What is the earliest time she could arrive in Rotherham by leaving Longridge at 0723? How long does the journey take?

Preston · Longridge · Ribchester · Blackburn
(including part Service 10)

Monday to Friday

	Code											⊕	○	10	▪					
Preston, Bus Station	dep.	0652	0722		0922	1022	1122	1222	1322	1422	1522		1635	1622	1662		1722	1818	1918	2018	2132
Ribbleton, Gamull Lane		0708	0738		0938	1038	1138	1238	1338	1438	1538		1651	1638	1708		1738	1834	1934	2034	2148
Grimsargh, Plough Inn		0713	0743		0643	1043	1143	1243	1343	1443	1643	⏐	1656	1643	1713		1743	1839	1939	2039	2163
Longridge, Stone Bridge		0721	0751		0951	1051	1151	1251	1351	1451	1551	1553	1604	1651			1723	1751	1846	1946	2046	2200
Longridge, Post Office		0723	0753		0953	1053	1153	1253	1353	1453	1553		1605	1653	1723↦		1725	1753	1848	1948	2048	2202
Longridge, Corporation Arms		0726	0756		0956	1056	1156	1256	1356	1456	1556	1609	1656			1728	1756	1851	1951	2051	2206
Ribchester, Ribchester Arms		0735	0805		1005	1105	1205	1305	1405	1505	1605	1618	1618	1705		1737	1805	1900	2000	2100	2214
Oaks Bar		0713	0743	0813	1013	1113	1213	1313	1413	1513	1613	1626	1626	1713		1745	1813	1908	2008	2108	2222
Salesbury, Bonny Inn		0715	0745	0815	▲	1015	1115	1215	1315	1415	1515	1615	1628	1628	1715		1747	1815	1910	2010	2110	2224
Wilpshire, Bulls Head		0718	0748	0818	0918	1018	1118	1218	1318	1418	1518	1618	1631	1631	1718		1750	1818	1913	2013	2113	2227
Lammack, Hare & Hounds Hotel																			1921	2021	2121	2235
Four Lane Ends		0726	0766	0826	0926	1026	1126	1226	1326	1426	1526	1626	1639	1639	1726		1758	1826	1922	2022	2122	2236
Blackburn, Boulevard	arr.	0737	0807	0837	0937	1037	1137	1237	1337	1437	1537	1637	1650	1650	1737		1809	1837	1932	2032	2132	2246

825	**Burnley** - BOLTON - MANCHESTER - BIRMINGHAM - COVENTRY - HEATHROW AIRPORT - **Gatwick Airport**	**825**
825	**Rochdale** - OLDHAM - MANCHESTER - BIRMINGHAM - COVENTRY - LEAMINGTON SPA - HEATHROW AIRPORT - **Gatwick Airport**	825
825	**Manchester** - BIRMINGHAM - COVENTRY - LUTON - HEATHROW AIRPORT - **Gatwick Airport**	825

Shows full East Lancashire/Manchester to Birmingham/Coventry service.

For Bank Holiday arrangements see below	806	825	730	924	825	830	825	850	825	825	850	825	923	735	808	820	821
Days of operation	D	D	D	NSuM	D	D	D	D	D	D	D	D	D	D	D	D	D
BURNLEY, Bus Stn., Stand 15						0700		0830			1230					2130	
Accrington, Infant St., Stand 'O'						0715		0845			1245					2145	
BLACKBURN, Boulevard Bus Stn., Stand Y						0730		0900			1300					2200	
Darwen, Bolton Rd., opp. Belgrave Church								0910			1310					2210	
BOLTON, Moor Lane, Bus Stn.								0935			1335				1735	2235	
Salford University, Museum & Art Gallery, Bus Stop	0415							0955			1355				1755	2255	
ROCHDALE, Yelloway Coach Stn., Weir St.									1105								
OLDHAM, Yelloway Coach Stn., 3 Mumps									1125								
Ashton-under-Lyne, Bus Stn., Stand C									1140								
MANCHESTER, National Coach Stn., Chorlton St......arr.	0425							1005	1205		1405				1805	2305	
MANCHESTER, National Coach Stn., Chorlton St......dep.	0430		0645		0810		1010	1210		1410	1630			1810	2310	
Stockport, Bus Stn., Stand A								1030			1430					2330	
Manchester Airport, Bus Stn., Stand C	0450						1045			1445				1830	2345	
Altrincham, Interchange Bus Stn., Stand F					0835			1235								
Sandbach Service Area, M6......arr.															0005	
Sandbach Service Area, M6......dep.															0040	0040
Stoke-on-Trent, Etruria Rd., Bus Stop, nr. Sentinel House (Y)														1910		
STOKE-ON-TRENT, Hanley, Bus Stn.	0635													1920	0100	0100
Wolverhampton, Pipers Row Bus Stn., Coach Stop			0750			0950	1150		1350	1550					0135	0135
BIRMINGHAM, National Coach Stn., Digbeth	0635		0825	0830		1020	1025R	1225	1220R	1425R	1625	1620R	1815		2020R	0210E	0210E
BIRMINGHAM, National Coach Stn., Digbeth......dep.		0700			0900		1100		1300	1500		1700		1900	2100	0210E	0210E
COVENTRY, Pool Meadow Bus Stn.		0740			0940		1140		1340	1540		1740		1940	2140	0245	0245
LEAMINGTON SPA, Coach Stop, Hamilton Terrace					1000				1600							
LUTON, Bute St. Bus Stn.		0905				1305									0445	
Uxbridge, Bakers Rd., Bus Stn., Stand O.							1540		1940					0510	
HEATHROW AIRPORT, Central Bus Stn.		0955			1155		1355		1555	1765		1955			0525	
HEATHROW AIRPORT, Terminal 4, Arrivals Forecourt		1005			1205		1405		1605	1805		2005				
GATWICK AIRPORT, Coach Stn., Ground Level		1050			1250		1450		1650	1850		2050		0700		

For Bank Holiday arrangements see below	352	361	296	352	361	352	361	363	363	363
Periods of operation									1	
Days of operation	D	D	D	D	D	D	D	S	F	D
BLACKPOOL, National Coach Stn., Coliseum	0850		0910	1050		1250		1300	1300	1750
Blackpool, Preston New Rd., Corner	0855		⏐	1055		1255		⏐	⏐	1755
Blackpool, Squires Gate, Fylde Transport Garage, Nat. Exp. stop.			0915					1305	1305	
Blackpool, Pontins Camp, National Express stop			0917					1307	1307	
St. Annes, Ashton Gardens			0920					1310	1310	
Ansdell, opp. Fairhaven Hotel			0925					1315	1315	
Lytham, Baths			0930					1320	1320	
PRESTON, Bus Station, Stand 68	0930		1000A	1130		1330				1830
Salford, University Museum & Art Gallery, Bus Stop	1015			1215		1415				1915
MANCHESTER, Nat. Coach Stn., Chorlton St., Stand B......arr.	1025			1225		1425				1925R
MANCHESTER, Nat. Coach Stn., Chorlton St., Stand B......dep.		1130			1330		1530			2000
Gorton, Hyde Rd., Debdale Park, Bus Stop, opp. Reddish Lane		1135			1335		1535			2005
Hyde, Bus Stn., Stand A		1145			1345		1545			2015
Hollingworth, Memorial, Bus Stop		1150			1350		1550			2020
Flouch Inn		1220			1420		1620			2050
Stocksbridge, Bus Stop, Coach & Horses		1230			1430		1630			2100
Sheffield, opp. Hillsborough Baths		1245			1445		1645			2115
SHEFFIELD, Central Bus Stn., Platform G......arr.		1255	1400		1455		1655R	1605	1605	2125
SHEFFIELD, Central Bus Stn., Platform G......dep.							1730	1605	1605	2125
ROTHERHAM, Bus Stn., Stand B4							1755	1630	1630	2150

6 The Newsagent From Monday to Saturday during one week in July a newsagent stocked the number of daily newspapers shown in Table 16.3 on the next page (the selling price of each newspaper is also shown on the chart).

Table 16.3 Number of copies of newspapers stocked

Week beginning 24 July	Price (p)	Mon	Tue	Wed	Thu	Fri	Sat
Express	32	70	70	70	70	70	80
Sun	25	80	80	80	80	80	100
Telegraph	35	70	70	70	70	70	90
Mirror	27	60	60	60	60	60	70
Mail	32	50	50	50	50	50	60
Star	25	45	45	45	45	45	45
Guardian	45	30	30	30	30	30	35
Independent	30	25	25	25	25	25	25
Times	25	20	20	20	20	20	20
Financial Times	60	12	12	12	12	12	15
Racing Post	80	8	8	8	8	10	12
Sporting Life	80	8	8	8	8	10	15

The number of copies remaining unsold at the end of each day, and sent back to the wholesaler, was as shown in Table 16.4. The newsagent employed 3 boys and 2 girls to deliver the papers, and each was paid £9.50 per week. 360 customers had their paper delivered, and the charge for this service was 15p per week for each customer. There is a gross profit of 30% on newspapers actually sold.

Table 16.4 Number of copies unsold each day

Week beginning 24 July	Mon	Tue	Wed	Thu	Fri	Sat
Express	4	10	8	9	5	3
Sun	5	8	8	7	3	2
Telegraph	2	6	4	2	2	1
Mirror	2	2	0	4	2	3
Mail	7	12	8	6	4	6
Star	4	4	9	0	6	0
Guardian	0	0	1	1	0	2
Independent	1	1	1	1	1	2
Times	1	1	1	1	1	0
Financial Times	0	0	0	0	0	0
Racing Post	1	3	2	1	0	0
Sporting Life	1	3	1	1	0	0

From the information, find

1 How many newspapers were sold on each day of the week for the week beginning 24 July.

2 What the takings were on each day for the sale of newspapers.

3 How much profit or loss there was from the delivery charge to customers over the cost of employing 3 boys and 2 girls.

4 How much gross profit per week there was from the sale of newspapers alone.

Hints

Add up the column for the number of papers stocked on each day. Add up the column for the number of copies unsold on each day. The difference will give you the number of copies sold on each day.

To find the actual takings on each day it may help to draw a chart similar to the ones shown for stock and unsold copies. Record how many of each paper were sold each day; leave enough room in each column to find the money taken, and then add up the totals.

Find the total money coming in (income) for charging 360 customers at 30p per week. Find how much it costs to deliver the papers, employing 3 boys and 2 girls. The difference is the profit or loss.

Find the total takings for the week and find the gross profit by calculating 30% of this figure.

7 The Student

The full grant for a student in 1995 was £1885 based on a 30-week year. Three male students shared a rented house during their first year at university and agreed a one-year tenancy with the landlord. The furnished terraced house was recommended by the Accommodation Officer.

The agreement was a rent of £315 per calendar month for 8 months and a retainer of £100 per month for the other 4 months, the students to pay for water, electricity and gas. The water charge was £28.50 per month for 8 months, but electricity and gas was charged as used. Electricity each quarter averaged 640 units at 6.4p per unit plus a fixed quarterly charge of £9.21, plus VAT at 8%, while gas each quarter averaged 7400 kWh at 1.43p per unit plus a fixed quarterly charge of £9.63, also with VAT at 8%.

The landlord allowed a rebate, however, of £30 in respect of fixed quarterly charges.

The students agreed insurance for personal effects for £3200 at 80p per year for each £100 insured.

No agreement was reached about cost of food.

Using these figures find

1 The total cost of renting and using this accommodation, with insurance, over 12 months.

2 The cost per student over 12 months (to the nearest penny).

3 The cost, to the nearest penny, to each student per week (52 weeks).

4 How much the grant allows per week, to the nearest penny, over the 30 weeks.

5 What is left over from the grant in these 30 weeks to cover food, books, social life, etc.

6 If the grant has to cover 52 weeks – the student cannot find holiday work – how much is left over per week for food, etc.

Hints

Find the cost of accommodation only. Next, find the cost of water charges. Find the cost of electricity for a quarter and then for a year, not forgetting VAT. Do the same for gas. Deduct the rebate allowed by the landlord. Now find the total cost of living in the house. Add on the insurance. This is the cost for 3 students. Find the cost per student over 12 months, and then over one week. The grant is for 30 weeks; find the amount per week and what is left over after covering accommodation. Do a similar calculation if the grant has to cover 52 weeks.

8 Smoker and Non-smoker

I am a non-smoker. My friend, Dave, smokes on average 30 cigarettes a day. He reckons a packet of 20 costs £2.74. It is a mild cigarette, but it says on the packet that it contains 5 mg of tar and 0.5 mg of nicotine.

From the sale of cigarettes it is estimated that the shop gets 15% of the cost of a packet, the wholesaler 7%, the manufacturer 13% and the government (in tax) 65%.

From this information work out

1 How many cigarettes Dave smokes in a year.

2 What it costs him in a year.

3 The maximum amount of tar that is smoked in a year.

4 The maximum amount of nicotine that is smoked in a year.

5 If all the money was put into a building society, instead of cigarettes, at 4% interest p.a. (work it out on half the total amount spent, i.e. an average for the year) how much money would have been saved?

6 How much the manufacturer receives in a year from this one person.

7 How much the government receives in tax in a year from this one person. (Tobacco in 1994 brought in £7297 million for HM Customs & Excise.)

Hints

$$1 \text{ mg} = \frac{1}{1000} \text{ gram}$$

The saving of money in the building society would be slightly higher than using an average, as interest is also earned on the interest, but this would introduce a complication.

9 Decorating

Fiona and Adrian want to decorate the livingroom of a house before they move in. The room was originally two rooms, and you can still see the two pillars where the dividing wall was knocked down. After preparing the surfaces they decided to wallpaper the walls, emulsion paint the ceiling, carpet the whole floor together with underlay, gloss paint the windows, clear varnish the doors, replace the large pane in the front window because it was cracked, and have new curtains for front and back windows.

From the diagram (Figure 16.1) and the information given, find the cost involved to complete the job, to the nearest £10, if Fiona and Adrian do all the work.

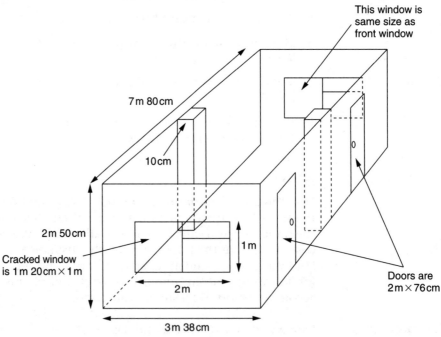

Figure 16.1 Living room to be decorated

Allow 1 roll of wallpaper less for windows and doors.
1 roll of wallpaper is 10.05 m × 52 cm (remember you can only buy whole rolls of paper).
Wallpaper is £11.99 a roll, ready pasted.
Emulsion paint is £4.99 for a litre tin and £9.99 for $2\frac{1}{2}$ litre tin. 1 litre covers 12 m². 1 litre of undercoat costs £5.99 and 1 litre of gloss paint costs £7.99 (1 litre is sufficient for windows and skirting board).

1 tin of clear varnish (sufficient for doors) costs £8.99.
Carpet is in 3 m, 3$\frac{1}{2}$ m, and 4 m widths. Cost is £12.99 per m^2.
Underlay is in 4 m widths, and the cost is £2.20 per m^2.
Glass cut to size is £8 per m^2.
Curtain material is in 1 m widths and is £9.99 per metre run.

Hints

Find the cost of separate items and then find the grand total. Head each item separately.

Wallpaper
Ignore walls and doors. Assume no waste. If necessary, draw another diagram of the walls stretched out in one long piece. Find how many strips of wallpaper are needed to go round the room (don't forget the pillars).
Now find the total length of wallpaper required.
What is the length of one roll?
How many rolls are needed? (Remember you cannot buy part of a roll.)
Subtract one roll to allow for windows and doors.
What is the cost of one roll?
Find the cost of all the wallpaper.

Paint
1 litre of emulsion paint covers 12 m^2.
What is the area of the ceiling?
How many litres are needed to cover the ceiling?
Which is the best buy of emulsion paint?
The gloss paint, undercoat and varnish are straightforward.

Carpet and underlay
You have got to buy the width of carpet given: when you cut some off to fit across the width you still have to pay for it.
Which carpet width will you use?
What length of carpet is needed?
What area of carpet is required?
Now find the cost of the carpet.
Underlay – you need a 4 m width; work out the area of underlay needed to run the length of the room. Calculate the cost.

Glass
Find the area of the cracked pane.
Find the cost at £8 per m^2.

Curtains
Allow *twice* the width of the window for a curtain to cover a window and an extra half metre longer than the window to make hems at top and bottom.
The material is 1 m wide.
How many widths are required to cover one window using the allowance above?
What length of material is needed to cover one window with the allowance given? How much is needed for 2 windows?
What is the cost of the curtain material?
What is the cost of the curtains?

Now find the total cost of doing the room, to the nearest £10.

10 The Garden

Moving into a new house, Anne and John found the back garden roughly dug and with only wire and posts to indicate boundaries. (The front garden had been turfed by the builders.) They decided to draw, on squared paper, a simple design for the back garden, which would give a sitting-out area, privacy from next door, and a garden plan that could be changed at any time. The drawing is shown in Figure 16.2 on the next page.

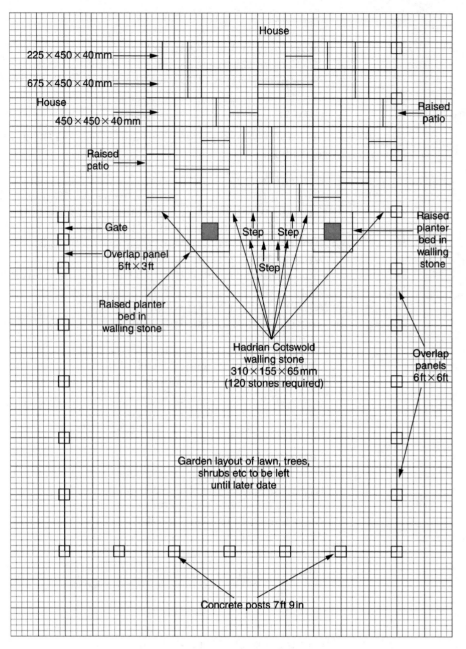

Figure 16.2 Simple garden plan showing patio, fence and posts

From the information on the drawing and the prices given, what would be the cost, to the nearest £10, of buying all the materials for the design?

Cost of materials

Bradstone Wetherdale Paving	$225 \times 450 \times 40$ mm	£1.82
	$450 \times 450 \times 40$ mm	£3.05
	$675 \times 450 \times 40$ mm	£4.74
Hadrian Walling Stone (Cotswold)	$310 \times 155 \times 65$ mm	£0.76 each
Concrete posts (intermediate)	7 ft 9 in	£6.30
Concrete posts (corner)	7 ft 9 in	£9.30
Overlap fencing	6 ft × 3 ft	£6.95
	6 ft × 6 ft	£9.70
Gate to match overlap fencing		£32

All prices subject to VAT at 17.5%
Prices include delivery.
Garden layout of lawn, trees, shrubs, shed and possible paths to be left until later date.

Hints

Count how many paving slabs, of each size, will be required, not forgetting the two leading up to the step. Find the cost. Count how many concrete posts (intermediate) and find the cost. Find how much the corner posts cost.

Count how many 6 ft × 6 ft overlap panels are required. Find the cost. Add one 6 ft × 3 ft panel and a gate.

Find the cost of the walling stones from the number given. Now find the cost of all the materials.

Add VAT for final cost and give answer to nearest £10.

11 The Holiday Venture

Lisa and her two friends in London have booked an apartment in Nice next July for two weeks from Saturday to Saturday. They want their car in Nice (or a hire car) and have decided to consider these choices:

1 drive their car to Dover, take the ferry to Calais and then drive to Nice;
2 drive the car to Dover, take the ferry to Calais, put the car on the train (Motorail) to Avignon, and then drive to Nice;
3 fly London to Nice and hire a car for two weeks;
4 drive the car to Folkestone, take Le Shuttle to Calais and then drive to Nice;
5 take the Eurostar train to Paris and then the train to Nice, and hire a car for two weeks.

It is agreed to go the cheapest way, and Lisa is asked to find out all the information for each journey. She comes back two days later and says she could give only present prices, which might change by next July, but the costs are as follows:
When using my car it will do 40 mile/gal. Petrol in England is 62.2p a litre. Petrol in France is 5.40 francs a litre. 1 gallon = 4.54 litres. 1 km = 0.62 miles. £1 = 7.70 francs.

Journey 1
London to Dover = 80 miles.
Dover–Calais ferry costs £225 return for car and driver.
Each additional adult costs £50 return.
Calais to Nice = 1225 km. If going this way then 2 overnight stops are required each way: allow £35 to cover each stop with food. (£35 should be enough for bed, breakfast, dinner and snacks during day for one person.)

Journey 2
London to Dover = 80 miles.
Calais to Avignon overnight by Motorail.
Car and driver costs £497 return. Each additional adult £114.
Avignon to Nice = 200 km.

Journey 3
London to Nice by air = £149 per person return.
Car hire = £167 per week.

Journey 4
London to Folkestone = 82 miles.
Le Shuttle (Folkestone to Calais) including all passengers is £154 single.
Calais to Nice = 1225 km. Allow overnight stops as in journey 1.

Journey 5
Eurostar train London to Paris is £95 per person return.
Paris to Lyon by TGV costs 286 francs single, per person.
Lyon to Nice by speed train costs 288 francs single, per person.
Allow one overnight stay in Lyon at £35 per person to cover stay and food. Car hire = £167 per week.

Which journey is cheapest and by how much over the next cheapest?

Hints

For three of the journeys you need to know the cost of petrol, per gallon, in England and France.

In journey 1, how much will it cost to drive from London to Dover?
How far is it in miles from Calais to Nice? How much will it cost?
How much will the ferry cost? How much for overnight stops?
Now find the total cost.

In journey 2, again find the cost of driving from London to Dover and back, and from Avignon to Nice and back. Add on the costs of Motorail.

Journey 3 is a relatively easy calculation.

The calculations for journey 4 are very similar to those for journey 1 except that they use Le Shuttle instead of the ferry.

There are no petrol costs in journey 5. Add up the train cost for each person, and do not forget one overnight stop.

Answers to Exercises

1 Number

Exercise 1

1 Forty-six
2 Five hundred and eight
3 Thirty-six
4 Fifty-two
5 Sixty-nine
6 Ninety-four
7 Four hundred and eight-three
8 Nine hundred and thirty-seven
9 Six hundred and eight
10 Three hundred and seventy
11 Two thousand one hundred and forty-seven
12 Four thousand eight hundred and thirty-six
13 Three thousand and fifty-eight
14 Seven thousand and forty
15 Thirty-eight thousand four hundred and seventy-six
16 Eighty-three thousand seven hundred and twenty-one
17 Fifty thousand four hundred and seventy-eight
18 Forty-six thousand two hundred and eighty-four
19 Forty thousand and sixty-five.
20 Five hundred and seventy thousand seven hundred and forty-five
21 Five million nine hundred and thirty thousand six hundred and fifty-seven
22 Four million sixty thousand eight hundred and seventy-four
23 Ten thousand and one
24 Three thousand and twenty-seven

Exercise 2

1 73	2 109	3 164
4 349	5 207	6 2583
7 5918	8 9006	9 7077
10 15 294	11 24 633	12 215 000
13 262	14 522 906	15 918 024
16 18 000 000	17 2 600 503	18 Two hundred
19 Fifty thousand	20 Two thousand	21 No hundreds
22 Eight hundred thousand	23 Three hundred	24 Four thousand

Exercise 3

1 48	2 24	3 68	4 99
5 74	6 129	7 110	8 299
9 525	10 707	11 1098	12 1315
13 846	14 1193	15 6126	16 2238
17 5477	18 8373	19 13 769	20 4740
21 2244	22 2441	23 6553	24 4272

Exercise 4

1 90	2 414	3 431	4 164
5 1366	6 583	7 188	8 667
9 1793	10 1797	11 303	12 1016
13 1127	14 1142	15 2812	16 4965
17 778	18 1934	19 2045	20 3750
21 856	22 5674	23 3873	24 3199

Exercise 5

1 490 miles	2 372 miles	3 40 miles
4 270 miles	5 387 miles	6 425 miles

7 202 miles		**8** 620 miles		**9** 322 miles	
10 491 miles		**11** 388 miles		**12** 367 miles	
13 637 miles		**14** 577 miles		**15** 668 miles	

Exercise 6

1 84	**2** 76	**3** 30 487	**4** 45
5 252	**6** 661	**7** 42 968	

8 (a) 203 (b) 217 (c) 196 (d) 260 (e) 298 (f) 362

9 1146	**10** 319

Exercise 7

1 17	**2** 178	**3** 34	**4** 14
5 26	**6** 25	**7** 16	**8** 168
9 179	**10** 219	**11** 186	**12** 1809
13 1291	**14** 274	**15** 107	**16** 286
17 2006	**18** 291	**19** 377	**20** 345
21 217	**22** 46	**23** 4216	**24** 679

Exercise 8

1 217	**2** 7	**3** 175	**4** 189
5 292	**6** 34	**7** 19 425	**8** 15; 263

9 Eight hundred and two thousand three hundred and eighty
10 Blackburn 43, Manchester United 45, Liverpool 15, Newcastle 11

11 12	**12** 559

Exercise 9

1 324	**2** 612	**3** 96	**4** 324
5 581	**6** 441	**7** 216	**8** 432
9 2231	**10** 560	**11** 2590	**12** 2262
13 3016	**14** 3431	**15** 2478	**16** 1112
17 62 084	**18** 13 068	**19** 30 060	**20** 229 042
21 2936	**22** 2460	**23** 1035	**24** 1152

Exercise 10

1 £184 per month	**2** 624 bottles	**3** £208
4 864	**5** (a) £592 (b) £7696	**6** £7385
7 1064	**8** £1008	**9** £884
10 £1304	**11** 4608	**12** (a) £306 (b) £15 912
13 £26 885	**14** £510	**15** 751
16 182		

Exercise 11

1 24	**2** 23	**3** 18	**4** 19
5 24	**6** 38	**7** 98	**8** 134
9 208	**10** 340	**11** 27	**12** 44
13 123	**14** 107	**15** 259	**16** 230
17 251	**18** 179	**19** 68	**20** 43
21 256	**22** 582	**23** 467	**24** 1053

Exercise 12

1 £16	**2** 325	**3** £13	**4** 36
5 1944	**6** £175	**7** Sister by £363	**8** 19
9 £14	**10** 28; £196	**11** £138	**12** 483 654

Exercise 13

1 11	**2** 7	**3** 23	**4** 13
5 2	**6** 55	**7** 12	**8** 9
9 9	**10** 11	**11** 2	**12** 4
13 6	**14** 24	**15** 5	**16** 22
17 24	**18** 8	**19** 32	**20** 5
21 48	**22** 11	**23** 64	**24** 20

Exercise 14

1 3600	**2** 60	**3** 120	**4** 360
5 3500	**6** 600	**7** 1400	**8** 2100

9 4300	**10** 3400	**11** 6300	**12** 9600
13 15 000	**14** 15 000	**15** 320 000	**16** 39
17 56	**18** 34	**19** 270	**20** 467
21 84	**22** 450	**23** 34	**24** 8
25 40	**26** 2300	**27** 220	**28** 40
29 510	**30** 620		

Exercise 15

1 60	**2** 100	**3** 30	**4** 20
5 70	**6** 150	**7** 400	**8** 600
9 1000	**10** 640	**11** 0	**12** 500
13 1000	**14** 70	**15** 1800	**16** 310
17 2000	**18** 4000	**19** 510	**20** 3600
21 300	**22** 500	**23** 0	**24** 500

Exercise 16

1 900	**2** 42	**3** 800	**4** 1500
5 3000	**6** 1600	**7** 15 400	**8** 25 600
9 2800	**10** 6500	**11** 1800	**12** 14 400
13 44	**14** 12	**15** 567	**16** 27
17 23	**18** 50	**19** 20	**20** 60
21 574	**22** 280	**23** 284	**24** 584

Exercise 17

1 19	**2** -10	**3** 3	**4** -17
5 4	**6** -8	**7** -12	**8** 10
9 -10	**10** -10	**11** 42	**12** -42
13 4	**14** -4	**15** -4	**16** -4
17 -4	**18** 4	**19** -4	**20** 4
21 -12	**22** 18	**23** -8	**24** $9, 8, 6, -4, -7, -9$

25 $-9, -8, -2, 0, 5, 6, 8$

26 (a) Brisbane (b) Moscow (c) 50 °C (d) 19 °C (e) 10 °C (f) 38 °C (g) 44 °C (h) 15 °C

Exercise 18

1 18	**2** 25	**3** 10	**4** 48	**5** 15
6 2	**7** -1	**8** 25	**9** 5	**10** 45

Exercise 19

1 20, 30	**2** 6, 10	**3** 16, 29	**4** 54, 2
5 0, 16	**6** 7, -1	**7** 6, 8	**8** $-7, 1$
9 9, 4	**10** $-9, -11$		

Exercise 20

1 D	**2** A	**3** B	**4** B	**5** C
6 D	**7** A	**8** D	**9** C	**10** D
11 A	**12** A	**13** D	**14** B	**15** C
16 C				

2 Fractions

Exercise 1

1 $\frac{8}{16}$	**2** $\frac{12}{9}$	**3** $\frac{2}{4}$	**4** $\frac{3}{9}$	**5** $\frac{4}{16}$
6 $\frac{9}{6}$	**7** $\frac{12}{8}$	**8** $\frac{9}{12}$	**9** $\frac{12}{18}$	**10** $\frac{4}{10}$
11 $\frac{16}{20}$	**12** $\frac{14}{16}$	**13** $\frac{6}{10}$	**14** $\frac{33}{24}$	**15** $\frac{24}{20}$
16 $\frac{15}{9}$	**17** $\frac{6}{16}$	**18** $\frac{20}{32}$	**19** $\frac{10}{4}$	**20** $\frac{6}{8}$
21 $\frac{12}{16}$	**22** $\frac{8}{10}$	**23** $\frac{20}{32}$	**24** $\frac{4}{6}$	**25** $\frac{9}{12}$
26 $\frac{25}{10}$	**27** $\frac{16}{12}$	**28** $\frac{14}{16}$	**29** $\frac{4}{8}$	**30** $\frac{20}{16}$

Exercise 2

1 $\frac{3}{4}$	**2** $\frac{4}{3}$	**3** $\frac{3}{5}$	**4** $\frac{2}{3}$	**5** $\frac{2}{3}$
6 $\frac{3}{4}$	**7** $\frac{1}{3}$	**8** $\frac{3}{4}$	**9** $\frac{4}{7}$	**10** $\frac{3}{5}$
11 $\frac{7}{10}$	**12** $\frac{5}{9}$	**13** $\frac{2}{5}$	**14** $\frac{2}{3}$	**15** $\frac{2}{9}$
16 $\frac{3}{7}$	**17** $\frac{6}{11}$	**18** $\frac{9}{16}$	**19** $\frac{7}{9}$	**20** $\frac{3}{8}$
21 $\frac{3}{8}$	**22** $\frac{3}{7}$	**23** $\frac{2}{3}$	**24** $\frac{4}{11}$	

Exercise 3

1 $\frac{1}{4}, \frac{1}{3}$ 2 $\frac{3}{8}, \frac{1}{2}, \frac{7}{10}, \frac{3}{4}$ 3 $\frac{1}{4}, \frac{1}{3}$

4 $\frac{2}{3}, \frac{3}{4}$ 5 $\frac{1}{3}, \frac{2}{5}, \frac{1}{2}$ 6 $\frac{1}{2}, \frac{3}{5}, \frac{2}{3}$

7 $\frac{3}{8}, \frac{1}{2}, \frac{5}{6}$ 8 $\frac{1}{3}, \frac{1}{2}, \frac{3}{5}$ 9 $\frac{7}{16}, \frac{1}{2}, \frac{5}{8}$

10 $\frac{5}{8}, \frac{2}{3}$ 11 $\frac{7}{12}, \frac{2}{3}, \frac{5}{6}$ 12 $\frac{11}{24}, \frac{5}{8}, \frac{2}{3}$

13 $\frac{3}{2}, \frac{7}{4}, \frac{15}{8}$ 14 $\frac{3}{8}, \frac{7}{16}, \frac{1}{2}, \frac{5}{8}$ 15 $\frac{2}{3}, \frac{3}{4}, \frac{13}{16}$

16 $\frac{1}{2}, \frac{9}{16}, \frac{5}{8}, \frac{2}{3}$ 17 $\frac{3}{4}, \frac{5}{6}, \frac{11}{12}, 1$ 18 $\frac{5}{8}, \frac{2}{3}, \frac{17}{24}, \frac{3}{4}$

19 $\frac{3}{4}, \frac{4}{5}$ 20 $1, \frac{5}{4}, \frac{3}{2}, \frac{15}{8}$ 21 $\frac{5}{8}, \frac{23}{32}, \frac{3}{4}, \frac{15}{16}$

22 $\frac{1}{5}, \frac{1}{4}, \frac{1}{3}$ 23 $\frac{2}{3}, \frac{11}{16}, \frac{3}{4}$ 24 $\frac{9}{16}, \frac{5}{8}, \frac{2}{3}, \frac{17}{24}$

Exercise 4

1 $1\frac{1}{4}$ 2 $2\frac{4}{5}$ 3 $1\frac{1}{2}$ 4 $3\frac{1}{2}$ 5 $1\frac{3}{4}$

6 $4\frac{1}{2}$ 7 $1\frac{2}{3}$ 8 $3\frac{2}{3}$ 9 $2\frac{2}{3}$ 10 $1\frac{1}{2}$

11 $2\frac{1}{2}$ 12 $3\frac{2}{5}$ 13 $3\frac{1}{4}$ 14 $2\frac{1}{2}$ 15 $2\frac{2}{5}$

16 $1\frac{5}{7}$ 17 $1\frac{3}{5}$ 18 $2\frac{3}{7}$ 19 $2\frac{2}{5}$ 20 $4\frac{1}{2}$

21 $1\frac{7}{9}$ 22 $5\frac{1}{2}$ 23 $1\frac{2}{3}$ 24 4

Exercise 5

1 $\frac{11}{4}$ 2 $\frac{23}{6}$ 3 $\frac{7}{2}$ 4 $\frac{9}{4}$ 5 $\frac{7}{4}$

6 $\frac{3}{2}$ 7 $\frac{5}{3}$ 8 $\frac{7}{3}$ 9 $\frac{11}{4}$ 10 $\frac{9}{5}$

11 $\frac{13}{5}$ 12 $\frac{19}{4}$ 13 $\frac{23}{10}$ 14 $\frac{11}{3}$ 15 $\frac{16}{3}$

16 $\frac{24}{5}$ 17 $\frac{17}{6}$ 18 $\frac{25}{6}$ 19 $\frac{34}{7}$ 20 $\frac{20}{3}$

21 $\frac{19}{7}$ 22 $\frac{43}{6}$ 23 $\frac{29}{4}$ 24 $\frac{18}{5}$

Exercise 6

1 $\frac{8}{15}$ 2 $3\frac{3}{8}$ 3 $\frac{2}{5}$ 4 $\frac{3}{4}$ 5 $\frac{5}{6}$

6 $\frac{5}{8}$ 7 $\frac{7}{8}$ 8 $1\frac{1}{8}$ 9 $\frac{11}{16}$ 10 $3\frac{19}{60}$

11 $1\frac{37}{60}$ 12 $5\frac{11}{12}$ 13 $3\frac{3}{20}$ 14 $5\frac{17}{24}$ 15 $4\frac{19}{60}$

16 $6\frac{7}{16}$ 17 $6\frac{29}{30}$ 18 $9\frac{5}{8}$ 19 $7\frac{7}{12}$ 20 $7\frac{31}{40}$

21 $5\frac{17}{60}$ 22 $7\frac{3}{16}$ 23 $3\frac{17}{24}$ 24 $2\frac{2}{5}$

Exercise 7

1 $\frac{1}{12}$ 2 $1\frac{3}{8}$ 3 $1\frac{5}{8}$ 4 $\frac{5}{12}$ 5 $1\frac{1}{12}$

6 $\frac{5}{12}$ 7 $\frac{7}{20}$ 8 $2\frac{13}{24}$ 9 $1\frac{7}{24}$ 10 $2\frac{1}{6}$

11 $\frac{11}{12}$ 12 $\frac{13}{20}$ 13 $2\frac{11}{16}$ 14 $1\frac{11}{16}$ 15 $\frac{17}{20}$

16 $2\frac{13}{16}$ 17 $\frac{23}{40}$ 18 $\frac{5}{8}$ 19 $1\frac{1}{24}$ 20 $1\frac{7}{12}$

21 $2\frac{7}{24}$ 22 $\frac{19}{60}$ 23 $4\frac{13}{16}$ 24 $1\frac{4}{15}$

Exercise 8

1 $\frac{1}{2}$ 2 $2\frac{5}{6}$ 3 90 4 $\frac{3}{7}$ 5 $\frac{1}{2}$

6 $\frac{2}{5}$ 7 $\frac{15}{26}$ 8 $\frac{9}{22}$ 9 3 10 $7\frac{2}{3}$

11 $2\frac{1}{3}$ 12 7 13 $5\frac{1}{3}$ 14 $6\frac{1}{3}$ 15 9

16 $2\frac{2}{9}$ 17 $3\frac{1}{2}$ 18 $4\frac{2}{3}$ 19 192 20 80

21 48 22 £54 23 25 24 45

Exercise 9

1 $2\frac{1}{5}$ 2 $3\frac{3}{8}$ 3 $2\frac{1}{4}$ 4 $1\frac{1}{4}$ 5 $\frac{6}{7}$

6 $3\frac{1}{2}$ 7 $2\frac{4}{5}$ 8 $2\frac{1}{8}$ 9 $2\frac{1}{5}$ 10 $2\frac{1}{9}$

11 $2\frac{6}{11}$ 12 $\frac{1}{2}$ 13 9 14 $1\frac{1}{8}$ 15 $\frac{2}{5}$

16 $\frac{7}{9}$ 17 $\frac{16}{49}$ 18 $2\frac{7}{16}$ 19 $2\frac{2}{5}$ 20 4

21 $1\frac{1}{2}$ 22 $2\frac{4}{15}$ 23 3 24 $1\frac{5}{13}$

Exercise 10

1 1 2 $\frac{5}{6}$ 3 9 4 $4\frac{2}{3}$ 5 $2\frac{1}{2}$

6 1 7 $\frac{11}{15}$ 8 $\frac{11}{16}$ 9 $2\frac{5}{6}$ 10 $3\frac{3}{16}$

11 3 12 $1\frac{7}{8}$ 13 $1\frac{1}{48}$ 14 $4\frac{2}{3}$ 15 $\frac{7}{12}$

16 $4\frac{4}{9}$ 17 $3\frac{1}{4}$ 18 $2\frac{4}{5}$ 19 3 20 $4\frac{2}{27}$

21 $4\frac{5}{8}$ 22 4 23 $4\frac{1}{4}$ 24 $7\frac{1}{2}$

Exercise 11

1 £40	2 270p	3 £90	4 24 ft; 8 ft
5 $1\frac{1}{3}$	6 $1\frac{7}{12}$	7 £40	8 £30
9 £45	10 £12	11 £35	12 12 ft
13 (a) £8 (b) £4	14 $\frac{7}{10}$ minute	15 50	16 112
17 48	18 $\frac{1}{12}$	19 £156 million	20 £9000

Exercise 12

1 C	2 A	3 D	4 B	5 A
6 C	7 C	8 D	9 B	10 C
11 B	12 A	13 C	14 D	15 C
16 C	17 A	18 C	19 B	20 D

3 Decimals

Exercise 1

1 2.64	2 Three point nought six five	3 5.6
4 3.5	5 2.63	6 8.41
7 24.93	8 62.59	9 7.04
10 0.67	11 98.4	12 130.92
13 40.06	14 13.24	15 Two point five

16 Three point eight 　　　17 Two point six five
18 One point eight seven 　　19 Forty-five point three four
20 Twenty-four point nought six 　21 Thirty-seven point eight
22 Twenty-eight point nought three 　23 One hundred and forty-six point four eight
24 Four point nought seven 　　25 Five tenths
26 One tenth 　　　　27 Four units
28 Two hundredths

Exercise 2

1 0.3	2 0.182	3 0.3	4 0.7
5 0.5	6 0.1	7 0.12	8 0.34
9 0.62	10 0.69	11 0.06	12 0.48
13 0.6	14 0.046	15 0.048	16 0.123
17 0.83	18 0.06	19 2.4	20 3.1
21 0.4	22 3.24	23 0.476	24 0.005
25 7.5	26 4.56	27 0.305	28 5.09

Exercise 3

1 $\frac{3}{5}$	2 $\frac{7}{20}$	3 $\frac{3}{8}$	4 $\frac{1}{5}$	5 $\frac{3}{5}$
6 $\frac{7}{10}$	7 $\frac{3}{10}$	8 $\frac{3}{20}$	9 $\frac{1}{4}$	10 $\frac{13}{20}$
11 $\frac{16}{25}$	12 $\frac{3}{4}$	13 $\frac{6}{25}$	14 $\frac{2}{5}$	15 $\frac{22}{25}$
16 $\frac{7}{25}$	17 $\frac{24}{25}$	18 $\frac{18}{25}$	19 $\frac{2}{5}$	20 $\frac{9}{20}$
21 $\frac{1}{8}$	22 $\frac{5}{8}$	23 $\frac{47}{50}$	24 $\frac{81}{250}$	25 $\frac{39}{100}$
26 $\frac{111}{200}$	27 $\frac{21}{50}$	28 $\frac{58}{125}$	29 $\frac{19}{20}$	30 $\frac{143}{500}$

Exercise 4

1 15.52	2 145.396	3 3.6	4 7.8
5 9.9	6 8.8	7 8.3	8 8.4
9 5.78	10 7.68	11 12.4	12 15.2
13 0.77	14 8.48	15 20.71	16 14.73
17 14.39	18 15.76	19 13.00	20 11.8
21 8.289	22 121.81	23 60.706	24 71.477

Exercise 5

1 2.8	2 7.26	3 4.2	4 3.3
5 4.6	6 2.41	7 2.25	8 3.30
9 13.22	10 15.13	11 1.89	12 2.5
13 1.5	14 1.6	15 16.7	16 26.71
17 6.55	18 23.47	19 11.97	20 4.31
21 370.19	22 33.75	23 10.58	24 24.47

Exercise 6

1 20.64	2 301.780	3 1.776	4 6.2
5 9.6	6 12.8	7 25.2	8 13.5
9 26.6	10 3.22	11 9.46	12 38.7
13 23.65	14 15.54	15 16.32	16 5.16
17 1.88	18 43.44	19 271.8	20 140.18
21 3.25	22 0.117	23 3.149	24 74.76
25 3.6716	26 2109.24	27 5.3235	28 32.778
29 31.941	30 40.733		

Exercise 7

1 370	2 0.037	3 34	4 57
5 343	6 56.7	7 8.4	8 50.4
9 3456	10 483	11 837	12 46
13 306	14 12 065	15 650	16 5250
17 8067	18 3.45	19 3.856	20 5.645
21 0.3678	22 45.65	23 0.087	24 0.456
25 0.064	26 4.565	27 0.0435	28 0.0075
29 0.5645	30 0.3876	31 0.060 78	32 4640
33 57.6	34 0.4567	35 0.546 08	36 0.045 067

Exercise 8

1 13.6	2 3.6	3 14.0	4 2.4
5 3.2	6 3.2	7 4.6	8 4.7
9 4.6	10 2.56	11 4.64	12 3.97
13 5.34	14 5.6	15 3.7	16 9.5
17 7.8	18 29.7	19 32.4	20 46.7
21 37.8	22 8.6	23 9.7	24 84.7
25 0.72	26 5.82	27 39.0	28 0.72
29 45.2	30 36.3		

Exercise 9

1 7.7	2 3.0	3 3.5	4 2.4
5 5.3	6 3.7	7 8.6	8 4.3
9 4.1	10 5.7	11 3.2	12 0.7
13 2.0	14 45.6	15 5.8	16 37.8
17 0.7	18 0.5	19 27.0	20 3.1
21 7.1	22 42.9	23 23.0	24 0.1
25 5.3	26 3.8	27 0.9	28 1.0
29 2.5	30 67.1		

Exercise 10

1 2.93	2 0.72	3 8.00	4 4.54
5 5.68	6 2.07	7 43.43	8 21.68
9 5.49	10 3.06	11 3.07	12 45.51
13 8.01	14 4.08	15 4.00	16 0.31
17 31.00	18 5.07	19 7.47	20 56.80
21 4.00	22 42.51	23 5.10	24 31.71
25 31.24	26 8.48	27 100.00	28 1.40
29 4.76	30 4.68		

Exercise 11

1 6500	2 500	3 0.077	4 360
5 360	6 7500	7 490	8 1900
9 15.0	10 36.0	11 26.0	12 4.1
13 3.0	14 780	15 4.6	16 6.0
17 32.0	18 3100	19 5.5	20 47 000
21 6.8	22 460.0	23 4.0	24 2.1
25 46.0	26 0.057	27 0.071	28 0.058
29 60 000	30 0.61		

Exercise 12

1 72.8	2 72.9	3 7000	4 0.0239
5 45.8	6 4.54	7 56.8	8 3780
9 4800	10 5.96	11 8.01	12 45.0
13 5000	14 4.45	15 6.81	16 356.0
17 357.0	18 4.00	19 36.7	20 40 800
21 0.003 45	22 6.75	23 4.91	24 9.01
25 3600	26 41.0	27 6.80	28 0.000 549
29 0.0607	30 6.00		

Exercise 13

1	0.6	2	0.375	3	0.$\dot{6}$	4	0.5
5	0.25	6	0.75	7	0.4	8	0.7
9	0.15	10	0.$\dot{6}$	11	0.2	12	0.9
13	0.33	14	0.375	15	0.35	16	0.625
17	1.75	18	0.65	19	1.5	20	1.$\dot{6}$
21	0.55	22	0.875	23	1.25	24	1.8
25	0.1$\dot{6}$	26	1.33	27	0.8	28	0.1
29	1.2	30	0.85				

Exercise 14

1	3.725×10^3	2	3.725×10^{-3}	3	4.6×10
4	6.3×10	5	8.7×10	6	4.845×10^3
7	3.865×10^3	8	2.831×10^3	9	3.78×10
10	3.749×10^2	11	4.1787×10^3	12	3.968×10^3
13	5.7865×10^2	14	3.7468×10^4	15	2.738×10^2
16	9.0696×10^4	17	3.856×10^3	18	5.6×10^{-1}
19	6.787×10	20	8.76×10^{-1}	21	7.45×10^{-3}
22	8.9×10^{-3}	23	6.186×10	24	1.35×10^{-2}
25	6.47×10^{-4}	26	$8.976\,45 \times 10^3$	27	3.657×10^5
28	6.31×10^{-2}	29	8.6965×10^2	30	8.6×10^{-5}

Exercise 15

1	2300	2	0.000 464	3	35.0	4	58.0
5	640	6	487	7	563	8	5850
9	5654	10	54.9	11	87.65	12	43 000
13	49 870	14	542.86	15	37.6	16	52 750
17	620.57	18	0.5654	19	0.930 65	20	0.647
21	0.027	22	0.006 843	23	0.589 056	24	0.002 76
25	0.046 957	26	0.000 418 47	27	0.4795	28	0.019 07
29	300.708	30	1483.5				

Exercise 16

1	B	2	C	3	D	4	C	5	B
6	C	7	D	8	B	9	A	10	C
11	D	12	A	13	B	14	C	15	A
16	B	17	D	18	B	19	D	20	C

4 Money

Exercise 1

1	£68.95	2	£26.53	3	£3.77	4	£9.89
5	£9.99	6	£13.96	7	£22.32	8	£33.50
9	£28.33	10	£57.37	11	£31.80	12	£54.53
13	£144.41	14	£471.16	15	£142.37	16	£655.13
17	£188.27	18	£195.52	19	£232.61	20	£596.52
21	£4.52	22	£4.01	23	£5.25	24	£9.26
25	£3.92	26	£4.56	27	£7.88	28	£51.63
29	£7.52	30	£83.69	31	£9.65	32	£0.63
33	£55.60	34	£26.68	35	£10.87	36	£7.14
37	£13.59	38	£7.54	39	£16.90	40	£6.59

Exercise 2

1	£51.40	2	£400.80	3	£238.26	4	£6.34
5	£3.63	6	£9.24	7	£7.41	8	£14.91
9	£26.04	10	£4.48	11	£38.80	12	£89.28
13	£195.14	14	£324.36	15	£11.52	16	£1123.92
17	£665.64	18	£305.52	19	£440.16	20	£2665.80
21	£385.08	22	£17.76	23	£3.23	24	£2.11
25	£3.15	26	£6.02	27	£3.48	28	£2.63
29	£4.07	30	£6.42	31	£7.32	32	£22.62
33	£13.47	34	£9.36	35	£0.78	36	£1.38
37	£1.08	38	£3.52	39	£17.29	40	£18.04

Exercise 3

1 £1.21	2 £0.86	3 £2.13	4 £2.31
5 £1.63	6 £1.21	7 £2.11	8 £1.41
9 £3.06	10 £2.51	11 £3.00	12 £1.56
13 £2.51	14 £2.33	15 £1.50	16 £2.38
17 £2.24	18 £1.94	19 £2.07	20 £3.07

Exercise 4

1 86p	2 £2.85	3 £3.26
4 £2.44	5 £47.29	6 £1770.56
7 £57	8 £280	9 £8904
10 £243.75	11 £39.18	12 £322.56
13 (a) £38.66 (b) £81.40	14 £42.83	15 (a) £12.38 (b) £5.96
16 £652.32	17 £116.48	18 £934
19 £28.95	20 (a) £6.24 (b) £4.47 (c) £12.80 (d) £19.16	

Exercise 5

1 C	2 C	3 A	4 C	5 D
6 A	7 D	8 C	9 A	10 C
11 A	12 C	13 A	14 D	15 C
16 C	17 D	18 D	19 A	20 B

5 Introducing the calculator

Exercise 1

1 114	2 220	3 168	4 599
5 436	6 9875	7 6214	8 83.72
9 217.48	10 104.97	11 388.08	12 5104.42
13 2954 m	14 993.8 miles	15 122.56	

Exercise 2

1 338	2 37	3 96	4 2261
5 −78	6 −81	7 22.1	8 72.1
9 49.9	10 7.35	11 25.9	12 25.1
13 1346.34	14 38.15	15 −390.96	16 119.83
17 115.39	18 14.665	19 362.82	20 5387.21

Exercise 3

1 576	2 1593	3 12 169
4 322.41	5 821.9666	6 12 916.662
7 £143.10	8 £7542.15	9 £62 372.76
10 293 020.16	11 19 452.51	12 1.240 848
13 88 966.355	14 7.544 596 5	15 14 392 373 000
16 31 948.80	17 3480.1137	18 612 286
19 25 680 304	20 358.542 16	21 2 658 827 600
22 423 264.37	23 28 381.632	24 84 177 988 000
25 44 576 211	26 2 538 747 300	27 20 868.528
28 15 126 650 032	29 294 947.74	30 24 exact, 5 approximate

Exercise 4

1 256	2 283	3 583	4 861
5 452	6 68	7 94	8 13.8
9 49.8	10 516	11 276.2	12 964.2
13 407.2	14 86.59	15 6534.3	

Exercise 5

1 8.54	2 12.13	3 5.83	4 13.67
5 40	6 30.61	7 0.06	8 0.20
9 30.70	10 0.04	11 6	12 128.05
13 8.78	14 5.79	15 0.23	16 0.07
17 616	18 0.06	19 35.83	20 0.05

Exercise 6

1 16.25	2 25.25	3 3.43	4 20
5 13.33	6 31.17	7 1.26	8 78.6
9 2.33	10 1.57	11 3.96	12 2.32
13 3.16	14 1176.97	15 1.85	16 7.33
17 5.27	18 1.61	19 30 083.81	20 27.82

6 Measurement

Exercise 1

	(a)	(b)	(c)	(d)
1	2000 m	6000 m	5000 m	20 000 m
2	1600 m	4800 m	5200 m	3400 m
3	1560 m	2340 m	3060 m	1800 m
4	3 km	8 km	12 km	50 km
5	2.5 km	5.6 km	4.25 km	1.8 km
6	1.25 km	0.88 km	0.06 km	0.24 km
7	25 m 40 cm	8 m 30 cm	48 m 75 cm	4 m 50 cm
8	5 m 24 cm	9 m 9 cm	82 m 18 cm	62 cm
9	3 kg	8 kg	24 kg	120 kg
10	1.5 kg	2.9 kg	7.85 kg	4.25 kg
11	0.9 kg	0.45 kg	0.248 kg	0.07 kg
12	2000 g	5000 g	15 000 g	21 000 g
13	1600 g	2500 g	820 g	2040 g
14	1 kg 280 g	1 kg 62 g	3 kg 590 g	3 kg 59 g
15	4000 ml	9000 ml	2000 ml	13 000 ml
16	2500 ml	3440 ml	400 ml	5090 ml
17	3 ℓ	8 ℓ	15 ℓ	120 ℓ
18	2.8 ℓ	1.75 ℓ	3.07 ℓ	8.008 ℓ
19	3 ℓ 60 ml	52 ℓ 300 ml	2 ℓ 950 ml	1 ℓ 82 ml

20 1.55 ℓ **21** 224 bottles **22** £1.30
23 0.55 kg **24** 360 seconds (6 minutes) **25** 24

Exercise 2

	(a)	(b)	(c)	(d)
1	24 in	72 in	144 in	240 in
2	21 in	40 in	62 in	102 in
3	3 ft 4 in	4 ft 10 in	6 ft 4 in	2 ft 11 in
4	6 ft	21 ft	27 ft	42 ft
5	10 ft	17 ft	23 ft	19 ft
6	4 yd 1 ft	2 yd 2 ft	6 yd 1 ft	8 yd 1 ft
7	60 cwt	100 cwt	160 cwt	200 cwt
8	50 cwt	85 cwt	10 cwt	75 cwt
9	48 oz	80 oz	71 oz	41 oz
10	24 pt	19 pt	15 pt	27 pt
11	60 fl oz	30 fl oz	44 fl oz	110 fl oz

12 13 pkts **13** 17 ton 15 cwt **14** £32.40
15 £518.40 **16** 20 lb **17** £54
18 50 bricks **19** 284 g **20** 40 pkts

Exercise 3

1 50 gal **2** 14 gal **3** 90 cm
4 2 m 25 cm **5** 55 lb **6** 86.82 kg
7 247.5p (£2 47.5p) **8** 25 m 20 cm **9** 40 lb
10 £1.15 **11** 40.5 ℓ **12** 180 cm by 135 cm
13 80 fl oz **14** 82.5 cm **15** 4545 g
16 90 m **17** 19 m 80 cm **18** 112.5 ℓ
19 6.62 **20** £1.35

Exercise 4

1 0500 hours **2** 1100 hours **3** 1800 hours
4 2100 hours **5** 0300 hours **6** 1130 hours
7 1600 hours **8** 2200 hours **9** 2030 hours
10 0725 hours **11** 0230 hours **12** 1615 hours
13 0630 hours **14** 2050 hours **15** 2045 hours
16 0924 hours **17** 0018 hours **18** 1230 hours
19 2230 hours **20** 1845 hours

Exercise 5

1 7 a.m. **2** 10 a.m. **3** 2 p.m. **4** 7 p.m.
5 3.30 a.m. **6** 2.30 p.m. **7** 7.45 p.m. **8** 4.20 a.m.
9 11.16 a.m. **10** 9.50 p.m. **11** 0.40 a.m. **12** 11.15 p.m.
13 9.42 a.m. **14** 12.50 p.m. **15** 5.15 p.m. **16** 9.30 p.m.
17 4.08 a.m. **18** 10.30 a.m. **19** 6.40 a.m. **20** 3.27 p.m.

Exercise 6

1	4 h	2	2 h	3	9 h 30 min
4	9 h 50 min	5	11 h 10 min	6	24 min
7	5 h 50 min	8	13 h 50 min	9	10 h 35 min
10	9 h 5 min	11	8 h 30 min	12	2 h 45 min
13	15 h 40 min	14	2 h 30 min	15	12 h 34 min
16	11 h 50 min	17	12 h 50 min	18	4 h 55 min
19	7 h 50 min	20	10 h 50 min		

7 Ratio and proportion

Exercise 1

1	1 : 2	2	2 : 3	3	4 : 5	4	2 : 3
5	3 : 2	6	3 : 1	7	5 : 2	8	3 : 4
9	3 : 2	10	5 : 8	11	7 : 10	12	3 : 5
13	2 : 1	14	8 : 5	15	3 : 7	16	5 : 8
17	2 : 3	18	1 : 3	19	1 : 4	20	5 : 3
21	3 : 5	22	3 : 4	23	5 : 3	24	6 : 5
25	2 : 3 : 5	26	3 : 2 : 1	27	3 : 2 : 2	28	7 : 5 : 3
29	6 : 4 : 3	30	9 : 5 : 4				

Exercise 2

1	(a) 2 : 3 (b) $\frac{3}{5}$ (c) $\frac{2}{5}$	2	(a) 3 : 2 (b) $\frac{3}{5}$ (c) $\frac{2}{5}$	3	(a) 2 : 3 (b) $\frac{3}{5}$
4	(a) 3 : 4 (b) $\frac{3}{7}$	5	(a) 9 : 2 (b) $\frac{2}{11}$	6	(a) 8 : 3 (b) $\frac{3}{11}$
7	(a) 23 : 5 (b) $\frac{23}{28}$	8	240	9	14 cwt
10	54 litres	11	1000 g	12	400 g

Exercise 3

1	£3; £2	2	£8; £4	3	£6; £14
4	£8; £6	5	£2.10; £1.40	6	£10; £15
7	70 cm; 30 cm	8	50 g; 75 g	9	90 ml; 210 ml
10	£20; £30; £30	11	£300; £800; £400	12	£18; £30; £12
13	1600 ml water; 400 ml chemical	14	1200 ml water; 800 ml antifreeze	
15	480 g brass	16	12 soft centres	
17	1 ton 10 cwt sand	18	120 g copper	
19	240 g fat; 120 g flour	20	250 tabloids	
21	4 cl cassis	22	36	
23	1925 g copper	24	12 blue	

Exercise 4

1	8 in	2	10 in	3	58 ft 4 in	4	250 m
5	2 km	6	5 km	7	60 cm	8	36 km
9	30 km	10	6.25 km	11	6 miles	12	(a) 15 ft (b) 10 ft
13	58 ft 4 in	14	6 km	15	210 km	16	922 km
17	300 km	18	80 cm	19	300 cm	20	16 cm

Exercise 5

1	65p	2	£1.50	3	99p	4	£147
5	£175	6	£28.50	7	175 g	8	10 flags
9	50p	10	12 oz flour	11	£430	12	135 cl
13	12.8 oz	14	17.5 ml	15	£160	16	£9.60
17	£82.50	18	7 cl	19	£38.08	20	£13.20

Exercise 6

1	C	2	A	3	D	4	D	5	B
6	D	7	A	8	B	9	C	10	C

8 Averages

Exercise 1

1	(a) 9	(b) 6	(c) 7	(d) 11
2	(a) 6	(b) 10	(c) 8	(d) 9
3	(a) 6	(b) 11	(c) 12	(d) 7

4 (a) £18   (b) £20   (c) £12   (d) £18
5 (a) £11.50   (b) £15.50   (c) £10.75   (d) £7.50
6 (a) £15   (b) £72   (c) £97   (d) £77
7 (a) £8.18   (b) £65.80   (c) £17.80   (d) £63.31
8 (a) 7 ft 4 in   (b) 2 ft 4 in   (c) 2 yd   (d) 5 yd
9 (a) 22.4 km   (b) 532 m   (c) 2.018 kg   (d) 8 cm 1 mm
10 (a) 2 h 28 min   (b) 5 yr 10 months (c) 2 ton 7 cwt   (d) 1 litre 2 cl 28 ml
11 54.6p   12 1 hr 46 min   13 £308
14 6 lb 4 oz   15 85 840 words   16 20.7 °C
17 51 cars   18 (a) £3120 (b) £312   19 £2.84
20 £6.80   21 84 marks   22 24 miles
23 £2.90 per kg   24 £246

Exercise 2

1 8   2 7   3 8   4 9   5 3
6 Mean 7.74 thousand; median 7.8 thousand
7 Mean 3.49 thousand; median 3.2 thousand
8 Mean 15.39; median $15\frac{1}{2}$; modal size $15\frac{1}{2}$
9 Mean £2322.8 million; median £2282 million
10 Mean 386.5 million; median 379.5 million

Exercise 3

1 A   2 C   3 B   4 B   5 C
6 B   7 D   8 C   9 B   10 D
11 B

9 Speed, distance and time

Exercise 1

1 (a) 10 mile/h   (b) 25 mile/h   (c) 30 mile/h
   (d) 15 mile/h   (e) 25 mile/h   (f) 25 mile/h
2 (a) 20 km/h   (b) 49 km/h   (c) 35 km/h
   (d) 36 km/h   (e) 90 km/h   (f) 47 km/h
3 (a) 24 mile/h   (b) 80 km/h   (c) 48 mile/h
   (d) 52 km/h   (e) 24 mile/h   (f) 72 km/h
4 (a) 30 miles   (b) 96 miles   (c) 720 km
   (d) 1260 km   (e) 1750 miles   (f) 133 km
5 (a) 60 miles   (b) 210 miles   (c) 168 km
   (d) 408 km   (e) 80 km   (f) 132 miles
6 (a) 4 h   (b) 3 h   (c) 7 h
   (d) 9 h   (e) 7 h   (f) 19 h
7 (a) $2\frac{1}{2}$ h   (b) $5\frac{1}{2}$ h   (c) $4\frac{1}{2}$ h
   (d) $3\frac{1}{2}$ h   (e) $5\frac{1}{2}$ h   (f) $4\frac{1}{2}$ h
8 (a) 3 h 15 min   (b) 4 h 45 min   (c) 5 h 45 min
   (d) 3 h 24 min   (e) 2 h 42 min   (f) 3 h 48 min
9 200 miles   10 24 mile/h   11 44 mile/h
12 88 mile/h   13 510 mile/h   14 4 days 6 h
15 24 mile/h   16 (a) 48.6 mile/h (b) 54 mile/h   17 40 mile/h
18 35 mile/h   19 70 mile/h   20 34 mile/h
21 50 mile/h   22 396 mile/h   23 4 h 15 min
24 55.8 mile/h

Exercise 2

1 B   2 A   3 D   4 A   5 D
6 C   7 B   8 D   9 A   10 C

10 Commercial arithmetic

Exercise 1

1 £190.85   2 £181.84   3 £115.20   4 £238
5 £249.60   6 £537.80   7 £278.10   8 £98.53
9 7 h   10 £6279

Exercise 2

1	£254.60	2	£238.48	3	£632.37	4	£989.90
5	£4201.97	6	£5805.35	7	£2220.81	8	£8879.11
9	£193.34	10	£74.65				

Exercise 3

1	38p	2	£1.00	3	£1.25	4	36p
5	61p	6	£4.70	7	£2.82	8	£4.70
9	£1.38	10	£2.22	11	£1.02	12	92p
13	£1.24	14	£3.36	15	£3.16	16	£1.56
17	60p	18	£1.88	19	£2.20	20	£1.44
21	£5.25	22	54p	23	92p	24	£5.22

Exercise 4

	(a)	(b)	(c)
1	1510 schillings	216 marks	750 marks
2	471 dollars	810 000 lire	59 175 pesetas
3	1275 francs	266.90 dollars	33 532.50 pesetas
4	30 200 schillings	15 000 francs	5 400 000 lire
5	54 marks	4931.25 pesetas	377.50 schillings
6	162 000 lire	94.20 dollars	450 francs
7	1661 schillings	21 697.50 pesetas	237.60 marks
8	376.80 dollars	1800 francs	3624 schillings
9	40 500 lire	32.40 marks	2958.75 pesetas
10	1350 francs	282.60 dollars	388.80 marks

Exercise 5

1	£10	2	£90	3	£1000	4	£10
5	£250	6	£25	7	£80	8	£500
9	£180	10	£240	11	£350	12	£36
13	£130	14	£1000	15	£55	16	£720
17	£0.60	18	£28	19	£95	20	£45
21	£170	22	£220	23	£15	24	£1200

Exercise 6

1	750 francs	2	540 000 lire	3	86.40 marks
4	32.40 marks	5	785 dollars	6	3945 pesetas
7	270 000 lire	8	125.60 dollars	9	2160 marks
10	219.80 dollars	11	70.65 dollars	12	1200 francs
13	1147.60 schillings	14	1500 francs	15	69.12 marks
16	47.10 dollars	17	4734 pesetas	18	86.40 marks
19	480 francs	20	7750 schillings	21	23 670 pesetas
22	140.40 marks	23	378 000 lire	24	634.20 schillings

Exercise 7

1	1.62	2	15.30	3	1.76	4	2.42
5	228	6	11.63	7	8.54	8	9.70
9	7.50	10	0.70	11	2.12	12	4.45
13	44.00	14	2.40	15	2690	16	7.60
17	0.97	18	2.23	19	16.40	20	1.765
21	201.63	22	1.65	23	7.84	24	2650

Exercise 8

1	£2.05	2	£16.01	3	£35.42	4	£12.49
5	£38.05	6	£40.93	7	£23.50; £27.60	8	£47.77
9	£73	10	£3140	11	(a) by £137	12	£7.99
13	£116.76	14	£22.20	15	£2050	16	£34.68
17	(a) by £320	18	£43	19	£120	20	£148

Exercise 9

1	£34	2	£10	3	£740	4	£7995
5	Bank by £280	6	(a) by £240	7	Dealer by £24	8	£280
9	£22	10	(a) by £52.80				

Exercise 10

1	£10.50	2	£10.50	3	£141	4	£308

5 £129.60	6 £280.80	7 £52.80	8 £320
9 £362	10 (a) £46.10 (b) £107.00 (c) £107.80		11 £486
12 £350			

Exercise 11

1 A	2 C	3 B	4 C	5 B
6 B	7 C	8 A	9 C	10 A
11 C	12 D			

11 Percentages

Exercise 1

1 $\frac{1}{2}$	2 $\frac{3}{4}$	3 $\frac{2}{5}$	4 $\frac{7}{10}$	5 $\frac{1}{5}$
6 $\frac{3}{20}$	7 $\frac{11}{20}$	8 $\frac{17}{20}$	9 $\frac{6}{25}$	10 $\frac{8}{25}$
11 $\frac{18}{25}$	12 $\frac{24}{25}$	13 $\frac{9}{100}$	14 $\frac{1}{3}$	15 $\frac{1}{8}$
16 $\frac{5}{8}$	17 $\frac{9}{40}$	18 $\frac{17}{40}$	19 $\frac{9}{50}$	20 $\frac{21}{100}$
21 $1\frac{1}{5}$	22 $1\frac{1}{2}$	23 $1\frac{2}{5}$	24 $2\frac{3}{10}$	25 $\frac{9}{400}$
26 $\frac{23}{50}$	27 $\frac{41}{50}$	28 $\frac{2}{3}$	29 $\frac{13}{30}$	30 $\frac{13}{25}$
31 $\frac{61}{100}$	32 $2\frac{1}{2}$	33 $\frac{29}{40}$	34 $\frac{7}{30}$	35 $\frac{23}{25}$
36 $\frac{11}{100}$	37 $\frac{7}{25}$	38 $\frac{19}{30}$	39 $1\frac{1}{4}$	40 $\frac{17}{100}$

Exercise 2

1 0.5	2 0.4	3 0.7	4 0.85
5 0.15	6 0.95	7 1.20	8 0.25
9 0.33	10 0.48	11 0.82	12 0.07
13 0.11	14 0.058	15 0.099	16 0.005
17 0.0012	18 0.035	19 0.725	20 0.0047
21 0.03	22 1.23	23 0.248	24 0.865
25 0.195	26 0.0007	27 0.946	28 0.71
29 0.1525	30 0.2825	31 0.0025	32 0.005
33 0.105	34 0.9	35 1.01	36 3.05
37 0.8025	38 0.57	39 0.195	40 0.0125

Exercise 3

1 50%	2 20%	3 75%	4 80%
5 90%	6 25%	7 60%	8 70%
9 10%	10 150%	11 $12\frac{1}{2}$%	12 150%
13 175%	14 $62\frac{1}{2}$%	15 $87\frac{1}{2}$%	16 36%
17 225%	18 $37\frac{1}{2}$%	19 30%	20 48%
21 350%	22 $17\frac{1}{2}$%	23 72%	24 $27\frac{1}{2}$%
25 45%	26 125%	27 68%	28 65%
29 120%	30 175%	31 15%	32 40%
33 84%	34 130%	35 35%	36 $42\frac{1}{2}$%
37 135%	38 96%	39 $112\frac{1}{2}$%	40 450%

Exercise 4

1 50%	2 70%	3 30%	4 75%
5 60%	6 25%	7 42%	8 86%
9 95%	10 9%	11 16%	12 57%
13 95%	14 210%	15 525%	16 94%
17 107%	18 119%	19 72%	20 8%
21 51.6%	22 74.8%	23 90.4%	24 8.4%
25 305.1%	26 100.8%	27 10.6%	28 207.5%
29 0.3%	30 56.8%	31 150.4%	32 7.25%
33 58.25%	34 300.06%	35 120.05%	36 10%
37 36%	38 210%	39 80.6%	40 17%

Exercise 5

1 60%	2 45%	3 64%	4 50%
5 20%	6 25%	7 $42\frac{1}{2}$%	8 35%
9 80%	10 70%	11 75%	12 20%
13 40%	14 37.5%	15 2.5%	16 40%
17 77.5%	18 35%	19 Maths by 4%	20 32%
21 62.5%	22 75%	23 15%	24 50%

Exercise 6

1	£10	2	£3	3	£24	4	£1.20
5	£14	6	£13.50	7	£6.60	8	£56
9	£32.50	10	£1.72	11	£0.84	12	£15.24
13	£1.80	14	£32.13	15	£18.09	16	£47.50
17	£69	18	£64.40	19	£44	20	£13.20
21	£20.80	22	£112.50	23	£40.70	24	£332.80
25	£42	26	£62 080	27	£324	28	£237.60
29	£692 250	30	£9890				

Exercise 7

1	3 miles	2	3 cm	3	7 km	4	5.6 litres
5	5.4 kg	6	6 cl	7	3 ft	8	0.2 kg
9	17 cm	10	9.1 km	11	112	12	72
13	4599	14	252	15	1.6 cm	16	252
17	3610	18	302 400	19	29 744	20	82 500
21	960 000	22	46	23	111	24	1 271 000

Exercise 8

1	£23.50	2	£35.25	3	£164.50	4	£28.20
5	£61.10	6	£21.15	7	£141.00	8	£70.50
9	£49.35	10	£98.70	11	£17.39	12	£31.02
13	£542.85	14	£1861.20				

Exercise 9

1	£94.50	2	£201.42	3	£343.44	4	£227.24
5	Credit £6.48	6	£90.18	7	£116.10	8	Debit £11.88
9	58 688	10	£192.94				

Exercise 10

1	£60	2	£1	3	£30	4	33p
5	£28.60	6	£182	7	£180	8	£93.60
9	£42.50	10	£46.90	11	£22	12	72p

Exercise 11

1	20% profit	2	25% loss	3	25% profit
4	36% loss	5	$33\frac{1}{3}$% profit	6	25% loss
7	$12\frac{1}{2}$% loss	8	10% profit	9	30% loss
10	9% profit	11	30% profit	12	40% loss

Exercise 12

1	£12	2	£40	3	£60	4	£240
5	28p	6	£8	7	£24	8	£40
9	£18	10	60p	11	£24	12	£90

Exercise 13

1	50%	2	60%	3	20%	4	60%
5	20%	6	$47\frac{1}{2}$%	7	(a) £240 (b) 120%	8	50%
9	47.2%	10	£15.60	11	£41.60	12	(a) £42 (b) £30

Exercise 14

1	£24	2	£30	3	£15	4	£44
5	£56.25	6	£22.50	7	£90	8	£2.25
9	£200	10	£365	11	£330	12	£59.25

Exercise 15

1	£36	2	£60	3	£30	4	£13.50
5	£156	6	£54	7	£172.80	8	£49.50
9	£190.80	10	£96	11	£1440	12	£29
13	(a) £48 000 (b) £200			14	(a) £75 000 (b) £250		

Exercise 16

1	£1123.60	2	£661.50	3	£324.48	4	£1373.88
5	£11 236	6	£9261	7	£23 820.32	8	£2268.45
9	£4160	10	£4336.05	11	£55 651.25	12	£23

Exercise 17
1 £1840	2 £3590	3 £8195	4 £3708.75
5 £62	6 £32 995	7 £336 195	8 £4072.50

Exercise 18
1. (a) 105 (b) 34 (c) 624 (d) £12
   (e) £18 (f) 0.5 m (g) £3240 (h) 337.5 m
2. (a) £51 (b) £22.05 (c) £105 (d) £40.70
   (e) £198.40 (f) £406 (g) £6562.50 (h) £54.45
3. (a) £68.20 (b) £115.50 (c) £140.40 (d) £86.10
   (e) £551.05 (f) £185.76 (g) £459.48 (h) £9350
4. (a) 62.5% (b) 28% (c) 42.5% (d) 87.5%
   (e) 57.14% (f) 36.36% (g) 66.6̇6% (h) 66.6̇6%
5. (a) £539.24 (b) £487.39 (c) £709.31 (d) £835.82
   (e) £335.99 (f) £493.09 (g) £645.53 (h) £813.84
6. (a) £12.75 (b) £21.76 (c) £78.54 (d) £277.27
   (e) £797.98 (f) £6.29 (g) £61.20 (h) £32.47

Exercise 19
1 B	2 D	3 A	4 D	5 B
6 C	7 A	8 C	9 B	10 D
11 B	12 B	13 C	14 A	15 C
16 A	17 C	18 B	19 A	20 C

12 Graphs, substitution, coordinates and surveys

Exercise 4
1. (a) 56.7 km (b) 15.4 miles 2 (a) 80.9 ha (b) 494 acres
3. (a) 38.7 litres (b) 8.8 gal 4 (a) 453.6 kg (b) 198.4 lb
5. (a) £26.30 (b) 1368 francs 6 (a) £258 (b) 496 dollars
7. (a) 98.6 °F (b) 21 °C; −17.8 °C 8 (a) £100 (b) £55
9. (a) 43 (b) 422 (c) 8.4

Exercise 5
1 12	2 10	3 27	4 20	5 24
6 28	7 6	8 4	9 30	10 4
11 5	12 13	13 5	14 3	15 3
16 2				

Exercise 6
1. (a) 16 (b) 5 (c) 16 (d) 8 (e) 0
2. (a) 9 (b) 32 (c) 22 (d) 43 (e) 12
3. (a) 21 (b) 8 (c) 46 (d) 10 (e) 26
4. (a) 42 (b) 17 (c) 68 (d) 21 (e) 32

Exercise 7
1. $P = B + \dfrac{S}{10}$ 2 $C = P + D + Pr$ 3 $P = 2L + 2B$ 4 $V = CR$

5. $S = \dfrac{D}{T}$ 6 86   7 23   8 55

9. 30   10 50

Exercise 8
A 2, 2	B 5, 4	C 3, 5	D 4, 7
E 3, −2	F 2, −4	G −1, −2	H −4, −3
J −5, 3	K −3, 7	L −6, −5	M 5, −5
N 7, 6	P −2, 5	Q −7, 6	R −3, −7
S 4, −8	T 6, 1	V −6, −2	Z 6, 9

1 549607	2 517618	3 574618	4 568798	5 527686
6 543767	7 570750	8 597747	9 560737	10 553728
11 507705	12 523698			

Exercise 9

1	2.5; 7.5; 3.6; 8.4	**2** 3.2; 15.6; 26.4
3	11.5; 13.7; 16.5	**4** 12.5; 19.4; 26.6
5	−6.8; 0.4; 12.8	**6** −3.4; 9.8; 28.2
7	15.8; 0; −7.8	**8** 15.4; 31; 38.4
9	11.4; 4.6; −4.6	**10** −4; 10; 43

Exercise 10

1

Marks	9	10	11	12	13	14	15	16	17	18
Frequency	1	2	4	8	13	6	4	3	0	1

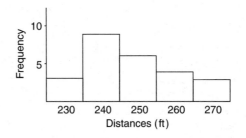

2

Distances	230	240	250	260	270
Frequency	3	9	6	4	3

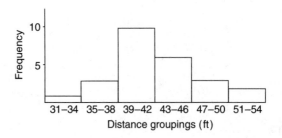

3

Groupings	31–34	35–38	39–42	43–46	47–50	51–54
Frequency	1	3	10	6	3	2

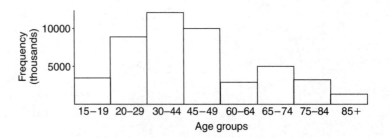

4

Age groups	15–19	20–29	30–44	45–49	60–64	65–74	75–84	85+
Frequency	3430	9061	12 313	10 670	2839	5169	3020	982

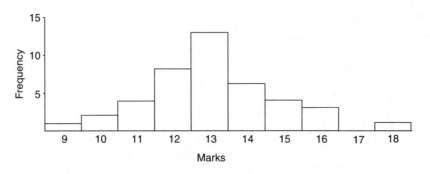

5   Age groups   15–19   20–24   25–34   35–44   45–54

Frequency					
Males	7	284	2346	3011	2641
Females	37	576	2815	3124	2632

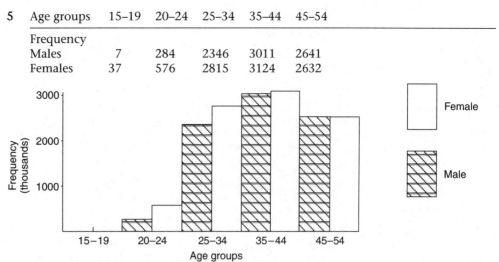

6   Frequencies of letters are:
a 29, b 4, c 9, d 7, e 28, f 9, g 5, h 18, i 19, j 0, k 1, l 12, m 5, n 12, o 25, p 8, q 0, r 22,
s 27, t 21, u 5, v 0, w 4, x 2, y 3, z 2

Exercise 12
1   (a) 9 (b) 15   2   6, 14, 10, 18, 14, 22
3   red   4   Start, collect glass, add orange, taste, add water, drink, stop
5   Between Add water and Drink   8   (a) green (b) yellow (c) red (d) red (e) blue

13 Plane shapes

Exercise 1
1   (a) 58°   (b) 116°   (c) 51°   (d) 67°
     (e) 58°   (f) 45°   (g) 75°   (h) 60°
3   (a) 40°   (b) 140°   (c) 140°
4   (a) 130°   (b) 50°   (c) 130°   (d) 50°
     (e) 130°   (f) 130°   (g) 50°
5   (a) 030° or 30° E of N   (b) 130° or 40° S of E
     (c) 220° or 50° S of W   (d) 255° or 15° S of W
     (e) 310° or 50° W of N
6   (a) 110°   (b) 80°

Exercise 2
1	28 cm	2	25 cm 6 mm	3	58 yd 2 ft	4	35 cm
5	2 m 65 cm	6	44 cm	7	7 cm	8	4 yd 2 ft
9	38 cm	10	2 cm 4 mm				

Exercise 3
1	216 cm²	2	480 cm²	3	28 m²	4	126 ft²
5	51 cm²	6	14 ft²	7	76.8 m²	8	24 ft²
9	17.28 m²	10	60 cm²	11	612 cm²	12	440 m²
13	224 cm²	14	104 yd²	15	96 m²	16	260 m²
17	875 ft²	18	474 m²	19	876 m²	20	2520 m²

Exercise 4
1	12 m	2	340	3	$3\frac{3}{4}$ m²	4	£30
5	17.6 m	6	£487.20	7	£149.25	8	7 rolls
9	£7.56	10	96 m²				

Exercise 5
1   22 cm   2   22.8 cm   3   10 cm 4 mm   4   13 cm 6 mm
5   28 cm or 26 cm   6   (a) 30 cm²   (b) 12 cm²   (c) 48 cm²
     (d) 225 mm²   (e) 14 m²
7   (a) 10.5 cm² or 1050 mm²   (b) 41.6 cm² or 4160 mm²
     (c) 196 in² or 1.36 ft²   (d) 9.45 m² or 94 500 cm²
     (e) 3.84 cm² or 384 mm²
8   (a) 6 cm   (b) 18 cm   (c) 5 cm   (d) 15 m
     (e) 14.4 m

9 (a) 70 cm²   (b) 60 cm²   (c) 40 cm²   (d) 36 cm²
    (e) 120 cm²   (f) 432 ft²   (g) 396 ft²   (h) 12½ m²
    (k) 210 ft²   (l) 56 m²   (m) 294 cm²   (n) 240 cm²

Exercise 6

1 22 cm	2 66 in	3 44 ft	4 132 m
5 110 m	6 33 cm	7 44 in	8 396 m
9 264 cm	10 110 cm	11 22 m	12 50$\frac{2}{7}$ cm or 50.29 cm
13 42 cm	14 35 m	15 77 m	16 28 ft
17 10$\frac{1}{2}$ cm	18 21 m	19 7 cm	20 8$\frac{3}{4}$ m
21 4.3 m	22 12.1 cm	23 26$\frac{1}{4}$ ft	24 15$\frac{3}{4}$ mm
25 14 m	26 33 cm	27 72 cm	28 37$\frac{1}{2}$ cm
29 47 cm	30 330 m		

Exercise 7

1   616 cm²   2   1386 cm²   3   12 474 ft²
4   346$\frac{1}{2}$ m²   5   3850 in²   6   38$\frac{1}{2}$ cm²
7   78$\frac{4}{7}$ cm² or 78.57 cm²   8   21$\frac{21}{32}$ in² or 21.66 in²   9   3$\frac{1}{7}$ m² or 3.14 m²
10   9$\frac{5}{8}$ m² or 9.63 m²   11   19$\frac{9}{14}$ cm² or 19.64 cm²   12   240$\frac{5}{8}$ m² or 240.63 m²
13   86$\frac{5}{8}$ cm² or 86.63 cm²   14   1886$\frac{1}{2}$ ft²   15   33 cm²
16   7 cm

Exercise 8

1   616 cm²   2   173$\frac{1}{4}$ cm² or 173.25 cm²   3   115$\frac{1}{2}$ cm²
4   2793 ft²   5   175 m²   6   96$\frac{1}{4}$ cm²
7   726 ft²   8   803 m²   9   1039$\frac{1}{2}$ cm²
10   3234 ft²

Exercise 9

1 A	2 B	3 D	4 B	5 A
6 C	7 D	8 C	9 B	10 B
11 C	12 A			

14 More use of the calculator

Exercise 1

1 4187	2 138.11	3 248	4 230.19
5 1262.45	6 822.72	7 243.28	8 193.07
9 −116.27	10 93.66	11 −67.52	12 11.16
13 2.71	14 10.41	15 8.10	16 31.52

Exercise 2

1   (a) 113.22   (b) 65.11   (c) 73.73   (d) 149.25
    (e) 59.96   (f) 48.27   (g) 344.47   (h) 97.11
2   (a) 18.23   (b) 8.22   (c) 34.38   (d) 171.03
    (e) 37.21   (f) 28.22   (g) 246.65   (h) 78.16
3   (a) 28.26   (b) 23.55   (c) 25.8422   (d) 78.6884
    (e) 59.503   (f) 22.1998   (g) 62.8942   (h) 109.9
4   (a) 1.91   (b) 4.14   (c) 2.97   (d) 14.67
    (e) 5.82   (f) 15.92   (g) 24.22   (h) 6.39
5   (a) 12.56 cm   (b) 47.1 cm   (c) 204.1 cm   (d) 78.5 in
    (e) 59.66 ft   (f) 23.55 cm   (g) 43.332 m   (h) 1256 mm
6   (a) 6.37 cm   (b) 2.55 ft   (c) 5.41 m   (d) 49.36 cm
    (e) 10.38 ft   (f) 30. 64 cm   (g) 5.73 in   (h) 104.11 cm

Exercise 3

1   (a) 64   (b) 37   (c) 5.4   (d) 12.35
    (e) 18.3   (f) 25.3   (g) 0.21   (h) 0.065
2   (a) 8.29 cm   (b) 5.17 cm   (c) 1.71 cm   (d) 4.37 cm
    (e) 7.49 ft   (f) 5.64 cm   (g) 3.99 cm   (h) 10.10 cm

Exercise 4

1 C	2 D	3 A	4 D	5 B
6 C	7 C	8 D	9 A	10 B

15 Space shapes

Exercise 1

1 60 cm^3	2 36 m^3	3 24 ft^3
4 130 cm^3	5 94.5 m^3	6 6480 cm^3
7 2508 cm^3	8 70 m^3	9 2592 in^3 or 1.5 ft^3
10 3800 cm^3	11 5100 m^3	12 23 296 ft^3
13 3696 in^3	14 184.8 cm^3 or 184 800 mm^3	
15 600 m^3	16 1540 cm^3 or 1 540 000 mm^3	
17 201.6 m^3	18 225.75 m^3	19 0.2 m^3 or 200 000 cm^3
20 29 400 in^3 or 17.01 ft^3		

Exercise 2

1 115.5 cm^3	2 14 700 cm^3	3 352 cm^3
4 32 400 in^3 or 18.75 ft^3	5 7.5 ft^3 or 12 960 in^3	6 12 ft^3
7 450 cm^3	8 30 cm^2	9 96 ft^3
10 2310 m^3	11 1694 cm^3	12 353.57 cm^3
13 187.5 gal	14 379.69 ft^3	15 274.625 cm^3
16 5775 gal		

Exercise 3

1 B	2 C	3 A	4 D	5 B
6 C	7 C	8 A	9 D	10 D
11 C	12 A			

16 Assignments

Exercise 2

1 Energy/water, male, 29.14%
2 Banking/finance, women, 9.15%
3 Other manufacturing industries, 45.25%
4 Transport and communication, 6.95%
5 1994 65.79%   1990 51.44%
6 1994 47.87%   1990 42.25%

Exercise 3

Local hospice – £258.40   Cancer Research – £226.10   Greenpeace – £161.50

Exercise 4

1 Approx 15 ft	2 Approx 95 ft	3 Approx 275 ft
4 Approx 36 mile/h	5 Approx 54 mile/h	6 Approx 68 mile/h
7 Approx 420 ft	8 Approx 550 ft	

Exercise 5

1 (a) Only when alternative flights are full
   (b) 1 h 45 min (c) Saturday (d) 1 h 35 min (e) 1715 hours
2 (a) Hourly; 0736 (b) 3 min (c) 31 min; 0548; Finsbury Park to Potters Bar
   (d) 0704; 46 min
3 (a) 41 min (b) 7 h 35 min (c) 7 h 5 min (d) 1 h 5 min (e) 1755 hours; 10 h 32 min

Exercise 6

1 Mon 450	Tues 428	Wed 435
Thur 445	Fri 458	Sat 548
2 Mon £147.19	Tue £138.32	Wed £142.18
Thur £145.42	Fri £152.63	Sat £184.26
3 £6.50 profit each week	4 £273.00	

Exercise 7

1 £3859.08	2 £1286.36	3 £24.74
4 £62.83	5 £38.09	6 £11.51

Exercise 8

1 10 950 cigarettes	2 £1500.15	3 2.74 g tar
4 0.27 g nicotine	5 £1530.15	6 £195.02
7 £975.10		

Exercise 9
£706

Exercise 10
£760

Exercise 11
Journey 4 is cheapest at £756.04 by £24.96 over journey 1.

Index